COMPARATIVE ANATOMY

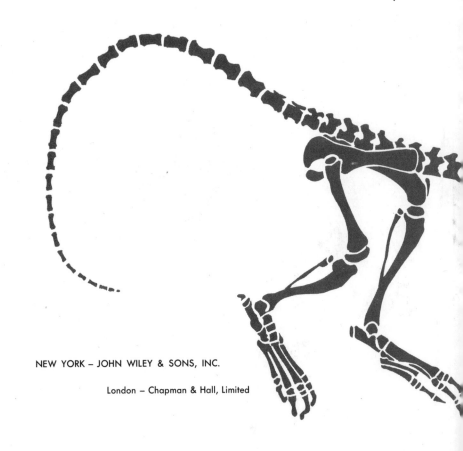

NEW YORK – JOHN WILEY & SONS, INC.

London – Chapman & Hall, Limited

WILLIAM MONTAGNA

Professor of Biology

Brown University

Providence, Rhode Island

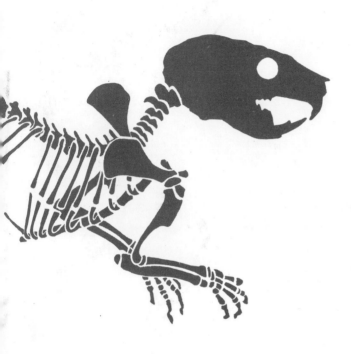

COMPARATIVE
ANATOMY

Library of Congress Catalog Card Number:
59–6775

Printed in the United States of America

DEDICATION

This book is dedicated to my teachers,
Professor Bernal R. Weimer of Bethany College
and Professor Howard B. Adelmann of Cornell University,
because they allowed me to become a biologist in my own way.
They were indulgent with me when I must have been very trying.

PREFACE

THIS BOOK is written for the college sophomore for a one-semester course. For the sake of brevity, many details have been eliminated, and compromises and generalizations have had to be made. Allusions to fossil forms, references to learned works, and terminology have been kept to a manageable minimum. Since developmental events give a better understanding of comparative anatomical detail, embryology has been emphasized more than is the usual practice in a course of comparative anatomy.

Biological disciplines do not need press agentry and apologies. It is neither necessary nor wise to emphasize man to make comparative anatomy interesting for beginning students; such emphasis usually leads to muddled impressions of phylogeny. In this book references to man are no more frequent than references to other animals. An exception to this is made in the chapter on the endoskeleton because human bones are large and can be studied with ease.

The study of comparative anatomy should be a thoughtful consideration of moving, changing systems; it should be more than an irksome catalogue of names

which must be learned. To really understand comparative anatomy, the student must develop an awareness of (1) the possible paths of phylogenetic ascension, (2) the homologies and analogies of organ systems, (3) the lability of tissues, (4) their infinitely beautiful and delicate structural patterns, (5) their unity of structure and function, (6) their functional adaptation, and, finally, (7) the profound influence which intrinsic and extrinsic forces exert on the maintenance of the integrity of tissues and organs.

The study of anatomy should be an adventure for the student. He should come to appreciate the changes that take place in the steps in phylogeny and in ontogeny. He must see that structure and function are complementary parts of the same principle and cannot be separated; the knowledge of one gives meaning to the other. The student must see beyond the unpleasantness of handling dead animals. He must discover the order that underlies the architecture of all living things. He must see how organs are constructed in order to understand them.

Most of the line drawings in this book were executed by Margaret C. Gould. Many of them were delineated by the author, and some, by interested students. To a large extent these are refinements of drawings that the author has put on the blackboard during his lectures. The majority of the excellent photographs were contributed by friends; proper credit of authorship is given under each of these illustrations. The author expresses gratitude to all who have helped in this venture and to students who have condoned his pedagogical experiments.

WILLIAM MONTAGNA

Providence, Rhode Island
January 1959

CONTENTS

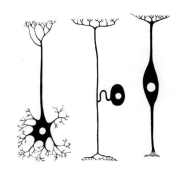

chapter *1*

THE CREDENTIALS OF VERTEBRATES   1

chapter *2*

DEVELOPMENT OF THE VERTEBRATE BODY PLAN
AND THE TISSUES OF THE BODY   9

chapter *3*

THE CHORDATA   30

chapter *4*

SKIN ·   43

chapter *5*

THE ENDOSKELETON ·   61

chapter *6*

THE MUSCULAR SYSTEM   133

Contents

chapter *7*

THE DIGESTIVE SYSTEM   155

chapter *8*

THE CIRCULATORY SYSTEM   191

chapter *9*

THE RESPIRATORY SYSTEM   233

chapter *10*

THE EXCRETORY SYSTEM   253

chapter *11*

THE REPRODUCTIVE SYSTEM   271

chapter *12*

THE SENSE ORGANS   297

chapter *13*

THE NERVOUS SYSTEM   315

chapter *14*

THE ENDOCRINE ORGANS   355

GLOSSARY   365

INDEX   385

COMPARATIVE ANATOMY

(a)

Figure 1. The figure at the top is of *Amphioxus*. The notochord (arrow) extends the entire length of the animal. The bottom figure is of an Ammocoetes of the lamprey. Its notochord (arrow) is also very large. Above the notochord in both animals the neural tube can be seen. Both animals show a typical pharynx.

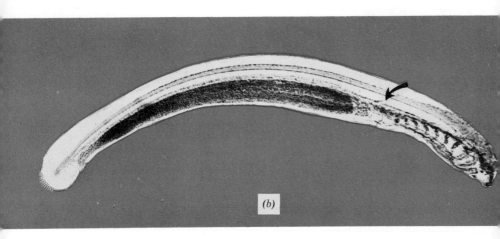

(b)

THE CREDENTIALS

OF

VERTEBRATES

Comparative anatomy introduces the student to the structural patterns of animals and to the similarities and differences in these patterns in the different vertebrates. This chapter is designed to acquaint the student with the characteristic features of vertebrates. It also presents a series of terms which must be learned before the descriptions that follow in subsequent chapters become intelligible.

All vertebrates have certain features in common. These are listed here in no particular order. The student must understand all of these points because they are the core around which the rest of the book is built. All vertebrates are (1) **bilaterally symmetrical;** one side of the body is similar to the other. (2) All show **cephalization,** or the concentration of sense organs and nervous tissue in the head, and a development of the head more advanced than that of the rest of the body. (3) The vertebrate body shows **metamerism** (segmentation), at least in the early embryonic stages; successive segments are different. (4) Whether in the adult or during embryonic life, all vertebrates possess a **notochord** (Figure 1). (5) They have a true **coelom,** lined entirely with **mesoderm.** (6) All have, at least during development, a **pharynx,** with **pharyngeal slits** or **clefts, arches,** and **pouches.** (7) The single **dorsal central nervous system** is hollow. (8) The digestive system is differentiated into a **mouth, pharynx, stomach, intestine,** and **cloaca.** (9) The **circulatory system is closed.** (10) A **ventral,** anteriorly located **heart** pumps blood to the body and keeps blood in motion and circulating.

Embryos follow the **law of cephalocaudal development.** Development progresses like a wave which moves from the anterior to the posterior regions. During early embryology the head is formed first, and the rest of the embryo is added on behind it by degrees. When each major organ system develops the more anterior parts are always differentiated before the posterior ones. The head, then, is the oldest and the best developed part of the embryo and of the adult. The tail is the most primitive region of the body, even in adult vertebrates.

All vertebrates have a certain structural organization or **body plan.** To understand the principles of anatomy one must have a clear idea of the body plan. One can learn a great deal about it by making a series of cuts at right angles to the long axis of a fish and studying the surface of each cut end. In the tail region, just above the center, is the **vertebra,** with an arch above and one below the body or **centrum** (Figure 2). The dorsal arch encloses the **nerve** or **spinal cord;** the ventral arch contains blood vessels. The notochord runs through the centrum of the vertebra. Two large masses of muscle occupy the dorsal portion of the body and two the ventral, these portions being separated by a fibrous sheet.

The body plan through the trunk region is similar to that of the tail, but other structures are present. The vertebra has a dorsal arch which encloses the spinal cord, and the notochord runs through the centrum. Underneath the vertebra is a large space, the coelom or **pleuro-peritoneal cavity** (Figure 3). The relation of the viscera to the coelom is peculiar. The gut is slung from the middorsal line of the coelom by the **mesentery,** a thin sheet of tissue which is composed of two layers of **peritoneum.** Thus the gut is inside the mesentery and outside the coelom. Over the gut the mesentery forms the **visceral peritoneum;** at the base of the mesentery the peritoneum continues laterally over the wall of the coelom to form the **parietal peritoneum.** Liver, kidneys, and other organs, which manifestly bulge into or hang within the coelom, are behind a covering of peritoneum. The peritoneal cavity contains only a small amount of **peritoneal fluid** which lubricates the viscera.

In all classes of vertebrates certain organs or structures can be identified and have a common origin. In different groups of animals specific organs or tissues which seem to have descended from similar organs in an ancestral organism are called **homologous.** The articular bone of the lower jaw of the fish, for example, is homologous with the malleus in the middle ear of mammals. Structures or organs which are similar in general structure or function but which have a different origin and development are called **analogous;** the tongue of the lamprey is analogous with that of the frog. When similar structures develop in unrelated forms, as the eye of the squid and that of vertebrates, the phenomenon is called **convergence. Parallelism** relates to structures that develop in-

2

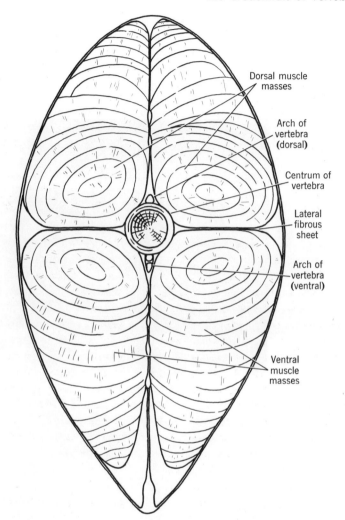

Figure 2. Transverse section through the tail of a fish.

dependently in closely related forms, as the incisor teeth of lagomorphs and those of rodents; hence it reflects a common genetic potential inherited from a common ancestor. Closely related forms which attain strikingly different form, as the lizards and the glass snake, have undergone **divergence.**

The sum total of the events in the development of an organism is called **ontogeny; phylogeny** is the history of the race or group. During

3

vertebrate development the embryos of the different classes do not look alike, but they have a superficial resemblance to each other. In addition, embryos go through developmental phases that appear to review their phylogenetic history. The **biogenetic law,** or **recapitulation theory,** is based on the principle that "ontogeny recapitulates phylogeny."

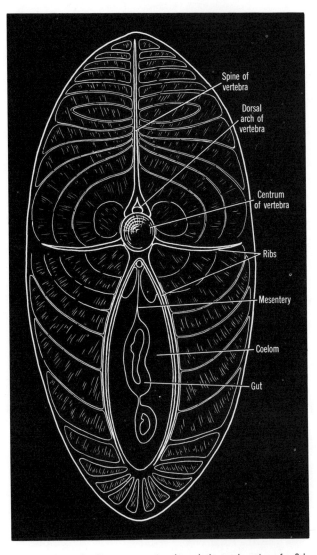

Figure 3. Transverse section through the trunk region of a fish.

This sweeping and misleading generalization has been taught uncritically to students of biology for many decades; the phrase is so euphonious that it is difficult to eradicate it once the student has learned it. The principle, however, is false. It is true that during development the embryo may show fragments of some of its ancestral developmental stages, but some structures are eliminated or bypassed, some developmental phases are shortened or prolonged, and some appear out of chronology. Some structures appear to spring spontaneously and others seem to have arisen as adaptations of organisms to their particular developmental conditions. Thus embryos recapitulate only some developmental events of only some of their ancestral forms. For example, all vertebrate embryos develop a pharynx that resembles that of fishes. In the embryos of fishes the pharyngeal pouches, arches, and clefts form the adult pharynx, jaws, gills and their skeletal supports. In vertebrates without gills the embryos go through phases that give a passing glimpse of the generalized embryonic anatomical features of this system in fishes and modify these building blocks to form very different structures; they never go through stages that resemble the adult fish. As DeBeer states it, "Ontogeny repeats fundamental steps in the ontogenies of ancestral forms, especially when these steps are of structural and functional importance to the individual," and "Phylogeny is due to modified ontogeny."

The studies of comparative embryology and anatomy, and of fossil remains in the sediments of the earth, have brought forth many facts which suggest that the vertebrates have arisen from some general stock. In 1859, in his *The Origin of Species,* Darwin constructed a scheme which re-emphasized the fact that animals are related, that they have come from common forms, and that they have differentiated or evolved into different groups through the accumulation of slow, gradual changes. These spontaneous congenital changes are transmitted to the species; the best adapted among them, or the fittest, survive, the less well adapted perish. Species do not stand still; they move and change constantly or undergo evolution. This book is not directly concerned with evolution, but the student cannot fail to see evolutionary trends in what follows.

In any discipline one must acquire facts and know how to express them. In anatomy the student must learn to describe clearly and precisely. To do this he will have to use terms which save time and space and which avoid awkwardness. Anatomical designations apply to animals which in their normal position stand on four limbs or with the belly down and the back up. (1) **Dorsal** denotes the back, (2) **ventral,** the belly, or underside. (3) **Anterior, cranial,** and **cephalic** denote the head or toward the head, (4) **posterior** or **caudal** denotes the tail or to-

5

ward the tail. (5) **Median** denotes the middle, (6) **lateral,** the sides. (7) **Superior** implies above, (8) **inferior,** below. (9) **Proximal,** near a given point, (10) **distal,** away from it. (11) **Central** implies near the middle, (12) **peripheral,** toward the edge or surface. (13) **Superficial** means near the surface, (14) **deep,** some distance below the surface. To describe the exact position of organs in the body it is convenient to divide the body by certain arbitrary planes. (1) A longitudinal plane through the axis of the animal which extends from dorsal to ventral is a **sagittal section.** A **median sagittal section** is one that divides the animal into equal halves; a **parasagittal section** is any plane parallel to the median sagittal. (2) A **frontal** or **horizontal section** is parallel to dorsal and ventral surfaces and is at right angle to a sagittal plane. (3) A **transverse** or **cross section** cuts across any level of the body at right angle to the sagittal and frontal planes.

Anatomical names have been compounded mostly from the Latin and the Greek. Occasionally the overzealous anatomist has combined the two in naming new structures and the results have been deplorable. Good or bad, names must be learned, and accuracy in learning them cannot be emphasized enough. The student should carefully write down each new term several times and learn its exact definition from the beginning.

SUGGESTED READING

Darwin, C. R., 1872, *The Origin of Species.* 6th edition.
De Beer, G. R., 1951, *Embryos and Ancestors.* Oxford, The Clarendon Press.
Huxley, T. H., 1895, *Darwiniana.* D. Appleton and Company, New York.

CHAPTER

2

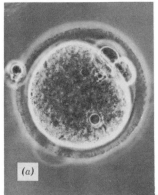

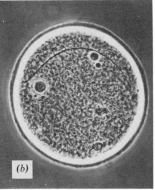

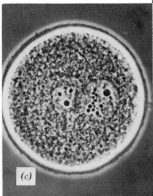

Figure 1. Living fertilized eggs of the rat seen under the phase-contrast microscope: (a) egg just fertilized; (b) later stage when the male and female pronuclei have formed; (c) the male and female pronuclei are well formed; (d) first cleavage. (Courtesy of Dr. R. J. Blandau, University of Washington.)

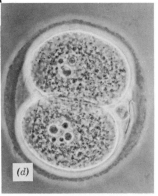

DEVELOPMENT OF
THE VERTEBRATE BODY PLAN
AND THE TISSUES OF THE BODY

INTRODUCTION

Vertebrates develop from the **fertilized ovum,** a single cell formed by the union of the male and female germ cells, the **spermatozoon** and **ovum,** respectively (Figure 1). All of the potentials for growth and development and all the wisdom of the body are encapsulated in these storehouses or archives of the race.

The fertilized ovum divides many times, each time forming smaller cells. During the early divisions, known as **cleavage,** the daughter cells remain undifferentiated, and each goes on dividing until a hollow sphere, called **blastula,** is formed (Figure 2). Although inherently alike, the cells on the surface of the blastula have different fates. Certain areas mapped out there form the **germ layers,** the primary tissues of the embryo (Figure 3). Since these presumptive tissues are on the surface of the spherical blastula, they must be rearranged to construct the vertebrate body plan. The potential **entoderm** flows on the inside, the **mesoderm** in the middle, the **ectoderm** on the outside, the **neural tube** on

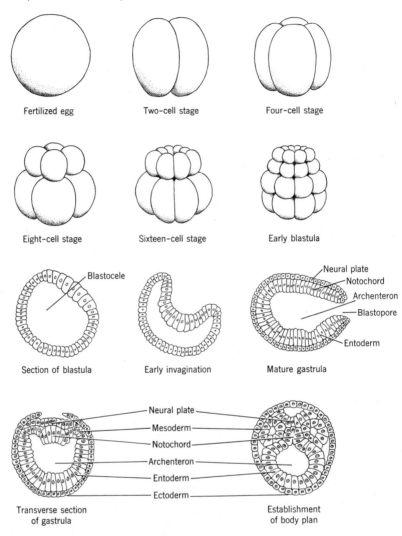

Fertilized egg

Two-cell stage

Four-cell stage

Eight-cell stage

Sixteen-cell stage

Early blastula

Blastocele

Section of blastula

Early invagination

Neural plate
Notochord
Archenteron
Blastopore
Entoderm

Mature gastrula

Neural plate
Mesoderm
Notochord
Archenteron
Entoderm
Ectoderm

Transverse section
of gastrula

Establishment
of body plan

Figure 2. Cleavage and gastrulation in the eggs of *Amphioxus*.

the dorsal midline underneath the ectoderm, and the notochord underneath the neural tube. Regardless of the shape and size of the egg, the germ layers must have this final arrangement.

The eggs of animals which develop outside the reproductive tract of the female are large and have stored in them all of the substances necessary for the development and growth of the embryo. The different

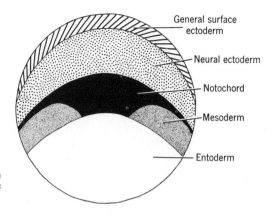

Figure 3. Surface of the blastula of *Amphioxus* showing the map of the presumptive germ layers.

sizes of egg are mostly due to the amount of foodstuff or **yolk** the egg contains. The **telolecithal** eggs of sharks, reptiles, birds, and monotremes have abundant yolk; the protoplasm is restricted to a small **germinal disc** at the upper pole of the yolk sphere (Figure 4). Balancing devices of different sorts maintain the yolk sphere oriented in such a way that the germinal disc remains at the surface no matter how the egg is rotated. The **mesolecithal** eggs of amphibians, cyclostomes, and many of the fishes have a moderate amount of yolk which tends to be concentrated toward the lower part, and the egg is divided into a dorsal **animal pole** and a ventral **vegetal pole** (Figure 5). The eggs of *Amphioxus* and cyclostomes are **isolecithal** and have a small amount of yolk evenly distributed in the cytoplasm. The eggs of eutherian mammals are also isolecithal, but the amount of yolk is so small that they can be called **alecithal** (see Figure 7).

The yolk, being inert, is an impediment to cleavage, and the mechan-

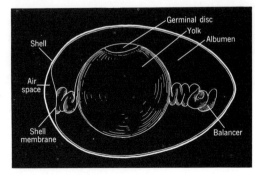

Figure 4. Egg of bird.

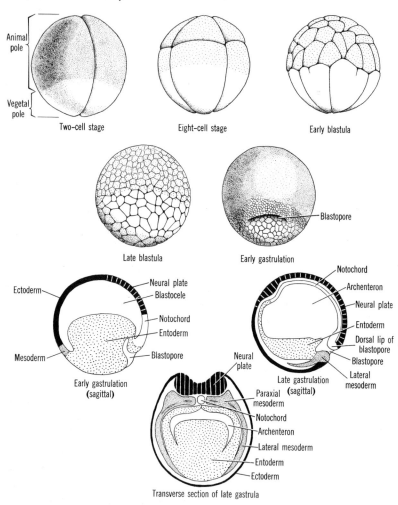

Figure 5. Cleavage and gastrulation in the eggs of amphibians.

ics of early differentiation are necessarily different for each type of egg. In spite of differences, however, the end results are the same.

CLEAVAGE AND GASTRULATION

The patterns of cleavage are strongly influenced by the amount of yolk in eggs. Isolecithal eggs are **holoblastic,** dividing completely and roughly evenly. Mesolecithal eggs are also holoblastic but divide unevenly. Telolecithal eggs are **meroblastic,** and only the animal pole or germinal disc divides; the yolk remains uncleaved.

Not all eggs fall precisely into one of these categories. The eggs of *Amia* and the gar pike have too much yolk to be mesolecithal and too little to be telolecithal. They are barely holoblastic, and cleavage takes place mostly at the upper fifth of the animal pole; a few meridional cleavage planes just manage to plow their way through the yolk in the last expression of holoblastic cleavage.

Eggs are polarized even before fertilization, with the animal pole turned dorsally and the vegetal pole ventrally, and are bilaterally symmetrical. After fertilization the first cleavage plane marks the future midsagittal plane of the embryo, separating the left and right halves.

Amphioxus

The first cleavage plane bisects the animal and vegetal poles longitudinally, separating the egg into two equal **blastomeres** (see Figure 2). The second plane, at right angle and perpendicular to the first, separates the egg into four equal blastomeres. The third cleavage is equatorial, at right angles to both preceding planes and separates the egg into eight blastomeres, the four dorsal ones being larger than the ventral ones. Cleavage continues until a single-layered blastula, with a hollow center called **blastocele,** is formed. The cells in the ventral half are larger than those in the dorsal part. The blastula has polarity and anteroposterior orientation.

Bilaterally symmetrical fields on the dorsal surface of the blastula represent the future germ layers (see Figure 3). When the blastula is fully formed the cells on its surface undergo swirling movements toward a specific posterior focal point; the presumptive mesoderm and notochord flow over the presumptive entoderm, overgrow it and become tucked in, or are **invaginated** at a posterior fold called the **dorsal lip** of the **blastopore** (see Figure 2); when this process is completed the single-layered blastula has become a double-layered **gastrula,** the central cavity of which is the **gastrocele** or **archenteron.** The blastopore, or the original site of invagination, indicates the posterior part of the embryo and is the orifice of the archenteron. The floor and the sides of the archenteron are lined with entoderm; the roof, however, is lined with the notochord on the midline and mesoderm on each side of it (see Figure 2). The entoderm later grows under the mesoderm, and the two edges come to fuse on the midline under the notochord (see Figure 2), the

13

archenteron, remaining lined completely with entoderm. When this is accomplished the typical chordate body plan is established. The outer surface is composed of ectoderm; a **neural plate** extends anteroposteriorly over the notochord, and the rest of the gastrula is covered with general surface ectoderm. The sides of the neural plate rise up, meet, and fuse over the middorsal line to form the neural tube. The two edges of the general surface ectoderm fuse over the neural tube, and the only tissue left on the outside of the embryo is the general surface ectoderm (see Figure 2).

This archetypical process of gastrulation is not possible in eggs with larger amounts of yolk; the establishment of the body plan must be achieved in some other way.

Mesolecithal Eggs

The relatively large amount of yolk in the vegetal pole makes cleavage difficult, and the eggs are unevenly holoblastic. The first cleavage plane cuts across the animal pole and extends slowly through the vegetal pole; the second cleavage forms at right angle to the first before the first has cut completely through the vegetal pole and divides the egg into four equal blastomeres. The third cleavage is equatorial and forms four small blastomeres in the animal pole and four large ones in the vegetal pole (see Figure 5). At the completion of cleavage the blastula has small cells at the animal pole and larger ones at the vegetal pole; a small blastocele is displaced toward the animal pole. The presumptive germ layers on the surface of the blastula are mapped out like those of *Amphioxus*. The movements of the mesoderm and notochord toward the blastopore are essentially similar to those that take place in *Amphioxus*. In gastrulation the materials of the animal pole at the blastopore overrun those of the vegetal pole to form a fold, the lip of the blastopore. As the materials go over the lip of the blastopore, they become reoriented in such a way that the notochord and mesoderm fall behind the entoderm, and the archenteron comes to be lined with entoderm.

Telolecithal Eggs

These eggs undergo meroblastic cleavage, only the germinal disc dividing, the yolk remaining uncleaved (Figure 6). When cleavage is complete the germinal disc is called **blastodisc;** this is homologous to the blastula. Gastrulation does not take place as in isolecithal and mesolecithal eggs. The presumptive germ layers on the surface of the blasto-

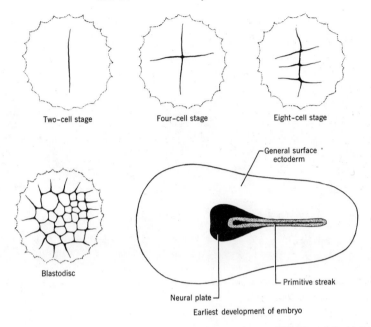

Figure 6. Cleavage and the formation of the primitive streak in the blastodisc of the bird's egg.

disc flow toward the posterior part and form a median thickening called the **primitive streak,** homologous to the lips of the blastopore (Figure 6). In this structure are dammed the presumptive neural plate, notochord, and mesoderm; these are fed out anteriorly and laterally between the ectoderm and the entoderm. Once the primitive streak is established, the germ layers proliferate from it and form the body plan. The edge of the blastodisc grows around the yolk sphere and eventually completely encloses it, forming the **yolk sac.**

Mammals

The three subclasses of mammals have three types of egg. **Monotremes** lay telolecithal eggs similar to those of reptiles and birds. **Marsupials** have eggs that contain a moderate amount of yolk, which is cast aside during cleavage. Later a yolk sac is formed around the yolk in a way similar to that of telolecithal eggs. **Eutherian mammals** have very small isolecithal eggs (Figure 7). Large amounts of yolk would be useless, since the embryos from early development draw their nutrition from the maternal uterus.

15

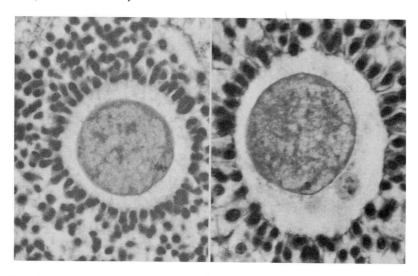

Figure 7. Two mature eggs in the ovary of the rat just before discharge. (Courtesy of Dr. R. J. Blandau, University of Washington.)

The first cleavage divides the egg into two blastomeres, one somewhat larger than the other. The second division is dischronous, the larger blastomere dividing before the smaller one, and for a brief period a three-cell stage precedes a four-celled one (Figure 8). This dischrony continues, and at the end a **blastocyst** is formed; this consists of a small cluster of cells, called the **inner cell mass,** which is attached to the inside of a thin-walled **trophoblast** (Figures 9, 10). The inner cell mass is de-rived almost entirely from the smaller, more slowly dividing cell, and the trophoblast, from the larger, more rapidly dividing blastomere of the first division. A cavity, the **amnion,** forms above the inner cell mass, and a yolk sac is formed below it; all of these structures develop inside the trophoblast (Figure 10). The plate of cells between the amnion and the yolk sac is the embryo proper. The neural tube, notochord, and mesoderm develop from a primitive streak similar to that of birds and reptiles. On the dorsal side, facing the amnion, the embryo devel-ops ectoderm; on the ventral side, entoderm, continuous with that lining the yolk sac. The ovum of eutherian mammals, not aware that it has no yolk, forms a large yolk sac, thus reflecting its evolutionary history.

The trophoblast is in contact with the uterus and together with the uterine lining becomes differentiated into the **placenta,** the organ of exchange between the embryo and the mother.

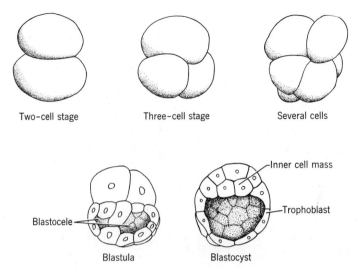

| Two-cell stage | Three-cell stage | Several cells |

Inner cell mass

Blastocele

Trophoblast

| Blastula | Blastocyst |

Figure 8. Cleavage in the mammalian egg.

Figure 9. Six-day blastocyst of the guinea pig showing a tropho-blast and inner cell mass. (Cour-tesy of Dr. R. J. Blandau, University of Washington.)

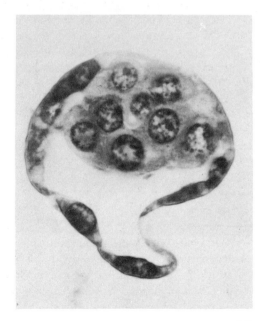

17

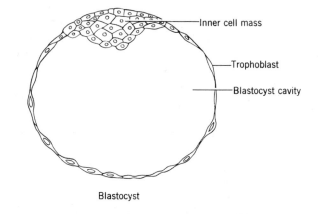

Inner cell mass

Trophoblast

Blastocyst cavity

Blastocyst

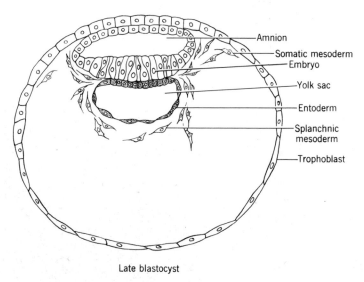

Amnion

Somatic mesoderm

Embryo

Yolk sac

Entoderm

Splanchnic mesoderm

Trophoblast

Late blastocyst

Figure 10. Development of the mammalian blastocyst.

THE FETAL MEMBRANES

Whether eggs develop inside or outside the female reproductive tract, their environment is not always suitable for development, and the embryos must make certain adjustments. Some of them develop **extraembryonic** or **fetal membranes** which provide means of protection, nutrition, respiration, and excretion.

18

The eggs of fishes and amphibians, with a limited amount of yolk, develop so rapidly that the embryos do not develop extra embryonic membranes. When these young hatch they are very different anatomically and physiologically from the adults and are called **larvae**. The swimming larvae of a peculiar family of teleosts, called *Carapidae*, develop three days after fertilization. During a period called **metamorphosis** the larvae assume the structure and physiology of the adults (Figure 11).

Reptiles, birds, and mammals, called **amniotes** because they develop inside an amnion, are in an advanced state of development when they hatch or are born. Very early in differentiation the embryos acquire fetal membranes called **amnion, chorion, allantois,** and **yolk sac.** The development of fetal membranes is related to the presence of a large amount of yolk in the egg and an embryonic life within a shell. This is one of the most interesting aspects of the mammalian evolution. The monotremes lay telolecithal eggs and develop within a shell like birds and reptiles; the eggs of placental mammals have neither yolk nor shell, but they behave as if they were telolecithal. The eggs of marsupials bridge the gap between those of monotremes and eutherian mammals.

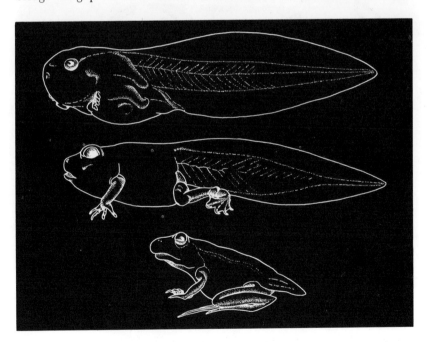

Figure 11. Three stages in the metamorphosis of the frog.

19

Birds, Reptiles, and Monotremes

The embryo proper develops from the blastodisc; the periphery of the disc grows around the yolk sphere and eventually completely encloses it (Figure 12). The advancing edge of the blastodisc around the yolk is composed of ectoderm on the outside and lateral mesoderm on the inside, next to the entoderm around the yolk. The mesoderm splits into an outer **somatic layer** against the ectoderm, the two layers comprising the **somatopleure** and an inner **splanchnic layer** against the entoderm, the two fused layers forming the **splanchnopleure**. The cavity between the layers of mesoderm is the extraembryonic coelom. The splanchnopleure, against the yolk, is the yolk sac. The connection of the embryo with the yolk sac grows at a slower rate than the rest and remains a small, tubular **yolk stalk**. A crescentic fold of somatopleure rises ahead of the early embryo, another behind it. These two folds grow towards each other and meet above the embryo, enclosing it into two cupolae, one inside the other (Figure 12). The inside cupola, the

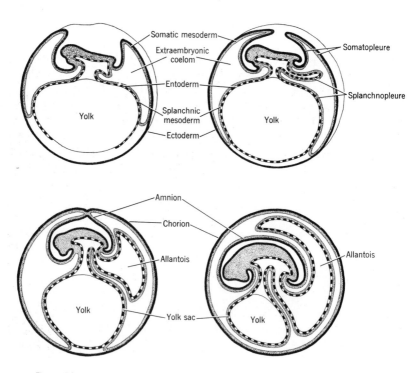

Figure 12. Development of the extraembryonic membranes in the egg of the bird.

amnion, is lined with ectoderm and covered with somatic mesoderm; the outside one, the chorion, has the same layers in the reverse order. The amnion, which is continuous with the body wall, slips over the yolk stalk and forms the fluid-filled vault around the embryo. Suspended in this fluid, the embryo is free from pressures and contacts and avoids dryness, adhesions, and deformities. The allantois first appears as a diverticulum from the yolk sac; it then grows into the extraembryonic coelom, where it expands and gradually obliterates the coelom (Figure 12). The allantois is lined with entoderm and covered with splanchnic mesoderm like the yolk sac. The splanchnic mesoderm of the allantois fuses with the somatic mesoderm of the chorion and the new layer, the **chorioallantoic membrane,** becomes rich in blood vessels and assumes a position just under the shell membrane of the egg. All of the respiration of the embryo takes place through the chorioallantoic membrane, which functions as the lung of the embryo.

Mammals

Gestation is the period during which mammalian embryos remain within the reproductive tract of the female. From the very first, mammalian embryos depend upon the maternal tissues for food and respiration, and the fetal membranes must be formed even before any differentiation of the embryo takes place. At the completion of cleavage the mammalian blastula consists of an inner cell mass suspended from the roof of a ball-like trophoblast. Cells from the underside of the inner cell mass form the entoderm, and other cells from the sides of the inner cell mass form the lateral mesoderm, which extends between the entoderm of the yolk sac and ectoderm of the trophoblast. The lateral mesoderm forms an outer somatic layer against the ectoderm of the trophoblast, the two combining to form the somatopleure, as in reptiles and birds; and an inner splanchnic layer combines with the entoderm of the yolk sac. An amnion forms by a folding of the somatopleure, as in reptiles and birds; after the amnion is formed the trophoblast is the chorion (Figure 13). In primates the amnion is formed as a cleft above the inner cell mass (see Figure 10), but regardless of the way it is formed the amnion is always composed of somatopleure.

The allantois forms as a diverticulum from the splanchnopleure of the hind gut; it grows into the extraembryonic coelom, as in reptiles and birds, and fuses with the somatopleure of the chorion. The size of the allantois is very different in different species, but its major function is to vascularize the chorion, which has no blood vessels of its own. The

21

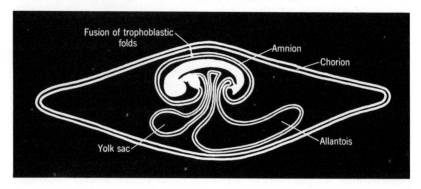

Figure 13. The fetal membranes of a mammalian embryo.

earlier blood vessels of mammalian embryos are formed in the yolk sac, but these vessels give way to **umbilical** or placental blood vessels.

Marsupials have a very brief gestation period and do not develop a real placenta. The outside wall of the chorion is smooth, and there is no intimate contact between it and the lining of the uterus. From the chorion of eutherian embryos rootlets or **villi** grow into the inner uterine wall. The villi are actually highly vascularized parts of the chorioallantoic membrane, and the degree of their intimacy with the uterus differs in different mammals. The chorionic villi and the uterine wall in which they become embedded form the placenta. The shape and size of the placenta depend upon the distribution of the villi over the surface of the chorion. In the horse, pig, and others the entire chorion is covered with villi, and the placenta is said to be **diffuse**. In ruminants the villi are clustered in numerous bean-shaped islands, and the placenta is known as **cotyledonary**. Carnivores have villi only in a band around the chorion; this is known as the **zonary** type of placenta. In bats, some primates, and rodents the villi grow from one or two rounded areas of the membrane to form a **discoidal placenta**. Placentas are also classified according to their function or the degree of intimacy that exists between the chorion and the uterus. In diffuse placentas the epithelia of the villi and the uterus remain intact, and the exchange of nutrients, gases, and wastes between fetal and maternal blood must take place not only through their respective blood vessels but also through the connective tissues and epithelia of the villi and uterus. This type is called **epitheliochorial placenta**. In the cotyledonary type of placenta the villi are more highly branched than those of the diffuse type; the uterine epithelium around the villi is destroyed, and the villi are in contact with the richly vascularized uterine connective tissue. This is the syndesmochorial placenta. In the zonary type of placenta the chorionic villi are still more intimately associated with the uterine tissue. The epithelium and the connective tissue of the uterine lining are eroded, and the chorionic villi come into contact with the bare endothelial lining of the uterine blood vessels. This is the endotheliochorial placenta. In the discoidal placenta of bats and some rodents and primates even the endothelium of the maternal vessels is eroded, and the chorionic villi form a complicated spongework through which circulates maternal blood. This is the hemochorial placenta. The most intimate placental relation is found in the rat and guinea pig, in which the chorionic villi are reduced to the bare endothelial lining of blood vessels which dangle in pools of maternal blood. This is the hemoendothelial placenta. These five types of placenta show a progressive elimination of the placental barriers between fetal and maternal blood. The hemoendothelial placenta is the most intimate, and a step further would be a complete mixture of fetal and maternal blood, a condition not known to exist normally. The embryo is attached to the placenta by the umbilical cord, through which pass the blood vessels and the stalks of the allantois and yolk sac.

All of these membranes are cast off at the time of birth as the afterbirth.

DERIVATES OF THE GERM LAYERS

Comparable tissues are derived from the same germ layers, whether in fish or mammals. The general surface ectoderm gives rise to the epidermis and all of the cutaneous structures, including the mammary glands, the lining of the anterior part of the mouth, the enamel of the teeth, the anterior lobe of the pituitary, and the lining of the anus. From the ectoderm of the neural plate and neural crest arise all of the nervous tissue and melanocytes. The entoderm gives rise to the lining of the pharynx, the respiratory system, some endocrine glands, and the entire gastrointestinal tract. The mesoderm forms the bulk of the organs and tissues.

The mesoderm is at first a sheath between the ectoderm and the entoderm; it is thicker along the sides of the neural tube and notochord than it is laterally. It becomes differentiated into segmentally spaced blocks called somites, or paraxial mesoderm, piled up along each side of the notochord and neural tube, intermediate or nephrogenic mesoderm, and lateral mesoderm (Figure 14). The lateral mesoderm splits into an outer somatic layer, and an inner splanchnic layer; the space be-

23

tween them is the coelom. This is the forerunner of the three major coelomic cavities of adult vertebrates: the **pericardial,** around the heart, the **pleural,** around the lungs, and the **peritoneal,** around the abdominal viscera.

The somites are at first solid masses of undifferentiated mesodermal cells called **mesenchyme.** Later each somite acquires a small cavity, and the mesenchyme rearranges itself in such a way that three distinct regions can be recognized (Figure 14). The cells in the ventromedial side of the somite, which comprise the **sclerotome,** migrate away and cluster around the notochord and the base of the neural tube, where they will give rise to the vertebrae and a part of each rib. The rest of the somite remains in its original position as a flattened doughnut; the part underneath the epidermis is the **dermatome,** from which the dermis of the skin in the dorsal and dorsolateral regions of the trunk differentiates; the part facing downward is the **myotome,** from which some of the skeletal muscle later develops.

From the intermediate mesoderm the reproductive and the urinary systems develop; from the splanchnic mesoderm come the blood vascular system and the smooth muscle coats and connective tissues of the gut. The somatic mesoderm gives rise to connective tissue, the limb buds and the skeletal and muscular tissues that develop in them, and the skeletal musculature and some skeletal elements of the ventrolateral body wall. From the entoderm come the lining of the pharynx and the entire digestive tract, the thyroid and parathyroid, the pancreas, liver, bladder, and the respiratory system.

When an organ is said to arise from a specific germ layer only the **parenchyma,** its characteristic tissue, is derived from that germ layer; actually, all organs have a supporting framework of connective tissue, or **stroma,** and blood vessels and nerves; every organ, then, is composed of the derivatives of several germ layers.

Generally speaking, each tissue and organ is derived from specific germ layers. This rule, however, is flexible; germ layers are fairly labile, and the same tissue under the proper stimulus could be formed by any of the primary germ layers.

THE TISSUES OF THE BODY

Tissues are aggregations of similar cells. There are only five major tissues in the animal body: the **epithelia, connective, muscular,** and **nervous tissues** and **blood;** all others are combinations of these five.

24

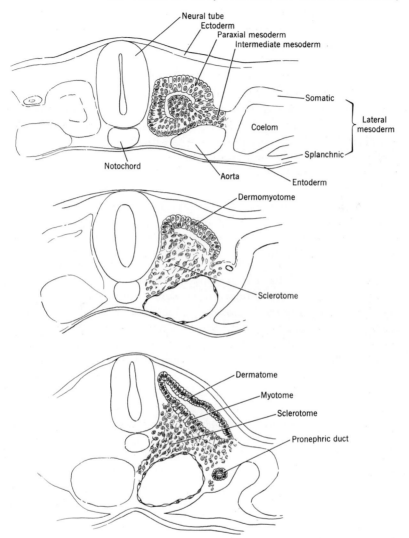

Figure 14. Differentiation of the mesoderm.

The Epithelia

An epithelium is a layer or layers of cells covering a free surface of the body and is characterized by numerous cells bound together by a small amount of intercellular material; epithelia may be formed from any germ layer. Epithelia are simple when one layer thick and strati-

25

fied when more than one layer. A **simple squamous epithelium** is a single layer of flat cells, the edges of which are more or less dovetailed and cemented together with those of adjacent cells; it is found lining the body cavities, where it is called **mesothelium,** and lining the lymph and blood vessels, where it is known as the **endothelium.** **Simple columnar epithelia** consist of long, closely packed, pillarlike cells found lining the intestine and some glands. **Simple cuboidal epithelia** are composed of cubic cells which line the tubules of glands. A **stratified squamous epithelium** has a basal layer of cuboidal or columnar cells with the cells above them becoming progressively more flattened as they approach the surface. A **stratified cuboidal epithelium** is found in the ducts of glands. In spite of their high degree of structural organization, epithelia are labile tissues which can readily change from one type to another, depending upon the functional demands made upon them.

The Connective Tissues

These tissues are characterized by the presence of widely separated cells and large amounts of intercellular substances in the form of fibers and a semifluid ground substance. **Collagenous fibers** which are white in color and nonelastic, are the most numerous and are found everywhere. **Elastic fibers** are abundant only in certain places and under certain circumstances, and the fine **reticular fibers** are numerous only around epithelial structures and blood vessels. The predominant connective tissue cells are the **fibroblasts** which form the fibers; others, such as **phagocytic cells,** which engulf debris, **mast cells,** which release heparin and histamine, and **white blood cells** are found in greater or lesser numbers. Loose or **areolar** connective tissue is found wherever a space needs to be filled and around every blood vessel and organ; **adipose tissue** or **fat** is a loose connective tissue. Dense connective tissue consists of **white fibrous tissue,** such as tendons, **elastic tissue,** the ligaments, and the **supporting** or **skeletogenous tissues,** cartilage and bone.

Blood

Blood and lymph are really connective tissues with fluid intercellular substance.

Muscular Tissue

There are three types of muscles: **cardiac, smooth,** and **skeletal,** all of which share the characteristic feature of contractility.

Nervous Tissue

Nervous tissue is composed of cells of various shapes and sizes and their peculiar supportive tissue, called **neuroglia**. In spite of differences in shape and size, nerve cells have the same structural plan, and their characteristic features are irritability and conductivity.

SUMMARY

1. Vertebrates arise from the fertilized egg.

2. Vertebrate eggs may be isolecithal with almost no yolk, mesolecithal with a moderate amount, and telolecithal with a very large amount. Isolecithal eggs are small, mesolecithal are moderate sized, and telolecithal can be gigantic. Isolecithal eggs are holoblastic and divide completely and equally. Mesolecithal eggs are also holoblastic but divide unequally. In telolecithal eggs only the small protoplasmic disc at the top of the large yolk sphere divides.

3. The egg of *Amphioxus* develops into a blastula with a hollow blastocele. During gastrulation the blastula becomes involuted, and the presumptive mesoderm and entoderm wind up inside the blastula, only the ectoderm remaining on the outside. The gastrula is at first a two-layered structure with a new cavity, the archenteron, the blastocele having been wiped out. Later, the gastrula attains three layers: the ectoderm on the outside, the entoderm on the inside, and the mesoderm between the two.

4. Mesolecithal eggs undergo holoblastic, uneven cleavage. The blastula is like that of *Amphioxus,* but the blastocele is small and displaced toward the dorsal portion; the cells in the animal pole are smaller than those in the vegetal pole. The process of gastrulation is somewhat similar to that in the eggs of *Amphioxus.*

5. In telolecithal eggs only the germinal disc at the dorsal part of the yolk sphere undergoes cleavage. The presumptive germ layers at the surface of the germinal disc flow toward the posterior median part of the blastodisc and become dammed in a thickened ridge called the primitive streak. From the primitive streak are fed out the neural plate, notochord, and mesoderm. Entoderm is formed underneath the blastodisc, ectoderm, on the surface of it.

6. At the end of cleavage the eggs of mammals have formed a blastocyst, consisting of a hollow sphere with an inner cell mass attached to the inside of the roof of a trophoblast. The embryo develops from the inner cell mass, the extraembryonic membranes, mostly from the trophoblast.

7. The embryos of most fishes and amphibians develop very rapidly and are hatched as free-swimming larvae. At metamorphosis the larvae are transformed into adult stages.

8. The embryos of reptiles, birds, and mammals are hatched, or born, at a more advanced stage. During their development the embryos live and develop within the amnion, which is in turn housed within the chorion. Amniotes also develop a yolk sac around the yolk, attached to the gut of the embryo by the yolk stalk. The allantois, a diverticulum from the hind-gut, grows into the chorionic space, expands within it, and becomes attached to the wall of the chorion. In mammals the fused allantois and chorion, and the lining of the uterus, form the placenta.

9. The vertebrate body plan is fully established at the completion of gastrulation, and the indifferent germ layers form the definitive tissues.

10. From the general surface ectoderm arise the epidermis and all of the cutaneous structures, the mammary glands, the lining of the anterior part of the mouth, the enamel of the teeth, the anterior lobe of the pituitary, and the lining of the anus. The neural ectoderm gives rise to all of the nervous tissue. From the mesoderm develop the connective tissue derivatives, all of the muscular system, the kidneys and their ducts, the gonads and their accessory ducts, the circulatory system and blood, and other structures. From the entoderm come the lining of the alimentary canal, the digestive glands, and the pharyngeal derivatives, including the larynx, trachea, lungs, gills, tonsils, thyroid, parathyroid, thymus, and other structures.

11. The body is composed of epithelia, connective tissues, blood, muscular tissues, and nervous tissues.

12. Organs are aggregations of tissues adapted to perform a specific function.

SUGGESTED READING

Arey, L. B., 1954, *Developmental Anatomy*. W. B. Saunders Company, Philadelphia and London.

Corner, G. W., 1944, *Ourselves Unborn*. Yale University Press, New Haven, Conn. This book, written by a master with consummate artistry, is as exciting as a novel. Every student of biology should read it.

Maximow, A. A., and W. Bloom, 1956, *A Textbook of Histology*. W. B. Saunders Company, Philadelphia and London.

Mossman, H. W., 1937, "Comparative Morphogenesis of the Fetal Membranes and Accessory Uterine Structures." Contributions to *Embryology*, Vol. XXVI, pp. 129–246. Carnegie Inst. Wash., Publ. 479, Washington, D. C.

Witschi, E., 1956, *Development of Vertebrates*. W. B. Saunders Company, Philadelphia and London. This is a thorough and beautifully illustrated book.

3

THE
CHORDATA

GENERAL INTRODUCTION

Taxonomy, the science of classifying and naming living things, provides a method that makes possible their specific designation. Even those who find the details of taxonomy unexciting cannot escape the fact that things must be named and separated from all others. In naming animals the taxonomist attempts to arrange them in a logical, formal order and groups them according to their common characteristic features. Some animals which are superficially very unlike are closely related and have stemmed from a hypothetical common ancestor. The grouping together of the sloth and the armadillo, the sheep and the ox, or the pig and the hippopotamus would seem to be illogical if the anatomy, development, physiology, and ancestral history of these animals were not similar. Valid classification is based on a large series of criteria, since it can be very misleading to place together animals which merely have similar structures. Wholly dissimilar animals may come to resemble one another by convergence. The Australian marsupials have attained striking resemblances to many totally different mammals.

The ancestral history of animals, called phylogeny, is reconstructed by the study of anatomy and development and of fossil remains. If the lineage of every animal were known, it would be possible to construct a precise natural hierarchy, beginning with the apparently simplest forms and progressing to the most complex ones; but the details of the phylogeny of most animals have been lost in time and only here and there fossil remains have been found that connect the past with the present. It is easier to be dogmatic about the distinctness of a group of animals if very little is known about its phylogeny than if numerous connecting links exist. Because of these uncertainties complete agreement is lacking among experts, and the system of classification is arbitrary and subject to change.

The crust of the earth is an impressive gallery of **fossils**. These are documents of plants and animals that have existed over the ages. In order to have some appreciation of the genealogies of living forms which have been compiled through assiduous search for fossil records, the student must first keep in mind the vastness of geologic time. From the study of the rate of disintegration of uranium to lead it has been estimated that some rocks in the crust of the earth are about 3 billion years old. Life may have originated 1500 million years ago, but recognizable fossils date back about 550 million years. Geologic time is divided into eras and periods; life evolved through four eras, which from the oldest to the most recent are the **Pre-Cambrian, Paleozoic, Mesozoic,** and **Cenozoic.**

Pre-Cambrian

Life probably originated some 1500 million years ago in the lower periods of this era. The early living things, however, were of such a nature that they left almost no recognizable fossil records. Fossils became numerous and intelligible in the upper Pre-Cambrian era.

Paleozoic

This era, which began about 505 million years ago, lasted 300 million years. Fragmentary fossil remains of the first known vertebrates appeared in the lower periods of the Paleozoic era, some 425 million years ago. In the middle of Paleozoic time vertebrate fossils became very clear; all the major groups of fishes became established, and amphibians and reptiles arose.

Mesozoic

Beginning some 205 million years ago, this era lasted about 130 million years. Bony fishes became numerous, and birds and mammals appeared. Dinosaurs were the most numerous land vertebrates. These curious reptiles evolved along lines so varied that they became adapted to nearly every inhabitable environment; most of them, however, became extinct at the end of the Mesozoic era.

Cenozoic

This extends over a period of about 75 million years and continues to the present time. The Cenozoic era is characterized by the abundance of birds and mammals and, during the last million years, the ascent of man.

CLASSIFICATION

The principle of classification is based on a so-called **hierarchy,** with each unit incorporating progressively larger units.

The following is the basic framework of taxonomic hierarchy:

Kingdom
Phylum
Class
Order
Family
Genus
Species

The most general division of this system is the kingdom, which separates living things broadly into plants or animals; there are progressively more phyla, classes, orders, families, and genera. The smallest category is the species, in which each group is composed of individuals so alike that they are nearly indistinguishable from one another; species are further divided into subspecies.

Since in such rigid hierarchical systems there are uncertainties about the precise position of some animals, each step is subdivided into new categories, such as subphylum, superclass, subclass, infraclass, etc. It is sobering to reflect that none of the steps of this hierarchy can be spoken of in absolute terms, and only species is more or less definable. George Gaylord Simpson defines a species as *a group of living things in which the hereditary characters of any member can be passed on to the descend-*

ants of any other member. In practice, however, there are pitfalls even in this definition. Authorities do not always agree about the exact family, genus, or even species of some animals.

The **phylum Chordata** is divided into the **subphyla Acraniata** and **Craniata** or **Vertebrata**. The Acraniata are included in this phylum because at least during their larval or developmental stages they have a pharyngeal gill chamber, a notochord, and a dorsal nervous system. There are three classes of Acraniata; the **Hemichordata**, which are worm-like animals that live buried in the sand; the **Urochordata**, or tunicates, which possess chordate features only as larval forms; and the **Cephalochordata**, to which belong the small fishlike *Amphioxus*.

In this book we are concerned only with the classification of living Vertebrata. For a more thorough consideration of vertebrate classification the student should consult Romer's *Vertebrate Paleontology*.

The first vertebrates were the fishlike, jawless **Agnatha**, from which sprang the jawed fishes, or **gnathostomes**. Offshoots of gnathostomes took to living on land, where the great diversity of environment forced them to differentiate in many directions. The subphylum Vertebrata is divided into two great superclasses: the **Pisces**, or fishes, and the **Tetrapoda**, or land vertebrates.

Subphylum	Superclass	Class
Vertebrata	Pisces	Agnatha—lampreys and hagfishes Chondrichthyes—sharks and rays Osteichthyes—bony fishes
	Tetrapods	Amphibia—frogs, toads, salamanders Reptilia—reptiles Aves—birds Mammalia—mammals

The reptiles, birds, and mammals are often referred to as the amniotes. This is not a term of classification; it simply signifies that the members of these three classes all develop within an extraembryonic, fluid-filled sac or amnion.

SUPERCLASS PISCES

Class Agnatha

These jawless, fishlike animals have a round, suckerlike mouth, a naked, slimy skin, numerous gill slits, and no paired fins. The class has several extinct orders, and the only living one is the **Cyclostomata,** which has two suborders: **Myxinoidea,** or hagfishes, and **Petromyzontia,** or lampreys. The larvae of lampreys, known as Ammocoetes, are ideal primitive forms to study in comparative anatomy.

Class Chondrichthyes

These fishes have a cartilaginous skeleton; they are characteristically sharklike, and their skin is usually covered with spinelike scales. They have no swim bladder. The two living orders are the **Elasmobranchii,** to which sharks and skates belong, and the **Holocephali,** to which the chimaeras belong.

Class Osteichthyes

The skeleton of these fishes is partially or entirely ossified. The most distinct features of the class are a bony **operculum** that covers the gills and a swim bladder that in some forms functions as a respiratory organ. The two large subclasses are the **Choanichthyes** and the **Teleostomi.** There are two orders of Choanichthyes: the **Crossopterygii,** or lobe-finned fishes, whose only living representative is *Latimeria,* and the **Dipnoi,** or lungfishes. The most characteristic feature of these orders is an open canal between the nostrils and the roof of the mouth through which air can be drawn in or expelled with the mouth closed; these fishes also have an elaborate swim bladder that functions as a respiratory organ.

Subclass Teleostomi. This subclass consists of the orders **Chondrostei, Holostei,** and **Teleostei.** Chondrostei have a skeleton largely composed of cartilage and represented mostly by fossil Paleozoic forms and three primitive living ones: *Polypterus,* the sturgeons, and the paddlefish. The Holostei, which include the gar pikes, and the bowfin *Amia* have a bonier skeleton than the Chondrostei. Together, Chondrostei and Holostei can be grouped under the order **Ganoidea.** The skin of the Ganoidea is covered with large **ganoid** or **cycloid scales,** and the tail is **heterocercal** or asymmetrical. The Teleostei are the modern bony fishes and are by far the most numerous forms of the Pisces.

SUPERCLASS TETRAPODA

Class Amphibia

Although still mostly aquatic, some of the members of this class live much of their life on land. Amphibians have four limbs which may be lost secondarily and lungs which may also be lost. The two great orders, the **Urodela** or **Caudata**, or salamanders, and the **Salientia** or **Anura**, or frogs and toads, are very different animals. A third order, the **Apoda** or **Gymnophiona**, comprise a small group of limbless, blind, wormlike, burrowing animals.

Class Reptilia

This extremely varied group is composed of both aquatic and terrestrial forms. The turtles of the order **Chelonia** are toothless animals enclosed in a boxlike armature of bone on the inside and horny scales on the outside. The order **Rhynchocephalia** has only one living representative, *Sphenodon*, probably the most primitive living reptile, which resembles a lizard and has a rudimentary third eye. The **Squamata** include lizards and snakes. These were formerly separated into **Lacertilia**, the lizards, and **Ophidia**, the snakes. It is evident that in spite of some striking gross differences, snakes are highly specialized lizards. The order **Crocodilia**, the crocodiles and alligators, consists of large amphibious animals with coarse bony plates in their skin.

Class Aves

Birds are warm-blooded and the only vertebrates with feathers. They have a horny beak that replaces the teeth, and their anterior limbs are specialized into wings. This extremely diversified class ranges from aerial to flightless forms; and flightless birds may be so specialized as to be completely terrestrial or completely aquatic. In spite of the great diversities in size, adaptation, and specialization, the general body form of birds has remained unchanged. The two superorders of living birds are the **Palaeognathae**, or **Ratitae**, and the **Neognathae**. To the Palaeognathae belong the large, flightless ostrich, the emu, the cassowary, the rhea, the kiwi, and the odd, partridgelike tinamous of South America. To the Neognathae belong all the modern, carinate birds; there are twenty-two different orders which are not listed here.

Class Mammalia

The mammals are warm-blooded vertebrates with hair and mammary glands. The whales, which are mammals, are the largest living animals. The class is divided into three subclasses: **Prototheria**, **Metatheria**, and **Eutheria**.

The Prototheria are egg-laying mammals, their young developing outside the reproductive tract of the mother. This subclass has the single order **Monotremata,** to which belong three genera: *Ornithorhynchus,* the duck-billed platypus, and *Tachyglossus* and *Zaglossus,* two kinds of spiny anteaters.

The Metatheria consist of the order **Marsupialia.** These primitive animals develop within the reproductive tract of the female but are born very prematurely and complete their development within the **marsupium,** a pouch of skin on the abdomen of the female. The opossum is a North American marsupial.

The Eutheria are the true placental mammals whose young develop entirely within the reproductive tract of the female. Depending on how they are grouped, there are sixteen or more orders in the Eutheria:

Order Insectivora. The moles, shrews, and hedgehogs are small, nocturnal, burrowing animals.

Order Dermoptera. The flying lemur, the only member of this group, is about the size of a cat, and has loose skin folds that extend from the body to the limbs, as in the bat. This animal takes flying leaps, extends its limbs, and glides with grace.

Order Chiroptera. The bat is characterized by greatly elongated metacarpals and digits and a membranous skin fold that stretches from the body to the limbs. Bats are all expert flyers; they show much difference in size, body form, and feeding habits.

Order Primates. The lemurs, monkeys, apes, and man are terrestrial or arboreal hairy animals with prehensile hands and feet and, in a few forms, a prehensile tail. They all have relatively large cerebral hemispheres.

Order Edentata. The armadillos, sloths, and anteaters are all related, in spite of the great superficial differences in appearance.

Order Pholidota. The pangolin or scaly anteater is a toothless animal completely covered with large, horny scales.

Order Lagomorpha. Even though this group of rabbits and hares is often included with the rodents, both their anatomy and their evolutionary history are sufficiently different to justify classifying them as a separate order.

Order Rodentia. The most distinguishing feature of the rodents is their long incisors, which have enamel only in front and which keep growing throughout life. This very large group includes mice and rats, beavers, and porcupines.

Order Cetacea. The whales are naked-skinned, aquatic mammals, many of which are gigantic in size. The fore limbs are modified into flat, finlike paddles, and the hind limbs are vestigial. The two sub-orders are the **Odontoceti**, the toothed whales, porpoises, and dolphins, and the **Mysticeti**, the toothless or whalebone whales.

Order Carnivora. The carnivores are rapacious flesh eaters with large canine teeth. The two suborders are these: the **Fissipedia**, cats, dogs, bears, otters, weasels, etc., and the **Pinnipedia**, to which the seals, sea lions, and walruses belong.

Order Tubulidentata. The aardvark, the only genus and species of this order, is sufficiently different from all other mammals to be considered a separate order. The aardvark has a few small teeth with no enamel, a long snout, and a very long tongue.

Order Proboscidea. The elephant is a very large animal whose nose and upper lip are modified into a long prehensile trunk.

Order Sirenia. The sea cow, or manatee, and the dugong, are large aquatic herbivores with no hind limbs.

Order Perissodactyla. These are large, odd-toed, hooved animals with the third digit forming the axis of the limb. The three suborders comprise an odd assortment: the **Equoidea** are the horses and zebras, the **Tapiroidea**, the tapirs, and the **Rhinocerotoidea**, the rhinoceros.

Order Hyracoidea. The coney is a short-tailed herbivore about the size and shape of a guinea pig; its upper incisors are like those of rodents, but the molars resemble those of ungulates. Its front feet have four nailed toes; its hind feet have three. The toes resemble those of ungulates.

Order Artiodactyla. These are even-toed, hooved, large herbivorous animals. The three suborders are **Suina**, which includes the pig and the hippopotamus; **Tylopoda**, which has a ruminant stomach and includes the camel and llama; and the **Pecora**, which has a very complex ruminant stomach, and includes the sheep, ox, giraffe, and deer.

Thirty-two orders of mammals have been described, but only those named here are extant; the others are extinct. All of the surviving orders have extinct families, genera, or species. The number of extinct families and genera is probably larger than that of the surviving, and most orders of mammals are on the decline. The great era of mammals, then, is passing.

It may surprise the student to find in this schema that man and the primates are placed not at the top of the orders of Mammalia but actually far down in the list between the bats and the Edentata. However, primates are the most generalized existing mammals. In spite of the size of their brains, primates have not developed very far in the hierarchy of specialization.

SUMMARY

1. The sequence of the ascension of life on earth took place over the following eras:

Eras	Millions of Years Since Beginning	Duration in Millions of Years	Ascension of Vertebrates
Cenozoic	75	75	Man Mammals and birds numerous
Mesozoic	205	130	Birds and mammals arise Reptiles and amphibians very numerous; reign of dinosaurs Bony fishes numerous
Paleozoic	505	300	Rise of reptiles Amphibians numerous All aquatic vertebrates numerous First vertebrates
Pre-Cambrian	2000	1500	First fossils Origin of life (?)

2. Vertebrate taxonomy is based upon an hierarchical system that can be expressed in the following way:

> Kingdom
> Phylum
> Class
> Order
> Family
> Genus
> Species

3. The following is a synopsis of the systematic classification of the Chordata:

Kingdom: Animalia
Phylum: Chordata

Subphylum:

A. Acraniata
   Class:
   1. Hemichordata—acorn worms
   2. Urochordata—tunicates
   3. Cephalochordata—*Amphioxus*

B. Craniata or Vertebrata
   Superclass:

   a. Pisces
      Class:
      I. Agnatha—jawless, fishlike animals
         Order:
         Cyclostomata
         Suborder:
            Myxinoidea—hagfishes
            Petromyzontia—lampreys
      II. Chondrichthyes—fishes with a cartilaginous skeleton
         Order:
            Elasmobranchii—sharks and rays
            Holocephali—chimaeras
      III. Osteichthyes—fishes with bony operculum and skeleton
         Subclass:
         1. Choanichthyes
            Order:
               Crossopterygii—*Latimeria*
               Dipnoi—lungfishes

   b. Tetrapoda
      Class:
      I. Amphibia
         Order:
         1. Urodela—salamanders
         2. Salientia—frogs and toads
         3. Apoda—caecilians
      II. Reptilia
         Order:
         1. Chelonia—turtles
         2. Squamata—lizards and snakes
         3. Crocodilia—crocodiles

III. Aves
    Superorder:
      Palaeognathae—ratites and tinamous
      Neognathae—carinate birds
IV. Mammalia
    Subclass:
    1. Prototheria—egg-laying mammals
      Order:
        Monotremata—duck-billed platypus, spiny anteater
    2. Metatheria—marsupials
      Order:
        Marsupialia
    3. Eutheria—placental mammals
      Order:
        1. Insectivora—moles, shrews, hedgehogs
        2. Dermoptera—flying lemurs
        3. Chiroptera—bats
        4. Primates—lemurs, monkeys, apes, and man
        5. Edentata—armadillos, sloths, anteaters
        6. Pholidota—pangolins
        7. Lagomorpha—rabbits and hares
        8. Rodentia—rodents
        9. Cetacea—whales
       10. Carnivora—flesh eaters
       11. Tubulidentata—aardvark
       12. Proboscidea—elephants
       13. Sirenia—sea cows
       14. Hyracoidea—conies
       15. Perissodactyla—odd-toed ungulates
       16. Artiodactyla—even-toed ungulates

SUGGESTED READING

Clark, W. E. Le Gros, 1957, *History of the Primates.* University of Chicago Press, Chicago, Ill.

Colbert, G. H., 1955, *Evolution of the Vertebrates.* John Wiley and Sons, New York.

Romer, A. S., 1945, *Vertebrate Paleontology.* University of Chicago Press, Chicago, Ill.

Simpson, G. G., 1945, "The Principles of Classification and a Classification of Mammals." *Bull. Am. Museum Nat. Hist.,* **85.**

———, 1952, *The Meaning of Evolution. A Study of the History of Life and of Its Significance for Man.* Yale University Press, New Haven, Conn.

CHAPTER

4

CHAPTER

4

Figure 1. Epidermis from the back of man.

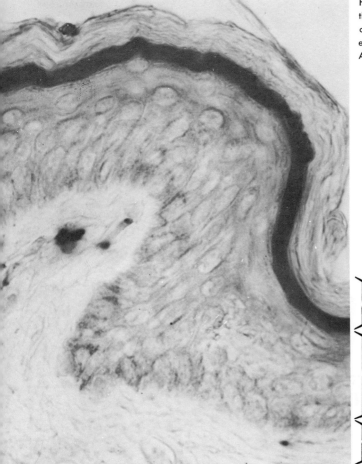

Figure 2. Melanocytes from the skin of a thirteen-and-one-half-week-old human embryo. (Courtesy of Dr. A. Zimmermann.)

Corneal layer

Malpighian layer

Dermis

SKIN

INTRODUCTION

Skin, the largest organ of the body, has the important function of manufacturing around the body an outer mantle that protects the tissues from becoming either desiccated or waterlogged. Skin is a marvelously versatile organ; it can form structures of such astonishing complexity as the feathers of birds; it can form scales, hair, spines, horns, claws, and hooves and a variety of glands that secrete many different substances. In any vertebrate the cells that form any one of these various structures could as well form any other. The differentiation of these cells is guided by certain forces which, when altered, can change the character of one organ into that of another totally different. Skin, then, is also a labile organ that can undergo profound changes to meet different demands.

The basic component elements of skin are the **epidermis** on the outside, a stratified squamous epithelium derived from the ectoderm, and the **dermis**, or **corium**, underneath, composed of connective tissue derived from the mesoderm (Figure 1). Although most of the recognizable gross features of the skin are formed by the epidermis, the dermis is the ground upon which the epidermal structures grow; it nurtures the epidermis and evokes certain genetic potentialities in it while suppressing others. Even though most of the structures described in this chapter are developed from the epidermis, let the student be constantly aware of the important role of the dermis.

The dermis has the property of combining with metallic salts, or tannic acid, to form an insoluble product called leather. In the processing of animal hides the epidermis is usually shaved off and only the dermis is used. Commercial furs are tanned hides with the hair left in place.

Such **external appendages** as scales, feathers, hair, horns, claws, nails, and hooves and the **internal appendages,** sebaceous glands, sweat glands, mammary glands, mucous and scent glands, all differentiate from the epidermis.

The epidermis consists of two main layers: the **Malpighian,** a variable thick layer of living cells at the bottom, and the **corneal,** a superficial layer of dead horny cells (see Figure 4). The basal cells of the Malpighian layer divide and rise gradually to the surface, manufacturing the horny substance **keratin** as they go. By the time they reach the corneal layer they die. The mission of these cells, then, is to form keratin and die.

Variable amounts and kinds of pigment impart color to the skin. The commonest is **melanin,** formed by the melanocytes (Figure 2) derived from the neural crest (see Chapter 8). The nomenclature for pigment-forming and pigment-bearing cells is unnecessarily confused, and for the sake of simplicity all pigment cells will be called **melanocytes.** Pigmented skin, then, has a triple origin: the epidermis is derived from the ectoderm, the dermis, from the mesoderm, and the melanocytes, from the neural crest.

COMPARATIVE ANATOMY OF THE SKIN

Amphioxus

The epidermis is a single epithelial layer covered with a thin cuticle. Single glandular cells or **goblet cells** secrete mucus which protects the surface from injury. The skin is not pigmented.

The dermis is very thin and barely distinct from the subjacent connective tissue.

Cyclostomes

The epidermis is a thin, stratified squamous epithelium which secretes a protective pellicle at the surface. Numerous **unicellular glands** scattered among the epidermal cells secrete so much mucus when the animals are disturbed that the water around them becomes turbid. The dermis is thin and contains melanocytes located just under the epidermis. The "teeth" in the buccal funnel are actually horny epidermal appendages.

Fishes

The epidermis of fishes is stratified, and the surface cells secrete a cuticular layer. Many unicellular and saclike multicellular mucous glands keep the body covered with mucus. Some fishes have epidermal poison glands at the base of the spines of the pectoral fins. The luminescent organs of deep-sea fishes are modified skin glands. Numerous melanocytes in the dermis produce black, red, and yellow pigments; these cells contract or expand under the influence of the pituitary and adrenal hormones, changing the color of the fish to adapt it to its environment.

Although some species have none, the most characteristic external feature of fishes is the presence of dermal bony plates or scales. The total covering of bony scales comprises the **dermal skeleton** of fishes. The **dermal bones** of the endoskeleton are believed to be derived from the dermal skeleton. The most spectacular scales are found in the ganoid fishes, whose ganoid scales consist of bony plates covered with a shiny layer of **ganoin,** also formed from the dermis. In the sturgeons ganoid scales are arranged in groups or rows and are crowded over the head, where they form the roof and sides of the skull. In the gar pike and others the entire skin is covered with an armor of rhombic bony plates (Figure 3*a*).

Elasmobranchs have **placoid scales** with a basal bony plate from which a spine projects through the epidermis (Figure 3*b*), giving the skin a sandpaper quality. The spines have a hollowed pulp cavity at the base filled with loose connective tissue (Figure 3*c*). Placoid scales are more like teeth than scales. At the edge of the mouth of elasmobranchs placoid scales undergo a gradual transition into teeth; this suggests that these scales are the archetypes of teeth.

Most bony fishes have **cycloid** or **ctenoid scales.** Cycloid scales are thin, oval bony plates with the distal free end marked with fine concentric lines (Figure 3*d*); coarse, unevenly spaced lines indicate the inter-

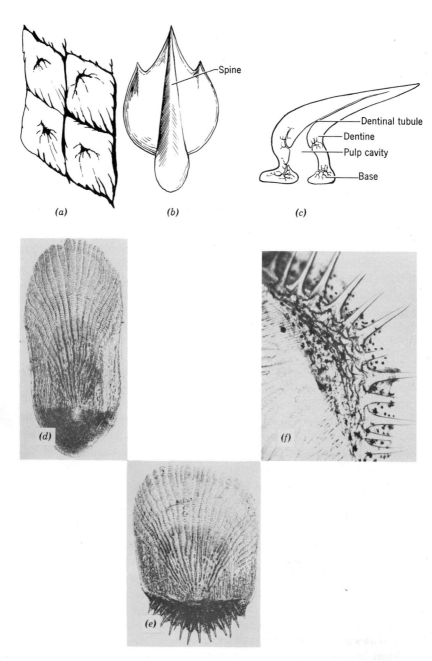

Figure 3.   Scales of fishes: (a) ganoid scales; (b) placoid scale of squalus, dorsal view; (c) placoid scale, longitudinal section; (d) cycloid scale of flounder; (e) ctenoid scale of flounder; (f) detail of teeth of ctenoid scale.

46

ruption of growth caused by the winter season or the preparation for spawning. Ctenoid scales resemble cycloid scales, except that the free edge has a serrated or comblike appearance (Figure 3*e,f*). Both types of scales grow from sockets in the dermis, and the base of the free end is covered with epidermis. The free ends of successive scales are **imbricated**; that is, they overlap like shingles. Usually these scales are so thin that they are translucent and allow the color of the melanocytes under them to show through.

Amphibians

The epidermis is thin in aquatic forms and thick in terrestrial ones. A distinct corneal layer of dead, keratinized cells is very thick in terrestrial forms. The dermis of aquatic forms is richly vascularized, the skin of these animals being an important respiratory organ.

Many multicellular, mucus-secreting glands keep the skin moist. All amphibians have small and large poison glands. The large, wartlike **parotoid glands** on the sides of toads, just behind the head, are poison glands which secrete adrenalinlike substances. Tree toads have on their toes suckerlike pads equipped with glands that secrete a viscid substance.

Although the extinct stegocephalians were covered with dermal bony plates, such scales are mostly lacking in modern amphibians. Dermal scales are found in some toads, and all caecilians have small fishlike scales buried under the epidermis. Cornified epidermal protuberances at the end of the hind toes of some toads resemble claws or **epidermal scales.**

Reptiles

The epidermis has a thick, compact corneal layer. Snakes and lizards have two fully formed corneal layers at any one time. The outer layer is cast off periodically, more or less intact; this is known as **ecdysis.** When the outer layer is shed the one underneath is exposed, and a new one is formed under it from the Malpighian layer. At the time of ecdysis a partially formed third corneal layer is found above the Malpighian layer.

The dermis has a thin superficial layer and a thicker deep layer. In some reptiles melanocytes are gathered in the superficial dermal layer, just under the epidermis; in others they are found within the epidermis.

The popular concept that reptiles are slimy is wrong, since their skin is dry. Snakes, alligators, and turtles have **scent glands** under the lower jaw or in the cloaca. The cloacal scent glands of some snakes secrete evil-smelling substances.

The skin of reptiles is characteristically covered with epidermal horny scales; turtles and crocodilians also have bony dermal plates. The plates of the turtle form a boxlike armor covered with large horny scales called **scutes. Tortoise shell** is the polished horny covering of large tortoises. Alligators and *Sphenodon* have dermal scales on the back and riblike dermal bones, called **gastralia,** in the dermis of the abdomen. Some lizards and large snakes have small dermal plates underneath the epidermal scales, and modified epidermal scales form spines around the head or back of some lizards. The rattle of the rattlesnake is composed of highly modified epidermal scales. The beak of the turtle is covered with a heavy layer of horn manufactured by the underlying epidermis.

The last joint of the toes of reptiles is covered with a claw composed of a dorsal convex horny plate, the **unguis,** and a ventral concave one, the **subunguis.**

Birds

The skin is relatively thin. The epidermis is composed of a desquamating horny layer and a relatively thick Malpighian layer. The thin dermis usually contains no melanocytes, these cells being restricted to the follicles of the feathers.

The skin of birds is notably free of glands other than the **uropygial gland,** located above the tail. This gland secretes an oily substance used by birds in preening their feathers. Some birds lack even this gland.

The tarsi and the toes of birds are covered with horny epidermal scales (Figure 4). The arrangement of these scales is so characteristic that they can be used as a means of classifying different orders and genera. In some orders of birds the males develop a bony spur covered with a horny cone at the back of the tarsus. Spurs are ornaments, but they are also used as weapons of combat. Horny spurs may be found on the wings of such birds as bustards and jacanas.

The last joint of the digits is covered with a claw, particularly well developed in birds of prey (Figure 4). Small clawlike corneal structures are found on the fingers of the wings of some young birds, and the maxilla and mandible of all birds are covered with a horny epidermal beak. The size and shape of the beak are among the most characteristic features of birds and reflect their feeding habits.

Since no other vertebrate possesses them, birds could be defined as vertebrates with feathers. Feathers have probably evolved from epidermal scales similar to those of reptiles. They grow over the skin in certain

48

tracts called **pterylae** (Figure 5); other regions, the **apteria,** appear to be naked, although they contain sparse, barely visible feathers. Most aquatic birds have small apteria, but penguins have none. Feathers grow from feather follicles, which are cylinders of surface epidermis sunk deep into the dermis. The architecture of the feather is extremely complicated; it is a rewarding experience for the student to examine one closely with the naked eye and under the low power of the microscope. The varieties of color, size, and shape of feathers are limitless. In general, three major types of feathers are recognized. Hair, or bristlelike feathers, growing around the mouth and face are called **filoplumes.** Fluffy down feathers with a weak central stem are the **plumulae. Plumae** are the large, stiff, contour feathers and those of the wings and tail. On the breast of herons and hawks are patches of feathers, called **powder down,** in which the feathers become fragmented as they emerge from their follicles, giving them a dusty appearance.

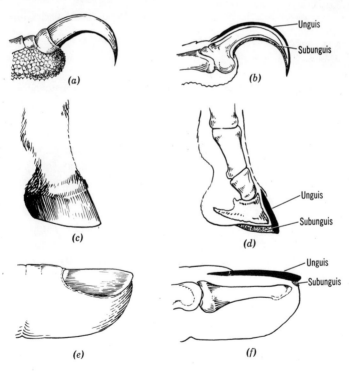

Figure 4. Claw, hoof, and nail: (a) claw of the osprey; (b) section through the claw; (c) hoof of the horse; (d) section through the hoof; (e) nail of man; (f) section through the nail.

Figure 5. Chick embryo showing pterylae and apteria.

Plumae have a stiff central shaft, or **rachis,** from the sides of which grow the **barbs** (Figure 6a). From these barbs grow short **barbules; hooklets** growing from the barbules are interlocked with the barbules in front of them to form a flat shield called the **vane** (Figure 6b). The vane can be spread apart by disengaging the hooks. Several pigments give feathers their color; irridescent or metallic sheens, however, are caused by the refraction of light or by spectral interference similar to that formed by a drop of oil on the surface of water. Feathers are shed seasonally, during molting, and are replaced by new ones; they are not shed all at once, and each species has a characteristic pattern of replacing them. Usually they are replaced gradually, so that the bird does not become naked and its flight is not appreciably impaired. Feathers are excellent insulating structures and provide the bird with a handsome and efficient thermoregulatory cloak.

Mammals

The skin of mammals contains a striking variety of external appendages and numerous and different glands. Just as feathers are peculiar to birds, only mammals have hair and mammary glands. It is not possible to give an accurate generalized description of mammalian skin, since even in the same animals there exist great topographic differences.

The epidermis, thick or thin, has a sharp transition between the Malpighian and the corneal layers. At the junction of these layers is a third, the **granular layer,** whose cells contain microscopically visible granules (Figure 7). The corneal layer is generally thick and flaky; as the cells are lost at the surface they are replaced by cells moving up from the **basal layer,** there being a balance between the rate of loss and the rate of cell division. Wherever the animal's body comes in contact with external objects, as on the soles or palms or in friction areas, the epidermis is many times thicker than elsewhere. It has a thick Malpighian layer, with a basal layer, a **spinous layer,** a distinct granular layer, a **hyalin layer,** and a very thick corneal layer (Figure 7). In most mammals the underside of the epidermis in contact with the dermis is rela-

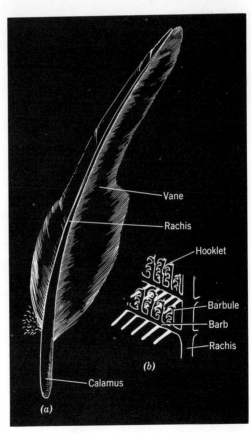

Figure 6.
(a) Feather (plume);
(b) anatomy of a feather.

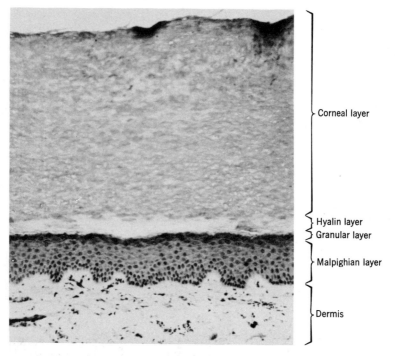

Corneal layer

Hyalin layer
Granular layer

Malpighian layer

Dermis

Figure 7. Epidermis from the palm of man.

tively flat, but in man it forms valleys and ridges, making the attachment very intimate.   The underside of the epidermis of the friction areas is more highly sculptured than elsewhere.

The entire surface of human skin is furrowed by numerous intersecting lines which form geometric figures characteristically different in each individual (Figure 8a). Everyone is familiar with the prints (Figure 8b) found on the underside of the fingers and toes of most primates; similar patterns are also found on the palms and soles.   In man these sculpturings, established in the four-month fetus, consist of delicate grooves and ridges that outline patterns so characteristic in each individual that they are infallible marks of identification.

Mammalian epidermis contains variable numbers of melanocytes (see Figure 2). These have long thin processes insinuated between the epidermal cells, to which they in some way transfer melanin. Skin is pink, yellow, brown, or black, depending on the quantity and quality of melanin it contains. In some mammals the melanocytes are located in the dermis.

52

The dermis of mammals is thicker than that of other vertebrates. That of the elephant and the rhinoceros may reach a thickness of several inches. The dermis is composed of a superficial thin layer under the epidermis and a deep, thicker layer which is tough and fibrous. Underneath the dermis is the **fatty layer** of the skin, the storage depot of energy, which is thicker in certain parts of the body than in others. The lard of pigs and the blubber of aquatic mammals represents an exaggerated expression of this layer; the blubber of whales may reach a thickness of several feet.

The skin of mammals is very glandular. Many, but not all, mammals possess simple tubular sweat glands; in most rodents sweat glands are found only on the soles and digital pads; guinea pigs and rabbits have none at all. Sweat glands are numerous in the skin of carnivores and ungulates, but in no other mammals are they so numerous as in the primates and particularly in man. Two types of sweat glands exist: large, **apocrine glands,** which secrete a milky fluid, and smaller **eccrine glands,** which secrete watery sweat. The sweat glands over the general body surface of man are mostly eccrine, whereas those of most other mammals are apocrine; in man apocrine glands are restricted to the axillae, the

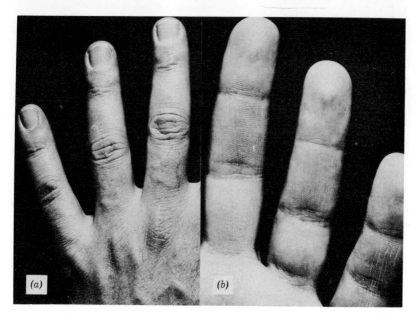

Figure 8. (a) Back of a human hand and fingers showing the pattern of interesting lines; (b) ventral side of fingers showing finger prints.

outer ear canal, the nipple of the breasts, the external genitalia, and around the orifice of the anus. The friction areas in the bodies of mammals, and particularly man, are very rich fields of eccrine glands.

Only mammals possess **mammary glands.** These complex, multilobulated, cutaneous glands produce milk and are functional only after the young are born; when suckling stops the glands regress to a resting state. They are under the control of hormones from the pituitary gland and from the ovary. In the Prototheria mammary glands are primitive and open to the surface at the bottom of depressions on the belly skin. The milk oozes over the hairs and is lapped up by the young. Another oddity of the Prototheria is that both parents attain functional mammary glands. In Metatheria and Eutheria glands are functional only in the female; they open to the surface through elevations called **nipples** or **teats.** In nipples the ducts open at the tip; in teats the ducts converge toward a common receptacle at the base called a **cistern;** a large single canal drains the cistern (Figure 9). Teats in mammals are much commoner than nipples. The number of teats or nipples is variable and usually reflects the size of the litter. Bats, man, horses, whales, and elephants, all of whom give birth to one or two young, have only two; mammals which have many young at one birth have correspondingly larger numbers of nipples or teats.

Mammary glands develop along the **milk line,** a thickened ectodermal ridge on the ventrolateral side of the embryo, extending from just inside the posterior limb to the axilla. Adult mammary glands may be located posteriorly between the hind legs, as in the cow and the horse; they may be distributed all over the milk line, as in the mouse, the pig, the cat and others; or they may be restricted to the pectoral region, as in most primates, elephants, and manatees.

Sebaceous glands secrete a fatty, oily substance that keeps the skin supple. Most of these glands open into the hair canals and are so intimately associated with hair follicles that they are a part of the **pilosebaceous units** (Figure 10).

The skin of some mammals possesses horny, epidermal scales similar to those of reptiles. Except for the belly, the entire body of the scaly anteater is covered with very large, shingled scales with the consistency of horn. The armadillo is encased in a shell formed by bony dermal scales fashioned in a mosaic pattern and covered with horny epidermal scales and hair. In most other mammals scales are less spectacular. Shingled epidermal scales are found on the tails of many rodents.

The toes and fingers of mammals terminate in a **claw, nail,** or **hoof** produced by the epidermis (see Figure 4). Claws, similar to those of

Figure 9. Diagram of a nipple on the left and a teat on the right.

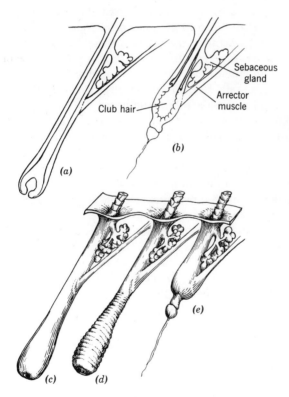

Figure 10. Schematic diagrams of human hair follicles: (a) longitudinal section of growing follicle; (b) longitudinal section of resting follicle; (c) growing follicle; (d) transition stage; (e) resting follicle.

reptiles and birds, are composed of the unguis, a convex dorsal shield, and the subunguis, which is concave and ventral. The two elements are about the same length.

Nails, found in man and other primates, are composed of a broad and flattened unguis and almost no subunguis (see Figure 4). Hooves, found in ungulates, consist of a very thick unguis which surrounds the front of the toe; a cleft of the posterior part of the toe, called the **frog,** is covered with thickened epidermis. The subunguis covers the ventral side of the toe (see Figure 4). These appendages are constantly worn through use and must grow at the same rate they are worn.

Some Artiodactyla and Perissodactyla possess horns. True horns are composed of keratin produced by the epidermis. Growing from the middle of the forehead of the rhinoceros are one or two solid horns composed of coarse keratin fibers cemented together and for this reason called **keratin fiber horns.** The horns of Artiodactyla consist of a core of bone growing from the frontal bone of the skull and covered with a heavy mantle of keratin. In a sense, these horns are derived both from the mesoderm and from the ectoderm. A similar type of horn, the **pronghorn,** found only in the American pronghorn antelope, has a bony core from the frontal bone, but the horny cap possesses one to three solid horny prongs. Unlike other true horns, the outer part of this horn is shed and replaced annually.

The deer family possess antlers, which are long extensions of the frontal bone. Growing antlers are completely covered with skin and are said to be **in velvet** because the skin is covered with a dense growth of short hair. At the completion of growth the skin dries and peels off. Antlers are shed annually; new ones grow to replace the old, usually increasing in size and adding more prongs each year. Fully grown antlers, then, are exposed bony projections of the skull and are not horns. The antlers of the giraffe are permanently in velvet.

The most characteristic feature of the skin of mammals is the hair. Hair grows from cylinders of epidermis called **hair follicles** (Figure 10). Every conceivable variation in shape, size, and color exists. Hair can take the form of spines, quills, and bristles; it may be long, fine, or coarse or so small as to be invisible to the naked eye. Some hair is colored, some is not. Regardless of these differences, the basic structure of the hair follicles and the essential composition of various kinds of hair are the same. Hair does not grow all the time, and follicles have periods of growth and rest. When a hair ceases to grow it forms a **club** at its base; this remains anchored in the follicle until a new hair grows alongside it, at which time the club is loosened and the hair is shed.

Most mammals shed most of their hair seasonally, but in some, as in man and the guinea pig, there is some shedding virtually all the time. The periods of growth and rest of hair follicles are varied, and this is reflected by the length of the hair they produce. The hair on the human scalp, which grows eight to ten inches a year and which may attain a length of six to ten feet, obviously must grow constantly for several years. Some of the fine hairs of the body, so short as to be barely visible, grow for only a very brief time.

Skin and the cutaneous appendages are remarkably well adapted to the environment. The thick wool of sheep and yaks is an obvious adaptation to cold climates. In no other mammals, however, is adaptation of the skin so striking as in the aquatic. The skin of these mammals has evolved along divergent patterns. The seal tribe has developed a rich fur, numerous skin glands, and a moderately thick layer of blubber under the skin. The chemical substances secreted by the glands of these animals are relatively water repellent and protect the skin and hair from the noxious effects of water. Walruses and manatees have scant hair and thicker skin, and whales and porpoises have neither hair nor skin glands, with the exception of the mammary glands. The epidermis of aquatic mammals is not only thicker than that of the terrestrial, but it is structurally different. The very thick horny layer rather than being flaky is comparatively solidly cemented and does not imbibe much water. The great whalebone whales have a spectacular cutaneous derivative called **baleen**. This consists of large sheets of keratin which grow from the roof of the mouth. The free edge of the baleen is greatly fringed and strains the foodstuff from the water.

In spite of a relatively simple basic structure, skin is a complex organ. It forms numerous suborgans which produce different and characteristic end products. The various epidermal external appendages mentioned, from scales to horns or baleen, are grossly different, but they are composed of keratin which, if not identical in all of these structures, is very similar. The wear and tear on skin is probably greater than that of any other organ, and it must be ready to repair and replace most of its structures. Skin, then, is an extremely active and versatile organ.

SUMMARY

1. The skin of vertebrates is composed of the epidermis, a superficial stratified squamous epithelium derived from the ectoderm, and the dermis, an underlying connective tissue layer derived from the mesoderm. The color of skin is due largely to the pigment melanin, formed by melanocytes derived from the neural crest of the embryo.

2. The epidermis consists of a Malpighian layer at the base, which is composed of living cells that proliferate and rise to the surface while manufacturing keratin, and a superficial corneal layer in which the dead cells from below come to rest and are finally shed.

3. The dermis is composed of a thin superficial layer under the epidermis and a thick deeper layer.

4. The epidermis gives rise to a large variety of external appendages, such as scales, claws, nails, hooves, spines, hair, and horns. It also gives rise to internal appendages in the form of various glands.

5. The dermis gives rise to horny scales and plates and in some mammals to the cores of hollow horns and to antlers. Dermal bony plates are believed to be the forerunners of the dermal bones of the endoskeleton.

6. The integumentary structures of aquatic animals are relatively simple and attain progressively more complexity in the terrestrial ones. In mammals the integument achieves its fullest expression of complexity. This evolutionary progression is observable in a cursory view of the comparative anatomy of the integument.

7. (*a*) *Amphioxus* has a simple epidermis and a barely distinct dermis.

(*b*) Cyclostomes have thicker epidermis and dermis and numerous mucous glands.

(*c*) Fishes have better developed epidermis and dermis and many mucous glands. From the dermis develop dermal scales: placoid, ganoid, cycloid, and ctenoid.

(*d*) In amphibians, particularly the terrestrial, the epidermis has distinct Malpighian and corneal layers. There are many mucous glands and special poison glands. The dermis is thicker, and dermal bony plates, except in a few forms, are lacking.

(*e*) Reptiles have the best development of epidermal scales and claws. With the exception of some scent glands, there are no cutaneous glands. Snakes and lizards shed the entire epidermal covering periodically. The dermis forms dermal scales only in Crocodilia and Chelonia and occasionally in the squamata.

(*f*) Only birds have feathers. Their skin, except for the uropygial gland, is aglandular. Epidermal scales cover the tarsi and toes; the toes terminate in claws; a spur covered with horny material is present in some forms, and the beak is always covered with a horny sheath derived from the epidermis.

(*g*) The epidermis of mammals forms hair, spines, quills, bristles, horns, claws, nails, hooves, scales, glands, etc.   The dermis forms bony plates only in the armadillo.

(*h*) Skin is a highly specialized, well-coordinated organ that, being exposed to the constant hazards of wear and tear, must be labile and ready to repair and replace damaged parts.

SUGGESTED READING

Hosker, A., 1936, "Studies of the Epidermal Structures of Birds." *Phil. Trans. Roy. Soc. London*, **B,** p. 226.

Montagna, W., 1956, *The Structure and Function of Skin.* Academic Press Inc., New York.

———, and R. A. Ellis, 1958, *The Biology of Hair Growth.* Academic Press, Inc., New York.

Noble, G. K., 1931, *The Biology of the Amphibia.* McGraw-Hill Book Company, Inc., New York.

CHAPTER

5

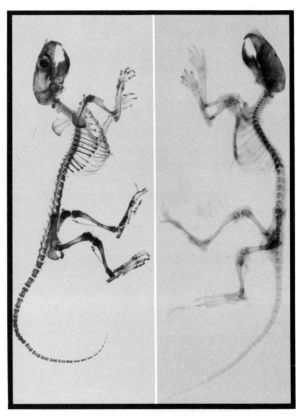

Figure 1. The skeleton of a rat: at the left, stained with alizarin; at the right, seen under X-rays. (From *The Genesis of the Rat Skeleton,* by D. G. Walker and Z. T. Wirtschafter, Charles C. Thomas, publisher. With permission of the publishers and authors.)

Alizarin stained   Roentgenogram

THE ENDOSKELETON

In a living animal bone is itself living. It is removed and replaced by degrees; it grows and repairs itself when injured; it undergoes constant incipient remodeling to keep itself in harmony with the changing stresses and strains forced upon it. The definitive shape of a bone is the result of **intrinsic** forces, or forces from within the bone itself, and **extrinsic** influences, such as the pull of muscle or the pressures from other bones, muscles, and tendons. Bones grow improperly and their characteristic shape is altered when the extrinsic forces are removed.

Bones have many functions: they are the rigid supports of the body, the levers for the muscles, and they protect the viscera. In many vertebrates bones house the blood-forming organs, and they are the storehouse for calcium.

The endoskeleton of vertebrates consists of bone, cartilage, and ligaments. These are all connective tissues with a common structural pattern. The bony skeleton consists of dermal bones (also known as **membrane** or **investing bones**) and **cartilage bones** (also called **endochondral** or **replacement bones**). Structurally, these two types of bones are identical. Dermal bones are formed directly from the mesenchyme, having apparently arisen phylogenetically as modifications of bony plates in the dermis of the skin. They have detached themselves from the skin and have become attached to the endoskeleton; they are found in the skull, the jaws, and the pectoral girdle. During development endochondral bones are preceded by a cartilage model. The cartilage is later gradually removed at the same pace at which bone is laid down in its place.

61

These bones are not formed by a conversion of cartilage but by a replacement of cartilage with bone. Endochondral bones occasionally bypass the formation of a cartilage model, as in some bony fishes in which only the anterior vertebrae are first formed in cartilage; the others are formed in bone directly from the mesenchyme. **Sesamoid bones,** nodules which develop within tendons that rub over convex bony surfaces, may form anywhere; the largest one is the **patella** or kneecap. Since the skeletons of living lower vertebrates and those of young embryos are cartilaginous, it is assumed that cartilage is a more primitive skeletal tissue than bone. The earliest known fossil remains of fishes have a bony skeleton; but this does not prove that one is more ancient than the other, and the matter is not settled.

The physical, chemical, and structural properties of cartilage and bone are different; but it would be misleading to emphasize only the differences because in spite of them they share basic similarities.

Cartilage is a glistening, translucent tissue found where the skeleton needs resiliency as well as strength. **Hyalin cartilage** is clear and bluish and is found in the ventral part of the ribs where they are attached to the sternum, on the articular surfaces of joints, in the rings of the trachea and bronchi, etc. **Elastic cartilage** has a faint yellow color and is found in the pinna of the ear, the external ear canal, and in the epiglottis. **Fibrous cartilage** is found in many places but particularly in the intervertebral discs. All three types of cartilage are composed of a very fine network of precisely oriented, infinitely small collagenous fibrils embedded in a solid matrix composed of esters of sulfuric acid called **chondroitin sulfates.** In elastic cartilage the matrix is traversed by numerous elastic fibers, in addition to the skeins of delicate invisible fibrils. Fibrous cartilage contains visible collagenous fibers. **Cartilage cells,** or **chondrocytes,** are surrounded and imprisoned by the matrix (Figure 2*a*). Communication between these cells and the blood vessels on the outside of the cartilage must take place by a seepage of substances through the matrix.

Cartilage is covered by the **perichondrium,** a layer of fibrous connective tissue which forms and maintains the cartilage. Although chondrocytes look very different from the cells in the perichondrium, they have arisen from perichondrial cells which have become trapped and isolated in their own secretion. Cartilage cells can divide within their confinement, and after division each daughter cell secretes or aids in the synthesis of more cartilage matrix, and each cell again becomes isolated. Cartilage, then, can grow by **apposition** from the perichondrium and from within by **intussusception.**

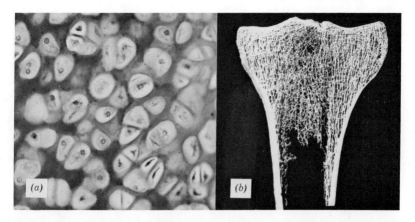

Figure 2. (a) Microscopic section of cartilage; (b) longitudinal section through a human tibia showing dense and spongy bone. (Courtesy of Dr. D. W. Fawcett, Cornell University.)

Bone is an opaque, hard tissue with little resiliency. Most bones have a **marrow** or **medullary cavity,** around which is a wall composed of **compact** or **dense** bone. The marrow cavity, particularly at the two ends of the bone, is crisscrossed and often filled with **spongy** or **cancellous** bone (Figure 2b). The chemical composition and the microscopic structure of dense and spongy bone are identical, even though their gross features are different. Bone is composed of a framework of collagenous fibers, permeated with calcium phosphate. The fibrous tissue gives bones strength and resilience; the inorganic salts make them rigid enough to be adequate levers. Bone is composed of about one third organic and two thirds inorganic materials. Bones that have been immersed in formic or acetic acid are **decalcified** and are composed only of organic materials. Such "bones" retain all of the gross details, although they can be bent with ease (Figure 3). If the carcass of a small animal is immersed in a solution of alizarin, the calcium salts of the bones combine with the dye and form a reddish compound. If later the flesh is macerated in a solution of potassium hydroxide and cleared in glycerin, the entire red bony skeleton can be seen through the transparent tissues (see Figure 1). The organic material of bone can be removed by incineration, leaving the inorganic material intact. A bone with its organic substance removed is whiter and lighter than a whole bone and is easily crumbled. Bone, being a living tissue, is composed of cells as well as of intercellular substances. Bone cells have numerous branching processes radiating from them. The cells and their processes

63

Figure 3. A decalcified human fibula: (*above*) straight; (*right*) tied in a knot.

are completely encased by the bony substance, so that the casing forms a perfect outline of them. The ends of one cell touch those of neighboring ones (Figure 4). Most bony tissue is composed of very fine laminae. At the two peripheries the laminae are arranged parallel to the surfaces; in the middle they are in concentric cylinders. Each of these concentric units has an **Haversian canal**, an open canal in the center which carries blood vessels and nerves and runs roughly parallel to the long axis of bone. The concentric units are referred to as **Haversian** systems (Figure 4). To appreciate the complexity of bony architecture the student should consult a book of histology. The outer surfaces of bones are covered with a closely adhering fibrous sheath called **periosteum**, and the **endosteum**, a more delicate fibrous membrane, lines the inner surfaces. A long bone is composed of a shaft, or **diaphysis**, and two ends, or **epiphyses** (Figures 5 and 6). The epiphyses articulate with other bones and are smooth and covered with cartilage. If the epiphyses are nearly flat, they are called **articular facets**; if rounded, they are called **heads** or **condyles**. Flat bones consist of two layers or plates of dense bone with spongy bone between them. The spongy bone between the plates of the bones of the skull is called **diploe**. The surface of dried bones is relatively smooth and is perforated by the **nutrient canals**, the numerous small pores through which enter the blood vessels and nerves. An adult bone has a number of characteristic markings upon it. Linear elevations are called **lines**, **ridges**, or **crests**, rounded ones, **tubercles**, **tuberosities**, **malleoli**, or **trochanters**, and sharp or pointed ones, **spines** or **styloid processes**. Smooth flat areas are called **facets**; small depressions, **pits** or **foveae**; large ones, **fossae**; and long narrow ones, **grooves** or **sulci**. A hole is a **foramen**; a large hole is a **meatus**. A **canal** is a tubular passage. Liberties are often taken in nomenclature; a canal, for instance, may be no different from a foramen.

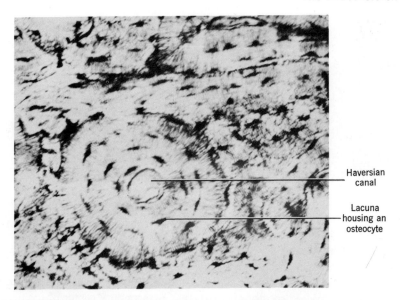

Haversian canal

Lacuna housing an osteocyte

Figure 4. (a) Section of bone seen under the microscope; (b) enlarged detail showing the structure of the bony lacunae which contain the bone cells.

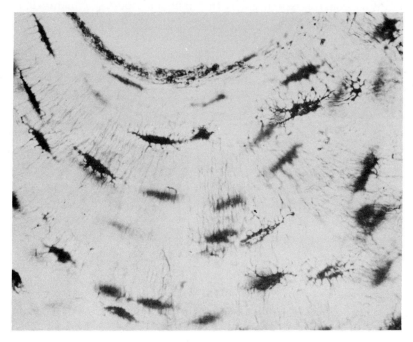

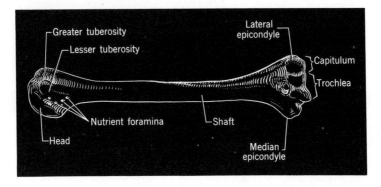

Figure 5. Humerus of man.

In cartilage bones the replacement of cartilage takes place first in the diaphysis. This is the **primary center of ossification,** which establishes the primary marrow cavity. In young animals the epiphyses of long bones are composed mostly of cartilage. **A secondary center of ossification** later appears in each epiphysis; these expand to form the secondary marrow cavities. A cartilaginous **epiphyseal plate,** which separates the diaphysis from the epiphysis, is the only mechanism in mammalian bones which provides for longitudinal growth (Figure 6). In adult bone this is fully ossified and appears as the epiphyseal line; growth in length is no longer possible (Figure 7). Increase in diameter is accomplished

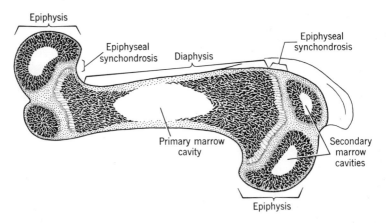

Figure 6. Humerus of a calf showing the centers of ossification and the epiphyseal synchondroses.

by a balance in resorption and addition of bone by the endosteum and periosteum, respectively. If no resorption took place, the marrow cavities would remain very small and the bone would be almost solid. In certain aquatic mammals bones have no marrow cavity and are called **marble bones.** The spongy bone in the epiphyses is not a haphazard gathering of bony threads or **trabeculae.** The trabeculae are oriented toward certain focal points of stress or strain, and each bony trabecula is traversed by another at a right angle to it (Figure 7), in this way gaining a maximum amount of strength.

The ends of adjacent bones in contact are modified into joints. If the joints are rigid, as in the bones of the skull or in the epiphyses of long bones, the two surfaces become dovetailed and interlocked in a union known as **synarthrosis. Sutures** are the lines that mark the places of contact of two such bones. A joint with freely movable bones is a **diarthrosis,** of which the two principal types are the **ball-and-socket joint,** as in the hip, and the **hinge joint,** as in the knee and elbow (Figure 8).

The skeleton can be divided into **axial** and **appendicular** portions. The

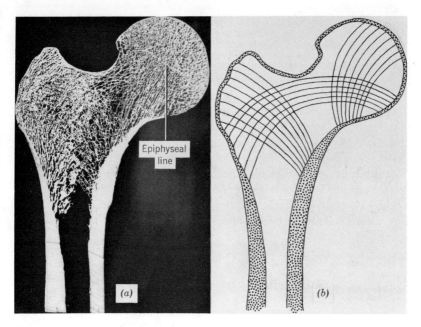

Figure 7. (a) Longitudinal section through a human femur showing the orientation of the spicules of spongy bone; (b) simplified diagram showing the same thing. (Courtesy of Dr. D. W. Fawcett, Cornell University.)

67

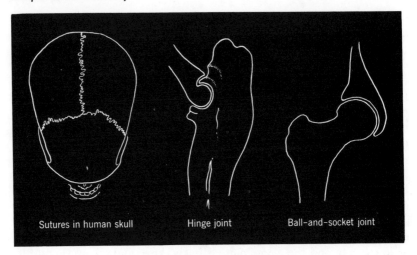

Sutures in human skull   Hinge joint   Ball–and–socket joint

Figure 8. Types of joints.

axial skeleton includes the skull and the vertebral column. For the sake of convenience we also include the **ribs,** the **sternum,** and the **branchial skeleton,** or the skeleton of the gill arches. The appendicular skeleton is composed of the bones of the limbs and of the **pectoral** and **pelvic girdles** which form the base and support of the appendages.

The most ancient endoskeletal element of vertebrates is the notochord, a flexible rod with a dense gelatinous core and a tough, fibrous sheath. All chordates possess a notochord. Phylogenetically, it is first seen in the larvae, but not in the adult tunicates. The notochord is the only skeletal element of *Amphioxus* and the larval lamprey or **ammocoetes.** The adult lamprey, the sturgeon, and many Chondrostei have a very large notochord which gives the body the main axial support. In most vertebrate embryos, however, the notochord is gradually replaced by the vertebral elements of the axial skeleton.

THE AXIAL SKELETON

Development of the Vertebra

During early development, before the germ layers come to lie in their final positions, the presumptive notochord is a part of the presumptive mesoderm. In the process of putting the germ layers in their definitive position the notochord comes to lie in the middorsal line, underneath

68

the neural tube (Figure 9). Later, the vertebrae develop around the notochord and, in some cases, obliterate it.

The skeleton develops from the mesoderm. Embryonic mesoderm or mesenchyme flows toward certain places of the body and becomes concentrated in **skeletogenous areas** from which skeletal elements develop. In order to explain as briefly as possible how the skeleton is formed, it is necessary to make broad generalizations. In describing these developmental sequences let the student be cautioned that some facts have had to be distorted: it is not known for certain that the development of the axial skeleton takes place exactly as described here. Many details in development are different in different classes and even in different species.

The dorsal or paraxial mesoderm is piled up on either side of the neural tube and notochord in blocks or somites (Figure 9). The somites are separated by **intersegmental blood vessels,** which we use as landmarks in tracing the movements to follow. Beginning with the most anterior ones and progressing in a cephalocaudal direction, the sclerotome, or the cells in the ventromedial part of each somite, migrate around the notochord, leaving intact the dermamyotome, the dorsolateral part (Figures 9 and 10). The mesenchyme from the sclerotome flows toward the notochord and becomes concentrated on either side of it, being heaped up toward the anterior part of the mass (Figure 11). Later, the anterior part of these mesenchymal condensations separates from the posterior part

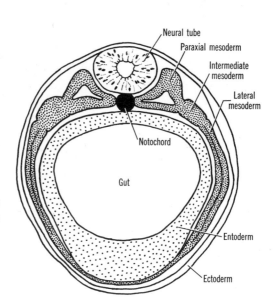

Figure 9. Transverse section of an amphibian embryo showing the organization of body plan.

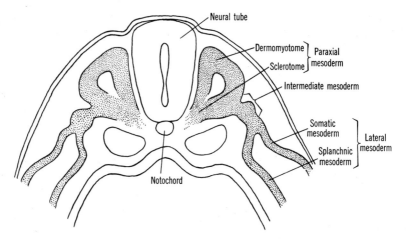

Figure 10. Diagram of a transverse section of an embryo showing the differentiation of the meso-derm and the migration of the mesenchyme toward the notochord.

and moves anteriorly toward the intersegmental blood vessels; the posterior mass moves posteriorly, creating a space between them and obliterating the original gap between the somites. The new mass of mesenchyme thus formed contains the intersegmental blood vessels and alternates with the dermamyotomes which remain in their original places (Figure 11). Two cartilages develop from the anterior mass and two from each posterior mass. Thus the site of each prospective vertebra is marked by eight cartilage plates called **arcualia**, four on each side (Figure 11). The anterior dorsal pair are the **basidorsals;** the anterior ventral pair, the **basiventrals.** The posterior dorsal pair are the **interdorsals;** the ventral pair, the **interventrals.** The basidorsals grow over the neural tube and fuse above it to form the **neural arch.** In the tail region the basiventrals fuse below the notochord, enclose the caudal blood vessels, and form the **hemal arch.** The interdorsals and interventrals rarely form arches. These elements are smaller than the anterior arcualia, and they grow around the notochord and contribute to the formation of the centrum. In some fishes, such as sharks, the interdorsals form **intercalary arches** (see Figure 18). The interventrals in the sturgeon form separate plates behind the basiventrals (see Figure 18).

In the elasmobranchs mesenchymal cells from each of the arcualia invade the sheath of the notochord and form a single cartilaginous ring or centrum. This is an **intrachordal centrum,** since it is formed just within the sheath of the notochord. In most vertebrates the mesenchyme remains outside the sheath of the notochord, and the type of centrum formed is **perichordal**. Two perichordal elements, or **intermedialia**, are formed on each side at the level of each developing vertebra (Figure 12). The anterior **hypocentrum** is in approximately the same place as the basiventral, and the posterior **pleurocentrum** overlaps with the interdorsals. The basiventrals and the interdorsals later are largely incorporated into the intermedialia. Unlike the arcualia, which produce cartilage plates before ossification sets in, the hypocentrum and pleurocentrum of bony fishes form bony elements directly.

The development of the centrum of modern vertebrates is not well known. In the tail of the bowfin (*Amia*) and in that of some lizards the hypocentrum and the pleurocentrum each form a separate centrum (Figure 12). This condition, known as **diplospondyly,** was common in extinct amphibians (Figure 12). Outside of the tail region, the centrum is formed by either one or the other of the intermedialia. In amphib-

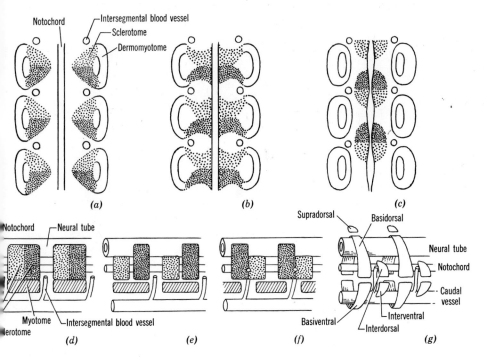

Figure 11. Schema of the development of arcualia: (a) (b) (c) show progressive migration of the mesenchyme of the sclerotome to around the notochord, seen in dorsal view; (d) (e) (f) correspond to (a) (b) (c), seen only in lateral view. (g) The full complement of arcualia.

71

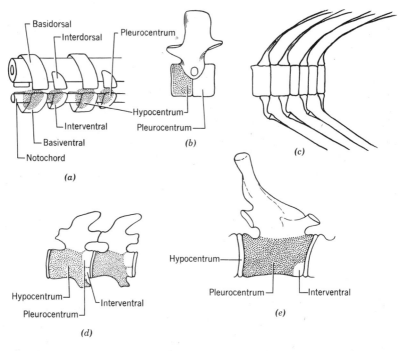

Figure 12. (a) Development of arcualia and intermedialia; (b) the centrum of the vertebra of an extinct amphibian. (c) Diplospondyly in the tail vertebrae of *Amia*; (d) the centrum in the vertebrae of modern amphibians. (e) The centrum in the vertebra of amniotes.

ians the hypocentrum forms the centrum and the pleurocentrum largely disappears (Figure 12). In the amniotes the hypocentrum forms the **intervertebral disc** and the pleurocentrum forms the centrum (Figure 12).

Each vertebra possesses one pair of ribs. The ribs may be fused with the vertebrae, or they may articulate freely with them. The origin of the ribs is also obscure. Some fishes have two kinds of ribs, both formed in the connective tissue **myosepta,** between the muscle masses. The dorsal or **intermuscular** ribs develop in the horizontal myoseptum between the ventral muscle masses. The ventral or **pleural** ribs grow between the coelomic wall and the muscle layer of the body (Figure 13). They originate as separate cartilages in the embryo and grow secondarily toward the basiventrals and fuse with them. The pleural ribs are probably the forerunners of the ribs of most other vertebrates, and the dorsal ribs of fish are extra structures of no great phylogenetic significance.

Additional skeletal elements, the **supradorsal** and **infraventral,** are sometimes formed in the dorsal and ventral myosepta, respectively. Supradorsals fuse with the neural arches and form the **neural spines** (see Figure 11); the infraventrals form the hemal spines of the hemal arches.

The development of mammalian vertebrae is abbreviated and therefore confusing. The vertebrae are formed from a cartilage model in which several centers of ossification appear. One appears in the centrum, one in each of the walls of the neural arch, and one in each of the ribs (Figure 14). Each center of ossification represents one or more embryonic elements.

The Vertebra

A "typical" structure in biology is one which embodies all of the features found in all related structures. Thus, a "typical" vertebra does not exist. Figure 15 represents two "typical" vertebrae from a fish. The tail vertebra has a neural arch and a neural spine above the centrum and a hemal arch and a hemal spine below the centrum. Lateral bony **transverse processes** project from the centrum. A trunk vertebra has a well-defined neural arch; its roof comprises the **lamina** and its

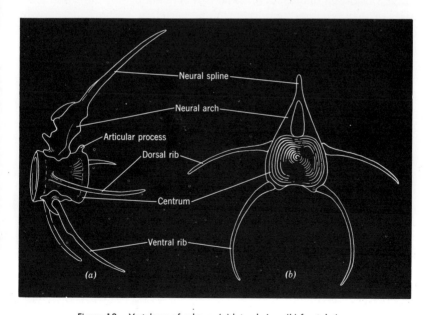

Figure 13.   Vertebrae of salmon: (a) lateral view; (b) frontal view.

73

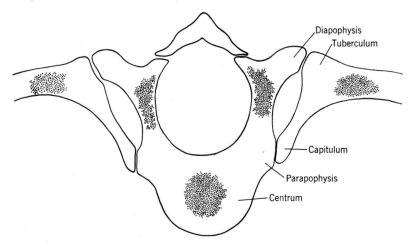

Figure 14. Developing mammalian vertebra and ribs, with the centers of ossification stippled.

lateral pillars, the **pedicles** or **roots**. The large transverse processes are extensions of the neural arch. The ribs articulate with the **costal processes** or they are fused with them. The vertebrae are interlocked with each other anteriorly by two bony processes, the **prezygapophyses**, and two posteriorly, the **postzygapophyses**. The postzygapophyses of one vertebra fit over the prezygapophyses of the vertebra behind it; thus the articular facets of one face upward and those of the other face downward. The neural arches of adjacent vertebrae do not form a continuous tunnel; there are gaps between adjacent pedicles. The pedicle of each vertebra has a large **posterior notch** and a smaller **anterior notch**. When vertebrae are yoked the posterior notch of one vertebra and the anterior notch of the vertebra just behind it form a lateral canal through which emerge the spinal nerves. Most of these features are clearly seen in Figure 16.

The centra of vertebrae may be concave, or **amphicelous**, at each end, as in fish and some reptiles; when concave only anteriorly, as in the reptiles, they are **procelous;** when they are concave posteriorly, as in gar pike, penguins, parrots, etc., they are **opisthocelous**. When the centra are flattened at both ends, as in those of man, they are called **acelous** or **amphiplatyan** (Figure 17); in birds they are saddle-shaped and are called **heterocelous** (see Figure 22).

Comparative Anatomy and Differentiation of the Vertebrae

Cyclostomes. The axial skeleton is very simple. In the hagfishes cartilage plates in front and behind each group of intersegmental blood vessels are the only vertebral elements present. The anterior ones correspond to the basidorsals, the posterior ones, to the interdorsals. There

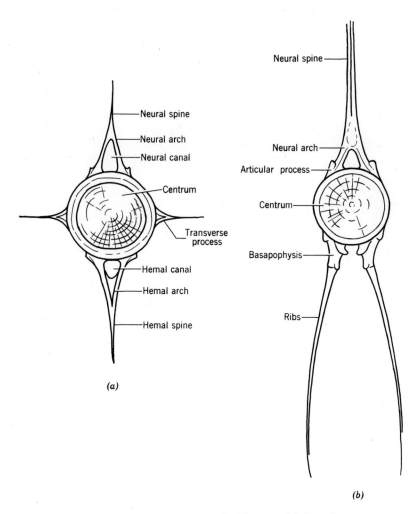

(a)

(b)

Figure 15. "Typical" vertebrae of a fish: (a) caudal; (b) trunk.

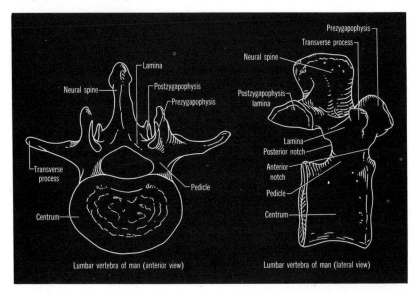

Figure 16. Lumbar vertebrae of man: (a) anterior view; (b) lateral view.

are no centra. In lampreys the basidorsals arch over the spinal cord (Figure 18). The very large notochord is the principal axial support in all cyclostomes.

Fishes. The vertebral column in the sturgeon is a strong reminder that the vertebrae of fishes have arisen from arcualia. The notochord is large and the primitive vertebrae consist of separate arcualia and no

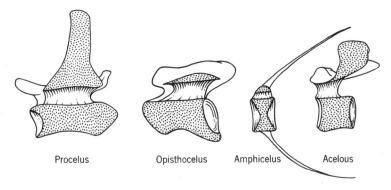

Figure 17. Types of articulations of centra.

centrum (Figure 18). The basidorsals and interdorsals arch over the spinal cord and form a neural arch. The basiventrals and interventrals form a row of shields at the base of the notochord. From the basiventrals short ribs extend laterally.

Fishes have two types of vertebrae: trunk and tail. Neither type has a complete neural arch in the shark; an additional cartilage plate, the intercalary arch, completes the tunnel (Figure 18). Caudal vertebrae have a hemal arch underneath the centrum which encloses the caudal vein and artery. In the anterior part of the tail the hemal arch gradually opens and the two pillars seem to differentiate into, or fuse with, the costal elements. The centrum of most fishes is amphicelous, resembling an hourglass, and the concavities enclose the gelatinous remains of the notochord. The vertebrae of elasmobranchs are cartilaginous and lack the refinements found in those of teleosts. The vertebrae of teleosts have no intercalary arch and the neural arch is more nearly complete. The spinous process and the neural and hemal arches are longer (Figure 19). At the anterior and posterior ends the neural arches have bony processes which interlock the vertebrae. In the tail vertebrae the hemal canal is larger than the neural canal. The trunk vertebrae have

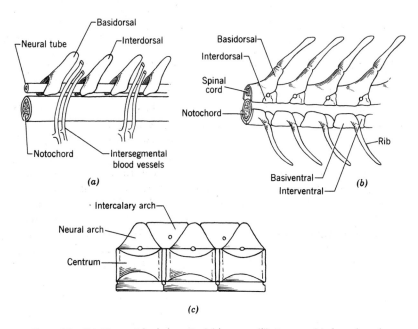

Figure 18. Primitive vertebral elements: (a) lamprey; (b) sturgeon; (c) elasmobranch.

77

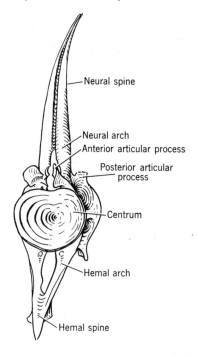

Neural spine

Neural arch
Anterior articular process
Posterior articular
process

Centrum

Hemal arch

Hemal spine

Figure 19.
Tail vertebra of a teleost.

no hemal arch, and in its place are the **basapophyses,** basal stumps, to which the ribs are articulated (see Figure 15). The trout, the herring, and other bony fishes have a second pair of ribs attached to the centrum. Additional ribs may be found in teleosts wherever connective tissue myosepta are found. The neural arches may have two spines; when this occurs the posterior one may be homologous with the intercalary arch.

Amphibians. For the first time the vertebrae begin to show regional differentiation, although in urodeles each vertebra has a similar basic architecture. The first vertebra behind the skull has no ribs and is the only cervical vertebra. All of the other vertebrae, including those of the tail, possess ribs. The trunk vertebrae have a shallow neural arch with short neural spines directed posteriorly. Each vertebra bears two conspicuous lateral processes; the dorsal one, the **diapophysis,** projects from the neural arch; the ventral one, the **parapophysis,** projects from the centrum. The ribs are two-headed, or **bicipital;** the ventral head, the **capitulum,** articulates with the parapophysis, and the dorsal head, the **tuberculum,** articulates with the diapophysis of the transverse process. The single sacral vertebra has larger diapophyses and parapophyses than those of the other vertebrae, and the rib which supports the pelvic girdle is much stouter than the other ribs. The first three caudal vertebrae resemble those from the trunk, but the fourth has a hemal arch. The centrum of urodele vertebrae, formed largely from the hypocentrum, is more solidly ossified than that of fishes, and it is amphicelous. Well-developed postzygapophyses project from the posterior end of the neural arch and fit over a pair of similar projections; the prezygapophyses project from the anterior end of the vertebra next to it.

The vertebral column of salientians has fewer vertebrae than that of urodeles. In the frog the single cervical vertebra is followed by seven trunk vertebrae. The short ribs, often erroneously referred to as transverse processes, are fused to the trunk vertebrae and flare out laterally. The ribs of the first three vertebrae are much stouter than those of the last four. The stout ribs of the single sacral vertebra support the pelvic girdle. Beyond the sacral vertebra the urostyle, a single long bone, probably represents fused caudal vertebrae (see Figure 57). There is no hemal arch. The centrum is either procelous or opisthocelous.

Reptiles. Reptiles, birds, and mammals have several cervical vertebrae. The first two are modified to support the skull. The **atlas,** the ring-shaped first vertebra, is composed of a neural arch dorsally and a small hypocentrum at the base. Two anterior concavities fit against the articular processes of the skull. The second vertebra, the **axis,** possesses a toothlike **odontoid process** on the anterior face of the centrum, which is the pleurocentrum of the atlas fused to the hypocentrum and pleurocentrum of the axis (see Figure 24).

The different orders of reptiles exhibit great varieties of differentiation of the vertebral column. Vast differences exist between the vertebrae of the alligator and those of the turtle. In the snakes nearly every vertebra has ribs. All reptilian vertebrae are procelous.

In the crocodilians all cervical vertebrae have posteriorly directed bicipital ribs, the **pleurapophyses.** The space formed on either side of the vertebrae between the fused heads of the ribs and the centrum is the **vertebrarterial canal** (Figure 20). The trunk vertebrae of the crocodilians are differentiated into **thoracic** and **lumbar.** The thoracic vertebrae have large transverse processes and bear ribs; in the first three thoracic vertebrae the ribs articulate with the parapophysis and diapophysis, but in the others the ribs articulate entirely with the transverse processes. The dorsal or vertebral parts of the ribs are bony, but the intermediate and the ventral, also known as **sternal** or costal parts, are cartilaginous. A hooklike bone, the **uncinate process,** projects posteriorly from the vertebral part of each rib and overlaps the rib behind it. A midventral

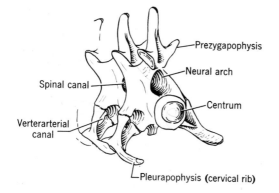

Prezygapophysis

Neural arch

Spinal canal

Centrum

Verterarterial canal

Pleurapophysis (cervical rib)

Figure 20. Cervical vertebrae of the alligator.

process, the **hypapophysis**, grows from the centrum of each of the anterior thoracic vertebrae and the cervical vertebrae. A series of bony processes, the **gastralia**, form a herringbone pattern in the posterior ventral abdominal wall. These riblike structures are of dermal origin and are homologous to the plastron of the turtle. Lumbar vertebrae have large transverse processes that are in reality fused ribs. The stout ribs of the two sacral vertebrae support the pelvic girdle. The caudal vertebrae also have laterally flaring transverse processes and hemal arches enclosed by **chevron bones** (Figure 21). These articulate between the centra, suggesting that they have arisen from the missing hypocentrum. All of the vertebrae are yoked together by large zygapophyses.

In snakes all vertebrae are similar and all bear ribs. In turtles the trunk region has only thoracic vertebrae, which, with the two sacral vertebrae, are fused with the plates of the bony shell or **carapace**. The

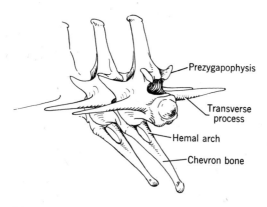

Prezygapophysis

Transverse process

Hemal arch

Chevron bone

Figure 21. Caudal vertebrae of the alligator.

ribs are expanded and fused with the dermal costal plates of the carapace. Only the cervical and caudal vertebrae of the turtle are movable. In summary, then, the reptiles show (1) a well-developed cervical region, the first two vertebrae, the atlas and axis, being specialized to allow the rotation and support of the skull; (2) the trunk, at least in the Crocodilia, is differentiated into thoracic and lumbar regions; (3) there are two sacral vertebrae; and (4) the centra of the vertebrae are procelous.

Birds. The vertebral column shows noteworthy specializations, and it is strikingly similar throughout the class. The number of cervical vertebrae varies from eight in some hummingbirds to twenty-four in some swans; the domestic fowl has sixteen and the pigeon, thirteen. The first two cervical vertebrae are modified into atlas and axis. The cervical vertebrae have a saddle-shaped or heterocelous centrum, large zyga-pophyses, and pleurapophyses, or fused ribs, directed posteriorly and forming the vertebrarterial canal. A hypapophysis grows from the ventral side of the centrum of the cervical, thoracic, and lumbar vertebrae. The thoracic vertebrae (Figure 22) have ribs composed of a dorsal and a sternal segment. From the dorsal segment a bony plate, the uncinate process, similar to that of the crocodilians, grows at an angle to the rib and overlaps the rib behind it. The neural spines are broad and blunt. In young birds the thoracic vertebrae are more or less movable, but in adults adjacent neural spines and the hypapophyses fuse with each other and bony splints form longitudinally across the transverse processes. These devices render the thoracic region completely immovable. The last two thoracic vertebrae, the lumbar, sacral, and first few caudal vertebrae are all fused together as the **synsacrum** and are surrounded by and fused with the bones of the pelvic girdle (Figure 23). All of the vertebrae in the synsacrum have large ribs, and the neural spines are expanded and also fused with one another to form a rigid median

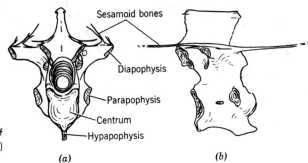

Figure 22. Thoracic vertebrae of a bird: (a) anterior view; (b) lateral view.

Sesamoid bones

Diapophysis

Parapophysis

Centrum

Hypapophysis

(a)

(b)

keel which extends from the first thoracic to the caudal vertebrae. Posterior to the synsacrum a few caudal vertebrae are freely movable. The **pygostyle,** a flat bone presumably formed from fused caudal vertebrae, is the terminal tail bone (see Figure 60). Thus the bird's vertebral column is movable only at the two extremities. The thoracic, lumbar, and sacral vertebrae are fused, and with the bones of the pelvic girdle they form a very rigid base for the attachment of muscle. The bird's body is compact and muscular and eminently adapted for speed in the air, water, or on land.

Mammals. The regional differentiation of the vertebral column is complete. With the exception of the sloths and manatee, the cervical region always has seven vertebrae, whether the neck is long, as in the giraffe, or short, as in the whale. The first two vertebrae are differentiated into atlas and axis (Figure 24). The vertebrarterial canal in most cervical vertebrae is bounded by a dorsal transverse process, attached to the pedicle of the neural arch, and a ventral pleurapophysis. In the seventh cervical vertebra the vertebrarterial canal may be incompletely formed or absent or the vertebra may go to the other extreme and bear a rib.

Thoracic vertebrae have long neural spines, large flaring transverse processes, and movable ribs. The usual number of thoracic vertebrae is twelve or thirteen, although the bottle-nosed whale has only nine, and the two-toed sloth, twenty-four. The ribs are mostly bicipital (Figure 25), but the posterior ones have only one head, the capitulum. This usually articulates with the parapophysis at the junction of two centra;

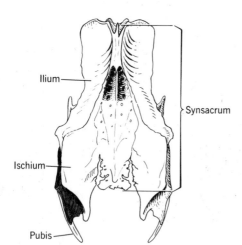

Ilium

Synsacrum

Ischium

Pubis

Figure 23. Synsacrum of a bird (dorsal view).

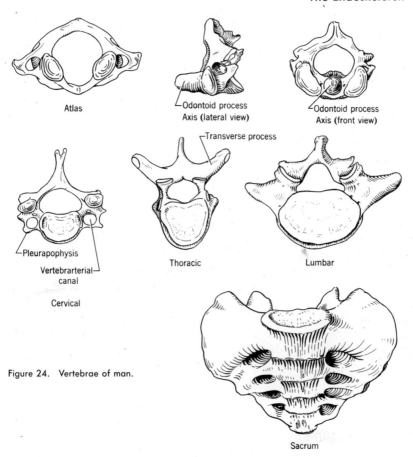

Atlas

Odontoid process
Axis (lateral view)

Odontoid process
Axis (front view)

Transverse process

Pleurapophysis

Vertebrarterial
canal

Cervical

Thoracic

Lumbar

Sacrum

Figure 24. Vertebrae of man.

the articular facet is formed by two half imprints, or **demifacets,** on each adjacent centrum. The tuberculum articulates with the diapophysis of the transverse process. The ventral portion of each rib is composed of cartilage and may or may not articulate with the sternum. The ribs that articulate directly with the sternum are the **true ribs;** those that are attached to the sternum secondarily by long cartilaginous processes are the **false ribs;** and the **floating ribs,** the most posterior, do not secure anchorage with the sternum at all. In man the first seven ribs are true ribs and the last two are floating ribs (Figure 26). Occasionally, the first or even the second lumbar vertebra may bear floating ribs.

The five or more lumbar vertebrae have a large, laterally projecting process on either side of the neural arch, usually called the transverse process. This is a costal or rib process; the real transverse process is a small protuberance on the dorsal side between the base of the costal process and the prezygapophysis (see Figure 28). The centrum is very broad and is flattened dorsoventrally.

The variable number of sacral vertebrae are usually fused together. They have very stout ribs for the attachment of the ilium, and the transverse process proper is a bony hump on the back of the sacral ribs (see Figure 28).

The number of caudal vertebrae depends upon the length of the tail; in man there are about five. Caudal vertebrae become progressively more primitive toward the tip of the tail. Those near the end have a hemal arch.

The centra of mammalian vertebrae are usually amphiplatyan or acelous; those of the cervical vertebrae of ungulates are opisthocelous. The centra are separated by intervertebral discs of fibrocartilage, derived from the hypocentrum. The center of intervertebral discs contains the **nucleus pulposus,** a mucoid, gelatinous remnant of the notochord (Figure 27), which has a strong capacity for binding water and acts as an effective shock absorber. In man, in an upright position, the intervertebral discs contribute a quarter of the length of the vertebral column.

All vertebrae have the same origin and develop on a similar pattern; with the exception of the caudal ones, each develops approximately the

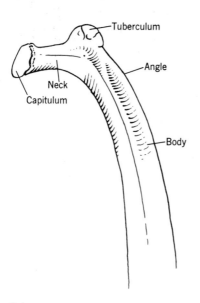

Figure 25. Bicipital rib of a calf.

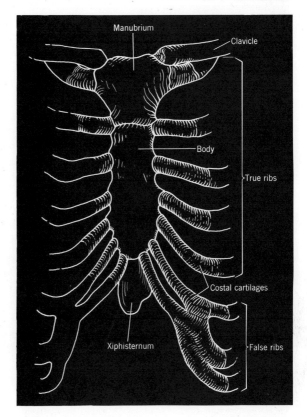

Figure 26. Sternum and rib attachments of man, with costal cartilages shaded.

same structures. These structures are modified differently in the different regions of the vertebral column, but with care all of the homologous parts can be found in each vertebra. Perhaps the most illuminating point of this similarity can be found in the modification of the ribs (Figure 28).

The Sternum

The sternum is found only in vertebrates that walk; fishes move in water by swinging the tail laterally and have none. It is best developed in tetrapods with strong anterior limbs that need a solid skeletal

85

frame for the attachment of their muscles. The origin of the sternum is obscure and its phylogenetic importance is questionable, since it seems to have arisen independently in each class. Thus it is difficult to theorize on the homologies of the sterna of each group. For example, in amphibians and in mammals sternal elements develop in the connective tissue of the embryo independent of the ribs. In reptiles and birds the sternum arises as two parallel cartilaginous bars, each united with the ribs on one side.

Amphibians. *Necturus* and some other urodeles have a sternum consisting of small bars of cartilage which extend laterally from the midline into the connective tissue septa between the muscles. The sternum of salientians is intermingled with the bones of the pectoral girdle, and the **omosternum,** the anterior part, is separated from the **xiphisternum,** the posterior part, by the **epicoracoid cartilage** (Figure 29).

Reptiles. The sternum of lizards and crocodiles is composed of a cartilaginous plate bounded anteriorly by the two coracoid bones of the pectoral girdle. A single median **interclavicle** projects anteriorly from the sternum as if it were an integral part of it (Figure 29). The costal cartilages are attached to the body of the sternum. Snakes and turtles have no sternum.

Birds. Flying birds have a large shield-shaped sternum, with a deep midventral longitudinal **keel** or **carina** (Figure 30), and bony extensions, the **xiphoid processes,** projecting posteriorly on either side. A bony **rostrum** usually projects anteriorly between the facets for the articula-

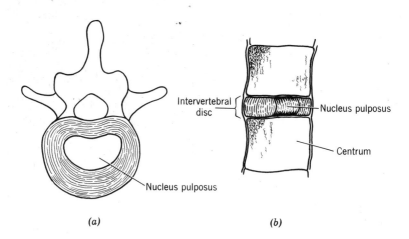

Figure 27. Intervertebral disc of man: (a) surface view; (b) longitudinal view.

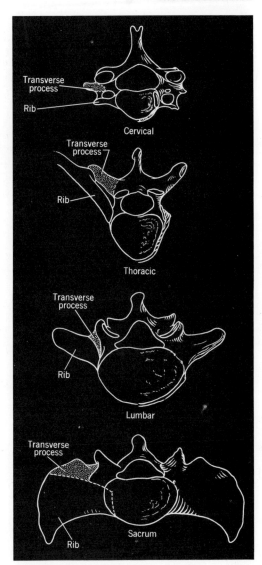

Figure 28. Schema of human vertebrae showing transverse process, stippled, and ribs, not stippled.

tion of the precoracoid bones. Laterally and anteriorly, the sternum forms two shelves for the articulation of the ribs and bears the imprints of these articulations. In Ratitae the flat, somewhat square or rhombic sternum has no keel (Figure 30).

87

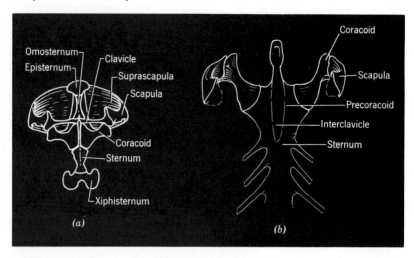

Figure 29. (a) Sternum and pectoral girdles of frog (ventral view); (b) sternum and pectoral girdles of alligator (dorsal view).

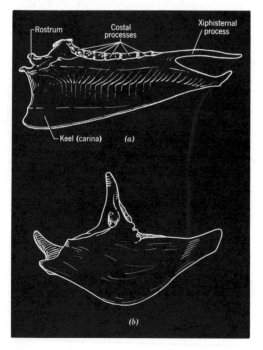

Figure 30. (a) Sternum of flying bird; (b) sternum of ratite (Emu).

Mammals. The sternum is composed of a series of bones and cartilages. The **manubrium**, the most anterior, is usually larger than the others and is the base of anchorage for the first pair of ribs and clavicles, when these are present. The xiphoid, the last sternal element, is partially or entirely cartilaginous, and there are no ribs attached to it (Figure 31). The other sternal bones, the **sternebrae**, vary in number in different mammals. In the cat, dog, sheep, and others the sternebrae are separate bones even in the adult. In man a separate manubrium articulates with the body of the sternum, formed by the fusion of three sternebrae. The sternum of some moles and bats has a median ventral bony keel.

The Skull

The skull is the protective skeleton of the head. It is found in its simplest form in the lower vertebrates and attains increasing complexity with phylogenetic ascension. Beginning with the ganoids, the skull consists of three separate components: the **chondrocranium** is the original and most ancient element; the **dermatocranium** arises from dermal bony plates in the skin of the head; and the **splanchnocranium** originates from the skeleton of the gill arches. The accounts which follow on the origin,

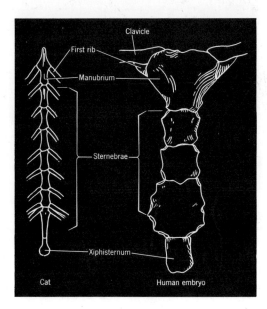

Figure 31. Mammalian sterna.

development, and structure of the vertebrate skull have been stream-lined, simplified, and abbreviated, and for the sake of clarity liberties have been taken. This has been done particularly in the case of the chondrocranium, which is different even in closely related forms.

With the early development of the brain are established the primordial vesicles of the nose, **olfactory**, eyes, **optic**, and ears, **otic**. Mesenchyme condenses around these vesicles and forms cartilaginous capsules. A pair of cartilage plates, the **parachordals**, develops between the otic vesicles alongside the anterior extension of the notochord. The para-chordals expand medially around the notochord, and their posterior portions fuse and form a **basilar plate** (Figure 32*a,b*). The parachordals also expand laterally and fuse with the cartilages of the otic vesicles. The **trabeculae**, which are two other cartilage bars formed just anterior to the parachordals, expand anteriorly to fuse with the olfactory vesicles and posteriorly with the cartilage plate formed by the expanding para-chordals (Figure 32). The cartilage capsules around the otic vesicles do not fuse with the chondrocranium. Two gaps remain: the **hypophyseal fenestra**, between the trabeculae, and the **basicranial fenestra**, between the fused parachordals. Several occipital vertebrae become fused to the back of the basilar plate, and the cartilage of this region begins to grow posterior to the brain and around the spinal cord. The fusion of all these cartilaginous elements gives rise to the chondrocranium. Poste-riorly is the **occipital** region, with the **foramen magnum** through which the spinal cord passes. Anterior to the occipital region is the **sphenoid** region, and anterior to it, around and between the olfactory vesicles, is the **ethmoid** region (Figure 32*c*).

In bony fishes and in the other classes of vertebrates the troughlike cartilaginous chondrocranium is replaced by bone. The cartilage of the occipital region forms the occipital bones: one **supraoccipital** above the foramen magnum, one **exoccipital** on each side of it, and a large **basioccipital** on its floor. The floor of the trough consists of a **basisphe-noid**, just anterior to the basioccipital, and a **presphenoid** in front of it. One **alisphenoid** develops on each side of the basisphenoid and one **orbitosphenoid** on each side of the presphenoid. A **mesethmoid** develops from the ethmoid plate, between the nasal vesicles, and the **ethmoturbinals** arise from the nasal vesicles. Each otic capsule gives rise to a series of three otic bones which lie between the alisphenoid and the exoccipital (Figure 32*d*).

When dermal bones become associated with the chondrocranium to form the sides and the roof of the skull the chondrocranium remains as its floor. Dermal bones appear first as bony scales in the heads of fishes.

90

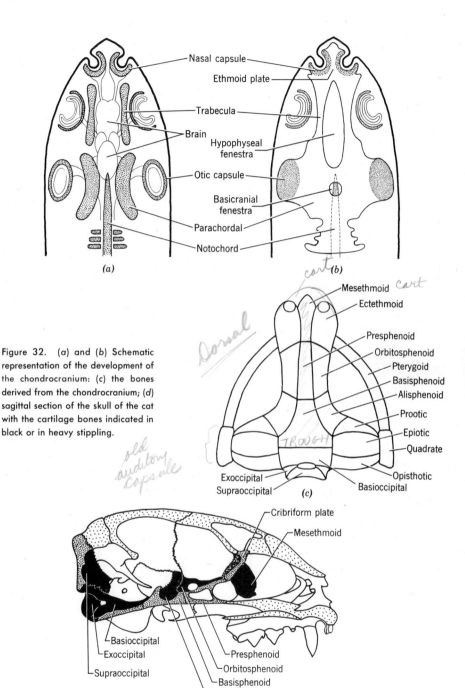

Nasal capsule

Ethmoid plate

Trabecula

Brain

Hypophyseal fenestra

Otic capsule

Basicranial fenestra

Parachordal

Notochord

(a)

(b) _cart_ _cart_

Mesethmoid

Ectethmoid

Presphenoid

Orbitosphenoid

Pterygoid

Basisphenoid

Alisphenoid

Prootic

Epiotic

Quadrate

Opisthotic

Exoccipital

Supraoccipital

Basioccipital

(c)

Dorsal

TROUGH

old auditory capsule

Figure 32. (a) and (b) Schematic representation of the development of the chondrocranium: (c) the bones derived from the chondrocranium; (d) sagittal section of the skull of the cat with the cartilage bones indicated in black or in heavy stippling.

Cribriform plate

Mesethmoid

Basioccipital

Exoccipital

Supraoccipital

Presphenoid

Orbitosphenoid

Basisphenoid

Alisphenoid

(d)

91

Gradually they become fused with and indistinguishable from the bones of the chondrocranium. The roof of the skull, anterior to the supra-occipital, is formed by the **parietals**, the **frontals**, and the **nasals**. Closing the gap on the sides posteriorly are the large **temporals**; anteriorly, the **maxillaries**. The maxillaries form the **maxilla**, or upper jaw, and most of the bony palate. The anterior part of the splanchnocranium is almost completely covered by dermal bones.

In fishes a series of cartilaginous gill arches supports the gills and forms a colonnade around the pharynx. These gill arches arise from splanchnic mesoderm. The first, or **mandibular**, arch is split into dorsal and ventral elements which contribute to the formation of the upper and lower jaws. The second, or **hyoid**, arch anchors the first arch to the cranium and supports the first gill or **hemibranch**. The other gill arches, with the exception of the last one, support the gills, and their number is somewhat variable in different orders of fishes. The visceral skeleton becomes reduced and modified in the classes of vertebrates which attain a fishlike pharynx only during early development.

The mandibular arch forms a dorsal **palatoquadrate** and a ventral **Meckel's cartilage** (Figure 33). Each of these meets its corresponding cartilage on the midline and fuses with it. The palatoquadrate and

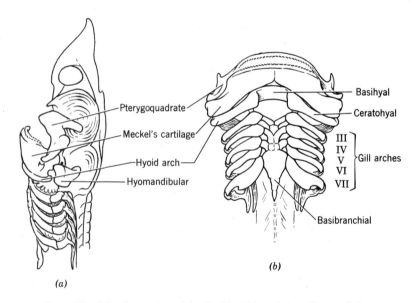

Figure 33. Splanchnocranium of the dogfish: (*a*) lateral view; (*b*) ventral view.

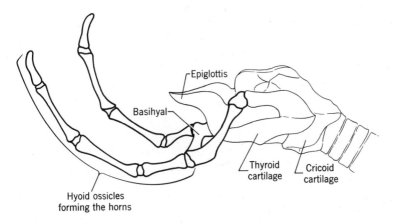

Figure 34. Hyoid bones of the cat.

Meckel's cartilages form the primitive jaws of vertebrates and in the sharks even bear teeth. Beginning with bony fishes and progressing to mammals, these elements are gradually replaced by dermal bones. In adult mammals all that remains of the first mandibular arch are the ossicles of the middle ear, the **incus** and **malleus**, derived from the palatoquadrate and Meckel's cartilage, respectively. The hyoid arch forms the **stapes** of the middle ear. In amphibia, reptiles, and birds the hyomandibular arch forms the **columella** of the ear. The rest of the gill arches of fishes form the so-called **hypobranchial skeleton** of higher vertebrates, comprising the hyoid apparatus and the cartilages of the larynx (Figure 34).

Comparative Anatomy of the Skull

Cyclostomes. The skull of myxines is so primitive that it consists of essential elements only. That of lampreys is better developed and is roofed over the brain. The peculiar visceral skeleton of cyclostomes, a continuous cartilage latticework just underneath the skin, is not homologous with the visceral skeleton of the other vertebrates.

Fishes. Elasmobranchs have a compact cartilaginous chondrocranium which is completely roofed over (Figure 35). A large, beaklike rostrum projects between the two olfactory capsules. Through the massive posterior part opens the foramen magnum, bounded by lateral **occipital condyles**; presumably, the occipital condyles articulate with the first

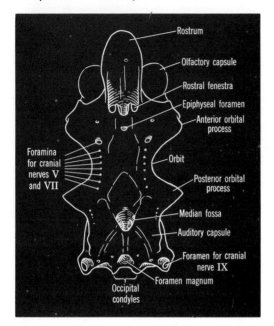

Figure 35. Chondrocranium of the dogfish.

vertebra, but actually the first few vertebrae are immovable. The primitive visceral skeleton is composed of seven arches. The first, or mandibular, arch, forms the jaws. The second arch has a large, upper **hyomandibular cartilage** and a lower **ceratohyal cartilage.** The chondrocranium and the splanchnocranium of elasmobranchs are not fused.

In the skull of Chondrostei and Holostei numerous dermal bones derived from dermal scales are gathered outside the chondrocranium, and the chondrocranium becomes simpler. There are more bones in the skull of teleosts than in that of any other vertebrate, but the exact homologies of these bones are obscure. From the chondrocranium arise the four occipital bones around the foramen magnum, the sphenoid bones, the otic bones, and, anteriorly, the ethmoid bones. The palatoquadrates are replaced by the **premaxillae** and **maxillae,** both of which bear teeth and form the bulk of the upper jaw. The **quadrate,** a cartilage bone forming the base of the upper jaw, is all that remains of the palatoquadrate. Meckel's cartilage is covered by a number of dermal bones, of which only the **dentary** bears teeth. The **articular** bone at the base of the mandible is derived from Meckel's cartilage.

Amphibians. In primitive extinct amphibians the vault of the skull was formed by a large number of bones. An **interparietal foramen,**

94

presumably representing the orbit of the **epiphyseal eye,** perforated the center of the skull. The skull of modern amphibians, however, shows a great reduction in both cartilage and dermal bones. Much of their chondrocranium remains cartilaginous, and in the occipital region only the two exoccipital bones are formed, each bearing an occipital condyle. The basioccipital and supraoccipital are not ossified. The entire skull is flattened dorsoventrally, shortened, and widened (Figure 36). In the upper jaw the premaxillae and maxillae largely replace the pterygoquadrate and bear teeth; the **vomers,** the **palatines,** and the **pterygoids** form the **primary** or **true palate.** These are all dermal bones and all of them may bear teeth. The quadrate at the angle of the jaw is derived from the pterygoquadrate. The articular is the only cartilage bone of the lower jaw and replaces Meckel's cartilage. The rest of Meckel's cartilage disappears and in its place are formed several dermal bones, of which the dentary bears teeth.

Reptiles. The skull has many cartilage and dermal bones. The chondrocranium is completely ossified, except for the ethmoid regions and the lateral extensions of the sphenoid. Four occipital bones surround the foramen magnum, and a single occipital condyle is formed mostly from the basioccipital. A bony **interorbital septum** separates the orbits in all reptilian skulls except that of snakes. The **ectopterygoid,** a dermal bone between the pterygoid and the maxilla, strengthens the upper jaw. The skull of the alligator illustrates the bones present (Figure 37). In the skull of turtles the postfrontals, parietals, and **squamosals** are expanded laterally; and on the anterior part, the nasals and **lacrimals** are absent. The palatal region of the alligators is very long, and the internal nares are pushed posteriorly very far on the

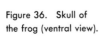

Figure 36. Skull of
the frog (ventral view).

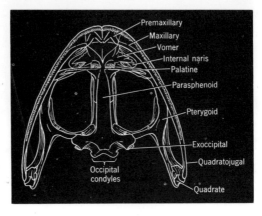

Premaxillary
Maxillary
Vomer
Internal naris
Palatine
Parasphenoid
Pterygoid
Exoccipital
Quadratojugal
Occipital
condyles
Quadrate

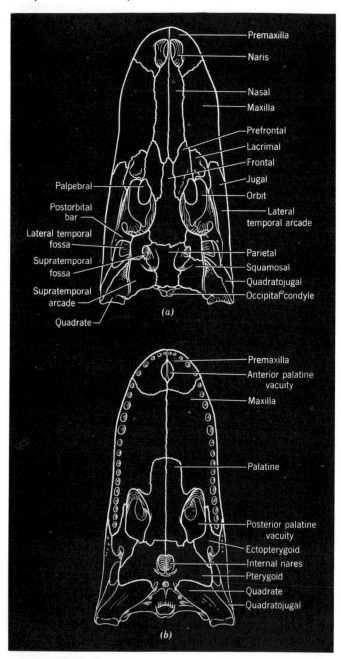

Figure 37. Skull of alligator: (a) dorsal view; (b) ventral view.

palate. The bony palate is formed by the maxillae, the palatines, and the large winglike pterygoids (Figure 37). The roof of the mouth of reptiles, and particularly that of Crocodilia, is different from that of Amphibia. The primary or true palate, such as that found in amphibians (see Figure 36), is composed of the vomers, palatines, and pterygoids. In reptiles the premaxillae and maxillae grow medially and form a shelf underneath the primitive palate, separating it from the roof of the mouth. This new shelf is the **false palate,** which, together with the palatines, pterygoids and ectopterygoids, extends back into the skull. The false palate is the floor of the nasal passageways, and the internal nares are displaced posteriorly (Figure 37). In snakes the two halves of the upper jaw are held together at their distal ends by elastic connective tissue. Each half is hinged to the skull by a movable quadrate (Figure 37). The jaw is composed of four movable bones: the quadrate, the pterygoid, ectopterygoid, and the maxillary (Figure 38). When the quadrate moves the entire series of bones of the palate moves. The lower jaw can be dislocated from the skull, and the two halves can move apart during the swallowing of large prey.

The lower jaw of reptiles is composed of dermal bones that completely invest Meckel's cartilage. The largest dermal bone, the dentary, bears the teeth. The articular, the only cartilage bone which replaces Meckel's cartilage, is jointed with the quadrate. In lizards and alligators the two rami of the mandible are fused by a suture, but in turtles they are completely fused. Turtles have no teeth, and the bones of the mandible are all solidly fused. In snakes the jaws are very loosely hinged.

Birds. The domed skull is larger and more spherical than that of reptiles. Its chief peculiarity is the disproportionately large size of the orbits (Figure 39). The bones are fused together so effectively that their sutures have disappeared. The anterior part of the skull consists of elongated premaxillae, maxillae, and nasals which are covered with a horny beak. The upper jaw continues posteriorly as the **zygomatic arch,** which consists of a posterior process from the maxilla and a slender **jugal** and **quadratojugal;** this articulates with a large movable quadrate. Finches, parrots, hawks, and others can move the mandible without moving the cranium. The four occipital bones are inseparably fused in the posterior floor of the skull, and there is one occipital condyle. The basisphenoid projects anteriorly in a rostrum, which is a dermal bone. The palate, formed by the pterygoid and palatine bones, is not rigid, and the pterygoids are hinged to the quadrate, where movements are transmitted by way of the palatines to the maxilla, which is also moved. Lateral from the basisphenoid, the alisphenoids and orbitosphenoids,

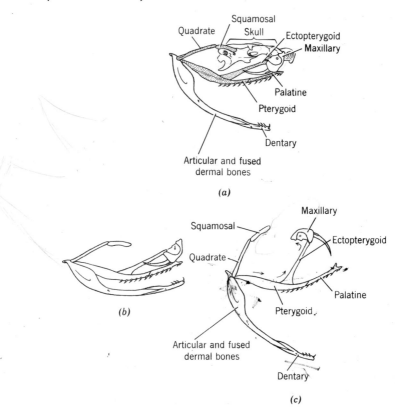

Figure 38. Skull of a rattlesnake: (a) lateral view of intact skull, with the bones of the jaw mechanism stippled; (b) and (c) the jawbone mechanism.

both derived from the chondrocranium, form much of the orbit (Figure 39). The mandible is similar to that of the reptile, but the dentary does not bear teeth. As in the reptile, the main remnant of Meckel's cartilage is the articular. The hyoid apparatus of birds is derived from the pharyngeal skeleton. The visceral cartilages from arches II and III form the body of the hyoid and the long cornua (Figure 40a). The cornua of woodpeckers are so long that they have to be wrapped around the skull (Figure 40b). Woodpeckers can extend the tongue a considerable distance when spearing grubs.

Mammals. The brain of mammals is larger than that of other vertebrates, and the skull has to be larger and more domed to house it. The skull reaches its greatest convexity in man. There are fewer bones than

98

in other vertebrate skulls; some of the dermal bones are lost, and individual dermal and cartilage bones have become fused. The most characteristic feature of the mammalian skull is the change in position of the quadrate and articular to the middle ear, in which they form the incus and malleus. The articulation of the jaws is by way of the dentary and the zygomatic process of the temporal bone; the temporal bone extends to cover the ear ossicles and forms a **tympanic bulla.** Only a few dermal bones form the roof of the skull: the nasals around the olfactory apparatus and the frontals above the orbits form the superior portion of the facial disc (Figure 41*a*). In animals with true horns the bony cores are extensions of the frontals; antlers are also bony protuber-

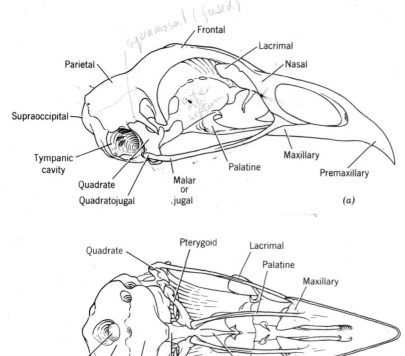

Figure 39.   Skull of bird: (*a*) lateral view; (*b*) ventral view.

99

ances of the frontals. The parietals form nearly the entire posterior vault of the cranium, with a contribution from the interparietal. The sides of the cranium are formed by the complex temporal bone. The lacrimals become incorporated in the anterior ventral part of the wall of the orbit, and the upper jaw consists of the premaxillae and maxillae, both of which bear teeth. The zygomatic arch, formed anteroposteriorly by the **zygomatic process of the maxilla,** the **malar** (or jugal), and the zygomatic process of the temporal bone flare laterally and posteriorly to form the lower margin of the orbits and the temporal fossae. A spur of bone, the **frontal process** of the malar, and the **postorbital process** of the frontals partially or completely separate the orbit from the temporal fossa; in most primates the separation is complete. The zygomatic process of the temporal bone forms the **mandibular fossa** for articulation of the lower jaw (Figure 41*b*).

The bony palate of mammals is a shelf formed by the fusion of the **palatine processes** of the premaxillae and maxillae, and the palatines posteriorly (Figure 41*b*). This shelf of bone is the floor of the nasal passages and is, therefore, the false palate. The primary palate is reduced to a median unpaired vomer attached to the base of the mesethmoid or nasal septum. The palatines form the posterior part of the false

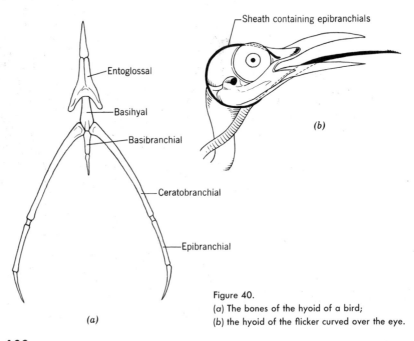

Figure 40.
(*a*) The bones of the hyoid of a bird;
(*b*) the hyoid of the flicker curved over the eye.

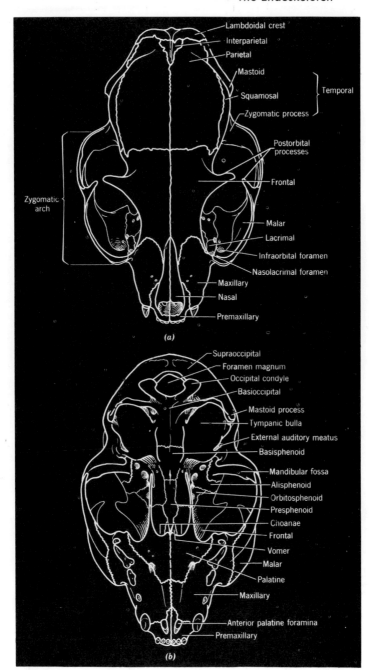

Figure 41.
The skull of
the cat:
(a) dorsal view;
(b) ventral view.

101

palate and the lateral walls of the nasopharynx. The large pterygoids of reptiles and birds are reduced to lesser bones. The four occipital bones are completely fused, each exoccipital forming one occipital condyle. The supraoccipital fuses with the interparietal to form a bone composed of cartilage and dermal elements. A sharp bony ridge, the **lambdoidal** or occipital crest, marks the separation of the occipital bone from the parietals; this ridge serves for the attachment of muscles from the shoulders and neck. The basisphenoid and presphenoid make up the floor of the skull anterior to the basioccipital. A saddle-shaped **sella turcica** on the dorsal side of the basisphenoid houses the pituitary gland. The alisphenoid, a triangular wing on each side of the basisphenoid, forms the posterior part of the orbit. The lateral processes of the presphenoid, the orbitosphenoids, also form a part of the orbits. The alisphenoid is believed to be derived from the pterygoquadrate and not from the chondrocranium. In the human skull the sphenoidal bones are fused into a single bone. From the olfactory capsules of the chondrocranium arise the mesethmoid, or nasal septum, and the **cribriform plate,** a bony plate against the olfactory lobe of the brain which is perforated for the passage of the fibers of the olfactory nerve. In *Ornithorhynchus* the cribriform plate actually has only two openings, and in Cetacea there are no perforations. Convoluted ethmoturbinals are attached to both sides of the ethmoid bone. Other turbinated bones, **maxilloturbinals** and **nasoturbinals,** are processes of the maxillae and nasals, respectively, and are dermal bones. These three spongelike turbinated bones form a complex maze through which air must pass on its way to the nasopharynx.

The temporal bone is incredibly complex. It forms the posterior portion of the zygomatic arch and the mandibular fossa and the squamous portion of the posterior lateral wall of the cranium; it is also fused ventrally and posteriorly with the tympanic bulla and **mastoid,** medial to the external auditory meatus. A styloid process, attached to the mastoid process, is supposed to be a remnant of the hyoid arch. The tympanic bulla houses the **petrous bone,** often fused with the mastoid to form the **petromastoid.** The petrous bone contains the **inner ear.** The mammalian skull has neither a quadrate nor an articular; these two bones have been reduced to minuscular ossicles, the incus and malleus, respectively, which are still jointed but have been displaced within the middle ear cavity (Figure 42).

Sinuses, or air spaces, lighten the skull, warm the inspired air, and give resonance to the voice. A pair of **frontal sinuses** is found on the anterior part of the frontal bone and communicates with the nasal passages. The large **ethmoidal cells,** or sinuses, found beneath the median

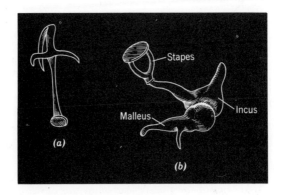

Figure 42. (a) Columella of bird; (b) mammalian ear ossicles.

wall of the orbit, also open into the nasal passageway. In the presphenoid a pair of **sphenoidal sinuses** is separated by a very thin septum and communicates with the nasal passageways. In the skull of man the mastoid process is riddled by the mastoid cells, spongy vacuities which communicate with the cavity of the middle ear. The bulk of the skull of animals with very large heads, such as the elephant, contains many large air-filled sinuses.

The mandible of mammals is composed of only one bone, the dentary. The two dentaries fuse anteriorly to form a suture, absent in the mandible of man and the bat. The jaw articulates with the mandibular fossae of the zygomatic process by the **condylar processes** (Figure 43).

The Teeth

Although teeth do not belong with the skeletal system, they are intimately associated with it.

The forerunner of the teeth of vertebrates seems to be placoid scales, such as those found near the edges of the jaws of elasmobranchs which become larger and undergo a gradual transition into teeth. Rows of triangular teeth are crowded into each jaw. Teeth are derived from the ectoderm and mesoderm of the **stomodeum;** they are composed of **dentine** and are covered with a crown of **enamel.** The teeth of elasmobranchs have no enamel. Teeth have a free crown above the surface of the gum and a root underneath the surface (Figure 44). Each tooth has a hollow **pulp cavity** which contains connective tissue, blood vessels, and nerves. A **cementum substance** around the roots of the teeth protects the dentine and binds the teeth to the jaw.

Lower vertebrates have numerous and widely distributed teeth. All

103

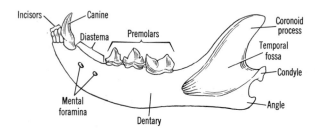

Figure 43. The mandible of a cat (lateral view).

the bones of the palate and pharynx of fish may bear teeth. The palatines and the vomer of amphibians, the vomer of *Sphenodon,* and the palatines and pterygoids of snakes all have teeth. Crocodilia and mammals have teeth only on the premaxillae and maxillae of the upper jaw and on the dentary of the lower jaw. The number of teeth is variable in all classes except the mammals, in which the number is so constant that it constitutes a specific mark of identification.

Toothless forms occur in nearly all classes of vertebrates. Turtles and birds show no traces of teeth even during their development. The ancestral birds, *Archaeopteryx, Ichthyornis,* and *Hesperonis,* had well-developed reptilian teeth. The monotremes, some Edentata, and some whales are toothless mammals.

In most vertebrates teeth are continuously replaced, and the dentition is called **polyphyodont.** Mammals with only two dentitions are **diphyodont;** the first provisional milk dentition is replaced by the permanent dentition. Marsupials, toothed whales, and some rodents have only one dentition and are **monophyodont.** The young of some bats and rodents shed their teeth in the uterus and are born with a permanent dentition. The teeth of most polyphyodont animals usually have no roots; they are attached to the jaw by fibrous connective tissue and are known as **acrodont** (Figure 45). The teeth of lizards are attached to the bone on the side and are known as **pleurodont.** The teeth of Crocodilia and mammals have long roots which fit into bony sockets called **alveoli;** this attachment is known as **thecodont.**

With the exception of those of mammals, all teeth in any one species of vertebrates are **homodont,** or similar. Such teeth are ill adapted for chewing and serve entirely for seizing and tearing food. The **heterodont** teeth of mammals are differentiated into **incisors, canines, premolars,** and **molars** (Figure 46). Although the toothed whales are homodont, they represent a regression from heterodontia. In the upper jaw incisors are

104

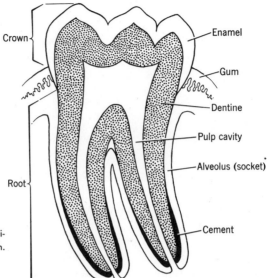

Figure 44. Diagram of a longitudinal section of a molar tooth.

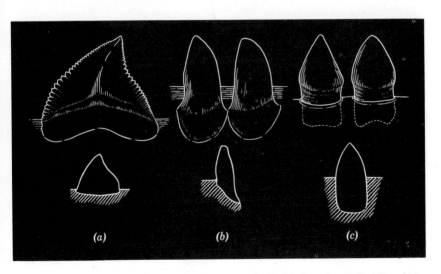

Figure 45. Types of tooth attachment: (a) acrodont (in shark); (b) pleurodont (in lizard); and (c) thecodont (in alligator).

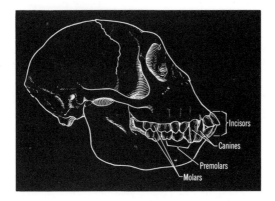

Figure 46. Skull of a Rhesus monkey showing heterodont dentition.

always located in the premaxilla. The tusks of elephants grow from the premaxillae and are incisors. In rodents and lagomorphs the incisors have very long roots and never stop growing (Figure 47). They must be worn or ground down at the same pace at which they grow, and it is important that contact between upper and lower incisors be unimpaired. These teeth are also peculiar in having enamel only on the anterior surface; since dentine wears more rapidly than enamel, the teeth develop a sharp cutting edge anteriorly. The tusks of elephants have almost no enamel; **ivory** is pure dentine. The sloths have no incisors on either jaw, and sheep have none on the upper jaw. The canines are usually long conical teeth, best developed in carnivores. The canines of boars and walruses form tusks. Rodents and herbivores have no canines, and the **diastema** is the place where canines would normally be (Figure 47). The premolars and molars are well differentiated in the carnivores, but there is little difference between them in herbivores. In herbivores these are the grinding teeth; their broad grinding surfaces are ridged with bands of enamel, between which is the partially worn,

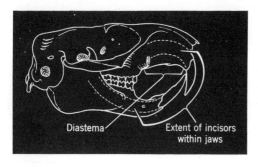

Diastema   Extent of incisors
within jaws

Figure 47. Skull of woodchuck showing the roots of the incisors.

106

softer dentine. The first set of premolars is shed and replaced by a permanent set; the molars are permanent from the beginning. This type of dentition is both monodont and diphyodont.

Heterodontia can be expressed in a **dental formula**. A series of numbers written above a line indicates, from left to right, the number of incisors, canines, premolars, and molars in the right side of the upper jaw; underneath the line are indicated the corresponding number of teeth in the right half of the lower jaw. Thus the dental formula $\frac{3.1.3.1}{3.1.2.1}$ for the cat indicates that in the upper right jaw there are three incisors, one canine, three premolars, and one molar, and three incisors, one canine, two premolars, and one molar in the lower jaw. The formula $\frac{0.0.3.3}{3.1.3.3}$ for the sheep indicates that in the upper right jaw there are no incisors and no canines, three premolars, and three molars; in the lower right jaw there are three incisors, one canine, three premolars, and three molars.

THE APPENDICULAR SKELETON

With the exception of the most primitive or aberrant specialized forms, all vertebrates have two pairs of free appendages braced against the body by cartilage or bones which form the girdles of the appendages.

It is generally agreed that the limbs of land vertebrates, which are four in number (tetrapods), have evolved from the paired fins of ancestral fish. Ancient vertebrates possessed continuous **fin folds** on each side of the body, which fused behind the anus, and a continuous dorsal median fin fold. According to the fin-fold theory, the fins of modern fishes have arisen through the persistence of certain parts of the fin folds and the dropping out of others (Figure 48).

The fins of ancestral fish were supported by bony or cartilaginous rays composed of three or more segments. The proximal elements are the **basals**, the middle elements, the **radials**, and the distal elements, the **dermal fin rays.** Groups of adjacent basals fused together to form a few large cartilages with which the radials articulate. The most anterior basal expanded toward the midventral line and fused with the corresponding one from the opposite side to establish a primitive girdle (Figure 49).

A direct lineage between the fin of the fish and the tetrapod limb is not known; the fins of lungfishes and those of the extinct Crossopterygii, however, suggest certain affinities. From the skeleton of these fishes it

107

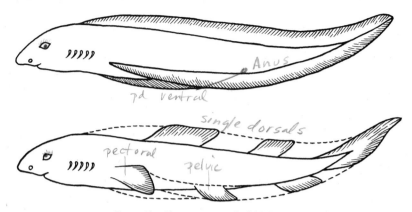

Figure 48.   The presumptive fin-fold theory.

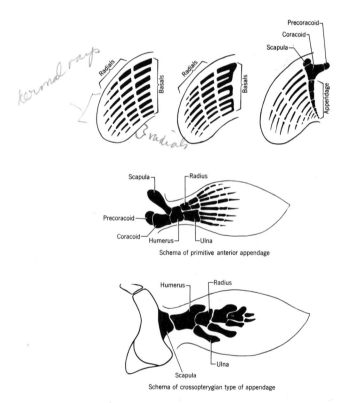

Schema of primitive anterior appendage

Schema of crossopterygian type of appendage

Figure 49.   Hypothetical development of the tetrapod appendages from a primitive fin.

108

appears that the girdles evolved from the fused basals and that some of the bones of the appendages arose from the radials. The appendicular skeleton of these fishes shows that the proximal skeletal elements of the extremities resembled those of more recent land vertebrates even before locomotion on land had come about (Figure 49). When vertebrates emerged from water the fins changed to appendages more or less capable of supporting the weight of the body. The tail, then, was no longer the main organ of locomotion. When the appendages became stronger they developed stronger girdles, which became attached to the vertebral column. The amphibians developed the first tripartite girdles. The bones of the pectoral appendages and girdles and those of the pelvic appendages and girdles developed in an identical way. Since there is a bone-for-bone correspondence in the pectoral and pelvic appendages and girdles, these bones are said to be **serially homologous** (Figure 50). The basic pectoral girdle consists of a **scapula, precoracoid,** and **coracoid,** which are serially homologous with the **ilium, pubis,** and **ischium,** respectively, of the pelvic girdle. In the appendages the **humerus, radius,** and **ulna** and **carpals, metacarpals,** and **phalanges** of the anterior appendages correspond to the **femur, tibia,** and **fibula** and **tarsals, metatarsals,** and **phalanges,** respectively, of the posterior appendages.

The generalized primitive tetrapod limb consists of a series of segments. The first segment, <u>stylopodium,</u> is composed of the humerus or femur;

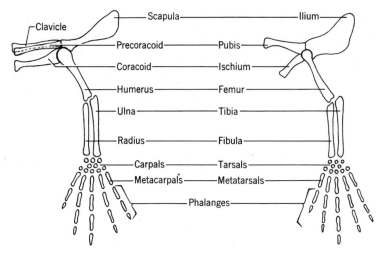

Figure 50.   Schema of serial homology.

the second segment, **zeugopodium,** the forearm or shank, is composed of parallel bones, the radius and ulna or tibia and fibula; and the third segment, **autopodium,** consists of the carpus, metacarpus, and digits or tarsus, metatarsus, and digits. The autopodium of tetrapods is typically **pentadactyl,** bearing five digits.

Between the zeugopodium proximally and the metacarpals or metatarsals distally is a series of carpal or tarsal bones. There are three bones in a proximal row, four in a middle row, and five in a distal row (Figure 51). The bone in the proximal row, distal to the ulna or fibula, is known as the **ulnare** or **fibulare,** that distal to the radius or tibia, **radiale** or **tibiale,** and the one between them is the **intermedium.** The middle row has four **centralia,** and each element of the distal row is at the base of one of the five metacarpals or metatarsals; these are the **distalia, carpalia,** or **tarsalia.** The **pisiform,** an additional element on the ulnar side considered to be a sesamoid bone, is found in nearly all tetrapods. There are five metacarpals or metatarsals and five digits composed of variable numbers of phalanges. In most tetrapods the number of carpals or tarsals is variously reduced, and even the penta-

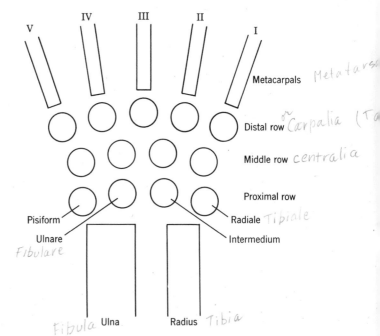

Figure 51. Schema of the complete carpal elements in a pentadactyle limb.

dactyl pattern is reduced and modified. The reduction may follow an entirely different pattern in the anterior and posterior appendages, even in the same order of vertebrates.

COMPARATIVE ANATOMY OF THE APPENDICULAR SKELETON

The Pectoral Girdle

Fishes. The pectoral and pelvic girdles of elasmobranchs are relatively primitive; they are simple, similar, and composed entirely of cartilage (Figure 52). In bony fishes the pectoral girdle is invaded by dermal bones, the largest and most important of these, phylogenetically, being the **clavicle** and the **cleithrum**. The girdle, then, is composed of the scapula and coracoid from the original girdle pattern and a clavicle, a cleithrum, and other dermal bones.

Amphibians. The earliest tetrapods have a single dermal bone, the interclavicle, added between the clavicles. The dermal bones tend to be reduced and to disappear altogether, although some discrepancies occur. The pectoral girdle of urodeles is primitive and consists entirely of cartilages or cartilage bones; that of salientians is well developed (see Figure 29). It has an anterior clavicle, which replaces the precoracoid, and a posterior coracoid; both articulate with the sternum medially and support the scapula laterally. The clavicle, coracoid, and scapula meet at the **glenoid fossa,** a depression which articulates the head of the humerus. The scapula is continuous dorsally with a cartilaginous **suprascapular process;** this is, in turn, partially covered by the cleithrum.

Reptiles. The most primitive pectoral girdle is found in *Sphenodon*, in which a T-shaped interclavicle is in contact with the clavicles anteriorly. Laterally, the girdle consists of the fused cartilages of the coracoid, precoracoid, and scapula; the precoracoid and scapula are partially ossified, and a large suprascapular cartilage extends laterally and dorsally. The pectoral girdle of alligators has a ventral precoracoid and a dorsolateral scapula; there are no clavicles, but an interclavicle is attached to the ventral part of the sternum (see Figure 29). In turtles the girdle is formed by a ventral flattened precoracoid and an elongated scapula which extends dorsally to the carapace. The scapula projects anteriorly as the **prescapular process** (Figure 53). The dermal elements of the turtle's girdle are incorporated into the plastron.

Birds. The pectoral girdle consists of a long, narrow, posteriorly directed scapula, a stout precoracoid that anchors the girdle to the sternum, and the wishbone, or **furcula,** composed of the clavicles and

111

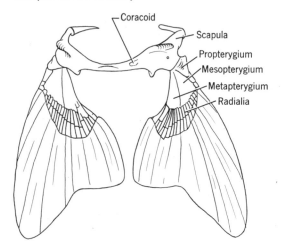

Figure 52. Pectoral girdle and fins of the dogfish.

the interclavicle (Figure 53) between the precoracoids. In some birds the interclavicle is fused to the rostrum of the sternum. Just medial to the glenoid fossa the three girdle bones form the wall of a large **foramen triosseum,** through which passes the tendon of the muscle that lifts the humerus. Ratites have no foramen triosseum.

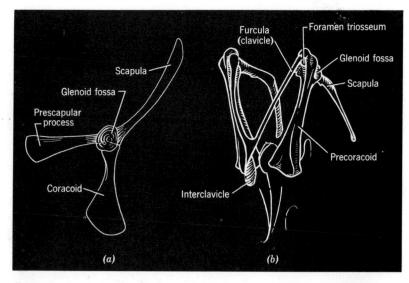

Figure 53. Pectoral girdles: (a) turtle; (b) bird.

Mammals. The primitive pectoral girdle of monotremes has a large T-shaped bone consisting of interclavicle and clavicles and associated with a precoracoid, coracoid, and scapula (Figure 54). Placental mammals have no interclavicle and precoracoid, and a vestigial coracoid process is an appendage of the scapula (Figure 55). The clavicle is often very small or absent, and the scapula is the largest and most important bone of the pectoral girdle. The mammalian scapula is triangular or fan-shaped (Figure 55); and the humerus articulates with the shallow glenoid fossa. The coracoid process is medial to the lip of the glenoid fossa. On the outer surface the spine, a bony ridge, terminates lateral to the glenoid fossa in an **acromion process**, with which the clavicles articulate when they are present. In monotremes, marsupials, and primates the stout clavicles anchor the girdle to the thoracic cage, but in the ungulates and carnivores, which have vestigial clavicles, the pectoral girdle is free.

The Pelvic Girdle

Unlike the pectoral girdle, which is enormously modified in different classes and orders, the pelvic girdle has remained relatively unchanged, and all three of the original bones can be recognized.

Fishes. The primitive pelvic girdle consisted of the enlarged cartilages of the basalia on each side. In elasmobranchs a pair of cartilages has fused in the ventral midline to form a **puboischiac cartilage** bar; the dorsolateral extensions are the **iliac processes** (Figure 56).

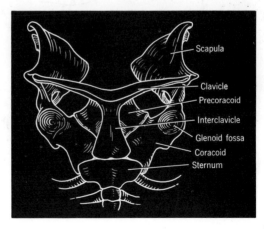

Figure 54. Pectoral girdle and sternum of the Spiny anteater, Echidna (ventral view).

Scapula

Clavicle

Precoracoid

Interclavicle

Glenoid fossa

Coracoid

Sternum

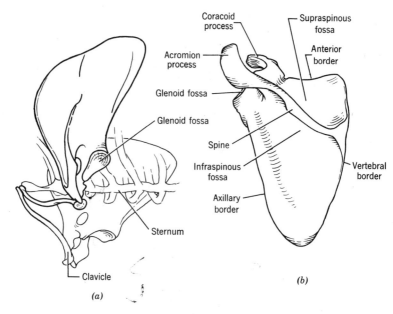

Figure 55. (a) Pectoral girdle of the sloth; (b) scapula of man.

Amphibia.　In urodeles a puboischiac plate is attached laterally to a flattened cartilaginous or bony ilium which extends dorsally and is attached to the sacral vertebra.　These structures meet in the **acetabulum**, a shallow depression in which the head of the femur rotates.　The pelvic girdle of salientians is U-shaped (Figure 57).　Two long slender ilia are attached to the ribs of the single sacral vertebra; posteriorly, where the two ilia are fused at the base of the U, is the pubis, a disclike structure composed of an anterior pair of fused calcified cartilages, and the ischia, a posterior pair of bones.　All three of these meet at the acetabulum (Figure 57).

Reptiles.　The pelvic girdle is best seen in the turtles, where the sutures of the three fused bones are visible (Figure 58).　Two pairs of ventral bones, pubes, anteriorly, and ischia, posteriorly, meet the ilia on the dorsal side.　The pubes and ischia extend to the ventral midline and fuse with the corresponding bone on the other side to form a **pubic** and **ischial symphysis**.　The seam of these symphyses remains cartilaginous.　An **epipubic cartilage** extends forward from the pubic symphysis, and a prominent **pectineal process** projects laterally from each pubis. Between the pubis and ischium is the puboischial or **obturator** foramen.

114

Figure 56. Pelvic girdle
and fins of the shark.

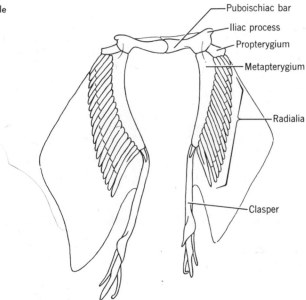

Figure 56. Pelvic girdle and fins of the shark.

Puboischiac bar
Iliac process
Propterygium
Metapterygium
Radialia
Clasper

The acetabulum is hemispherical, and in its concavity the sutures of each of the bones of the girdle can be seen (Figure 58). The large ilium makes contact with the two sacral ribs. In alligators the pubic bones are movably jointed with the ischia and do not form a part of the wall

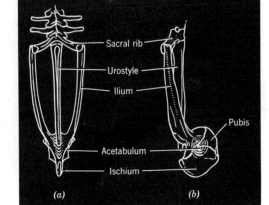

Figure 57. Pelvic girdle of the frog: (a) dorsal view; (b) lateral view.

Sacral rib
Urostyle
Ilium
Pubis
Acetabulum
Ischium

(a)   (b)

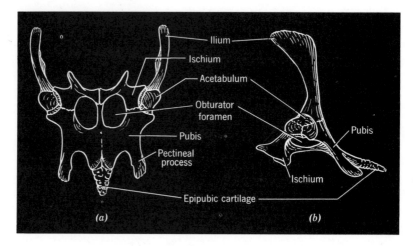

Figure 58. Pelvic girdle of the turtle: (a) ventral view; (b) lateral view.

of the acetabulum (Figure 59). In lizards an epipubic cartilage projects anteriorly and an **hypoischial cartilage** projects posteriorly from the symphysis. Snakes have no pelvic girdle, although vestiges of it may be found in the python.

Birds. The three bones are flat plates fused together and attached to the synsacrum (Figures 23 and 60). The ilium is the largest bone; the ischium is less than one third its size and is attached to its posteroventral border, enclosing the ilioischial foramen. The pubis is a narrow bone along the ventral border of the ilium extending from the pectineal

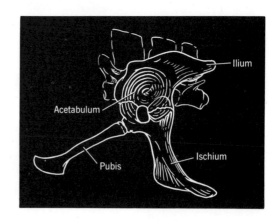

Figure 59. Pelvic girdle of the alligator.

116

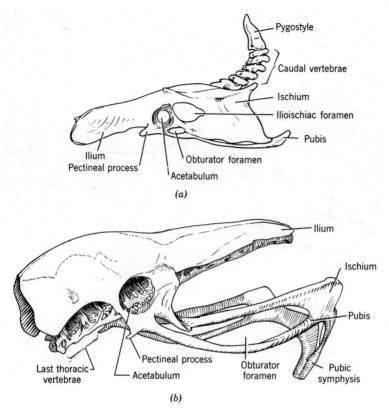

Figure 60. Pelvic girdles of (*a*) a flying bird; (*b*) the ostrich.

process, below the acetabulum, to the rear of the synsacrum; a slitlike obturator foramen separates the pubis from the ilium. The deep acetabulum is perforated by the acetabular foramen. The pubes extend beyond the ischia but do not form a symphysis. In the ostrich the large pubes fuse in the midventral line to form a plow-shaped pubic symphysis (Figure 60). In the Rhea the ischia form an ischial symphysis.

Mammals. The ilium, pubis, and ischium are completely fused into a single innominate bone. The ilium, the largest bone, articulates with the sacrum. The anterior and dorsal border of the ilium is curved and flared into the crest of the ilium (Figure 61). On the outer ventral part the pubes meet in the midline to form the pubic symphysis. The ischium extends back from the acetabulum and is expanded laterally

117

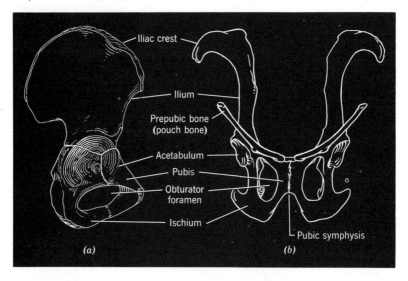

Figure 61. Innominate bone of (a) a new-born child; (b) a marsupial.

and posteriorly into the ischial tuberosity; a limb, or ramus, of the ischium swings from each side to the midventral line toward the pubic symphysis, and may form an ischial symphysis. The acetabulum is bounded anteriorly by the ilium, ventrally by the pubis, and posteriorly by the ischium. In young animals the three bones can be seen separately (Figure 61a). An additional bone, the cotyloid or acetabular bone, helps to form the acetabulum, except in monotremes, rodents, and bats. The acetabulum of monotremes, like that of reptiles and birds, is perforated by a foramen. Monotremes and marsupials have a pair of epipubic or marsupial bones projecting anteriorly from the pubes and articulating with them (Figure 61b). The obturator foramen is found between the ilium and the ischium. The degree of spread and flaring of the ilium is related to the normal position of the animal in locomotion. Even among the primates, those which tend to be bipedal have a wider and more flared ilium. In animals in which the pelvis does not directly support the weight of the viscera the ilia are small, narrow, and closer together.

The Appendages

Fishes. The skeleton of the paired fins consists of three basal cartilages or bones: an anterior propterygium, a middle mesopterygium, and a posterior **metapterygium** (see Figure 52). Numerous segmented radial cartilages or bones grow distal to the basal segment, and dermal rays extend from the radials. There is great variation in the structure of the fins of bony fishes. The number of separate skeletal elements tends to be reduced, and the dermal fin rays take over much of the skeletal support. The pelvic fins are similar to the pectoral fins, but they are smaller; they are large in elasmobranchs, and in the males they are modified to form **claspers** (see Figure 56). In some teleosts the pelvic fins are small or absent or they have moved very much forward, just posterior to the pectoral fins.

The tail of a fish is its principal organ of locomotion. According to their shape, two major types of tail can be found (Figure 62): heterocercal, in sharks, sturgeons, and paddle fishes; and **homocercal**, the typical, symmetrical fishtail, in most modern fishes.

Amphibia. Although the limbs of urodeles are weak, their bones are well formed. The humerus, the first bone of the fore limb, articulates distally with the two parallel bones, radius and ulna. Distal to these, the carpal bones are reduced in number by fusing with each other. The hand of urodeles usually has four digits, although some have only three or two. When four digits are present the first one has disappeared.

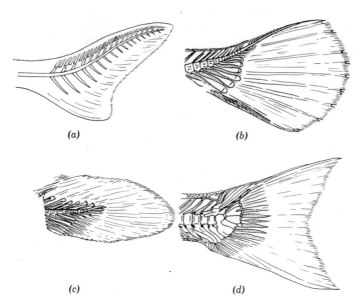

(a) (b)

(c) (d)

Figure 62. (a) Typical heterocercal tail; (b) intermediate herterocercal tail; (c) diphycercal tail; (d) homocercal tail.

In the hind limb the femur articulates with the tibia and fibula. Distal to the tarsal elements are five toes, although occasionally there may be four. In salientians the limbs are stronger and more specialized. There is nothing unusual about the humerus and femur, but the radius and ulna have become fused into a single bone, as have the tibia and fibula also (Figure 63). The fore limb has four toes, but the hind limb has five. In the hind limb the proximal row of the tarsus consists of two elongated bones, the **astragalus** on the inside and the **calcaneus** on the outside; the distal row has five small bones, one resting at the base of each long metatarsal. The digits are very long. An additional bony element, the **prehallux,** is usually found on the medial tibial side of the tarsus.

Reptiles. The pectoral and pelvic appendages show no striking modification, and only the autopodium needs to be mentioned briefly. The

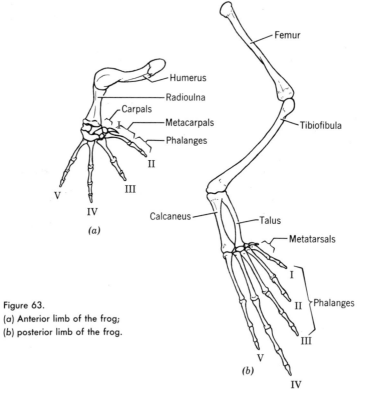

Figure 63.
(a) Anterior limb of the frog;
(b) posterior limb of the frog.

carpus is primitive and is composed of numerous bones. In *Sphenodon* only the centralia, the tarsals in the middle row, are fused. An additional tarsal bone, the pisiform, is found on the ventral ulnar side of the tarsus. In the turtle and alligator the centralia of the carpus and tarsus are fused with each other and with the proximal row. In the fore limb the intermedium is often fused with the radiale.

Birds. A variety of profound modifications has occurred. The fore limbs or wings are modified for flight, and the hind appendages can perform a large number of functions. The wings have a reduced number of carpals and digits, and the bones have acquired pneumatic channels to reduce their weight. The humerus of flying birds can always be recognized by its light weight, large, convex head, and large lesser tuberosity, continuous with the flaring **detoid ridge.** On the under surface of the greater tuberosity is a large hole, the **pneumatic foramen.** The radius is slenderer and less curved than the ulna, and on its posterior dorsal border the ulna bears the imprints of the **secondary flight feathers** (Figure 64a). The ulna projects proximally beyond the notch for the articulation with the humerus to form the elbow or **olecranon process.** Even though bird embryos have thirteen carpal elements, the adult has only two free carpals, the radiale and the ulnare. The radiale is formed by a fusion of the radiale, intermedium, and one centrale; the ulnare is formed by the fusion of the ulnare with the pisiform (Figure 64b,c). The rest of the carpal elements are fused to the base of the metacarpals, which together form the **carpometacarpus.** The carpometacarpus contains a very small metacarpal II, a stout metacarpal III, and a curved, slender metacarpal IV. Metacarpal I appears briefly during early development; metacarpal V disappears late in development (Figure 64b). The digits are much reduced. Digit II has two phalanges, the second forming a small claw; digit III has a broad, flattened first phalanx and a long, clawlike second; digit IV has only one very small basal phalanx (Figure 64a). In the kiwi the wings are vestigial, and only metacarpal III and digit III persist in the adult. The developmental history of the wing of the bird is controversial, and some believe that the digits and the respective metacarpals represent numbers I, II, and III, whereas others believe that they are III, IV, and V. These assumptions, however, are not valid, and the existing digits are II, III, and IV.

The posterior appendages of birds have developed along different lines from the wings (Figure 65). The femur has an almost spherical head which fits into the acetabulum and a greater trochanter that flares out lateral to the head. The distal end of the femur has a deep groove

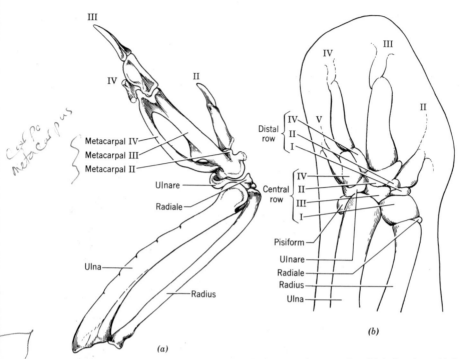

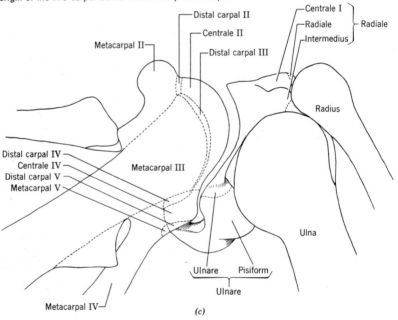

Figure 64. (a) The bones of an adult wing; (b) the wing of a seven-day-old chick embryo; (c) the origin of the two carpal bones and the carpometacarpus.

122

or notch in the center, dividing it into a lateral and median condyle. A patella, attached to the tendon which glides over the joint, is a sesamoid bone.   The tibia is fused on its distal end with the proximal row of tarsals to form the **tibiotarsus**.   One or two large bony crests, the **cnemial process,** extend anteriorly from the tibiotarsus; this attains great size in swimming birds.   The fibula is a short, slender bone on the outside of the tibiotarsus.   With the exception of that in penguins, the fib-

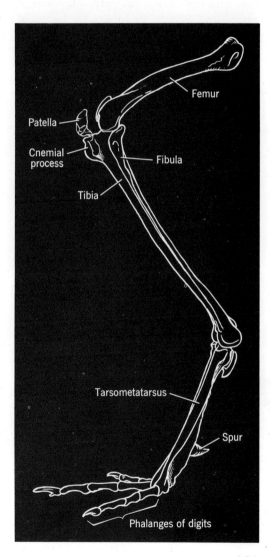

Figure 65.
Bones in the leg
of a bird (lateral view).

Femur

Patella

Cnemial
process

Fibula

Tibia

Tarsometatarsus

Spur

Phalanges of digits

123

ula is as long as the tibiotarsus. The terminal part of the tibiotarsus has two malleoli. The **tarsometatarsus** is one of the most characteristic bones in the avian skeleton. It is composed of the fused metatarsals I, II, III, and IV, to the proximal ends of which are fused the centralia and distalia. Metatarsal V is wanting. In general, the feet of birds have four digits which correspond to numbers I, II, III, and IV. The first is very small in most birds, and in some it is absent. The emu has three toes, and the ostrich has only two. The length of the digits of birds is varied and reflects the locomotor habits of the species; jacanas, which walk on water lily pads, have very long digits. Birds are **digitigrade;** they walk entirely on their toes, with the tarsometatarsus always above the ground.

Mammals. The appendages show great varieties of specialization. The fore limbs show less modification and have remained closer to the primitive pentadactyl pattern. The humerus articulates distally with the **semilunar notch** of the ulna. Mammals have a large elbow or **olecranon process.** In some mammals the radius articulates proximally

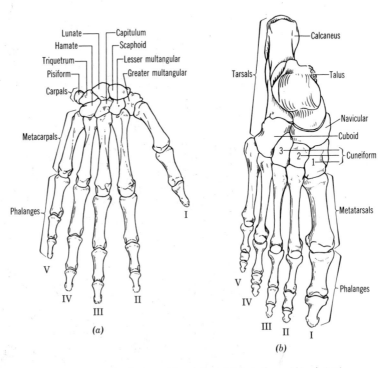

Figure 66. (a) Hand of man (dorsal view); (b) foot of man (dorsal view).

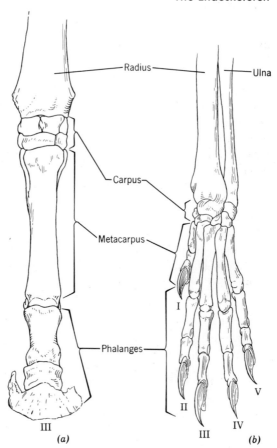

Figure 67.
(a) Foot of horse;
(b) foot of cat.

Radius

Ulna

Carpus

Metacarpus

I

Phalanges

II

V

III

(a)

III

IV

(b)

with the ulna in such a way that the hand can rotate from a prone to a supine position without moving the whole limb.   In the horse, and in a few other mammals, the radius is fused with the ulna.   The hand has several free carpals.   Although each carpal has been given various names in comparative anatomy, here we use only those in common use for the carpals in the human hand.   The proximal row has a **scaphoid** on the radial side, a **lunate** in the center, and a **triquetrum** on the ulnar side.   Naming them from the radial to the ulnar sides, the distal row has the **multangulus majus**, or **trapezium**, the **multangulus minor**, or **trapezoid**, the **capitate**, and the **hamate** (Figure 66a).   The metacarpals are nearly always elongated and form the body of the hand.   In ungulates the metacarpals are long and stout and often fused into a **cannon bone** (Figure 67a).   The digits have two or three phalanges, the distal one

125

bearing a nail, claw, or hoof. The flippers of aquatic mammals have many phalanges.

In the hind limb the femur is not particularly different from that of other vertebrates. In the shank, or leg proper, the tibia is large, but the fibula is small and often fused to the tibia. In the foot (see Figure 66*b*) the tibia articulates with the **talus** or astragalus; this in turn articulates with the calcaneus, the large heel bone. The **navicular** is a large third tarsal which articulates with the anteromedial side of the talus. A distal row of tarsals is composed, naming from medial to lateral sides, of **cuneiform I, II, and III** and a **cuboid.** The cuneiforms articulate with the navicular, the cuboid, with the calcaneus. The metacarpals form the body of the foot. The digits are similar to those in the fore limb; they are composed of two or three phalanges, the distal one of which bears a claw, nail, or hoof. **Plantigrade** animals walk on the whole foot (man, bear, and rodents); digitigrade animals walk on their toes (cats and dogs, Figure 67*b*); and **unguligrade** animals walk on their hooves (horses, pigs, and cows).

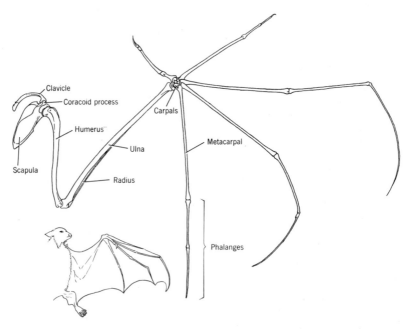

Figure 68. Pectoral girdle and wing of a bat.

Special modifications of the limbs are numerous. In the bat the anterior appendages have very long digits between which is stretched a thin skin membrane (Figure 68). In the horse, and in most of the grazing mammals, the metacarpals and metatarsals are very long, reduced in number, and fused (Figure 67*a*). When the digits of mammals are reduced the first digit usually disappears first, followed in order by digits V, II, and IV. The pig has four toes, the rhinoceros three, the camel two, and the horse only one. During the development of the horse four digital rays and several carpal and tarsal elements appear. Although the adult horse has only one digit, number III, the remains of meta-carpals or metatarsals number II and IV are fused on each side of the stout metacarpal III. Some aquatic mammals have almost completely lost some of the appendages. In the seals the appendages are greatly modified as flippers. In the porpoises the pelvic appendages are absent, and only vestiges of the girdles remain. In whales even the vestiges of the pelvic girdle have disappeared.

SUMMARY

1. The skeleton is composed of cartilage and bones. Bones which in development are preceded by a cartilage model are called cartilage or endochondral bones; those that are formed directly from mesenchyme are called membrane or dermal bones. Except for this developmental difference, the two types are structurally identical. Each bone consists of an outer dense or compact wall and inner spongy bone.
2. Bones that come in contact form either immovable joints (synar-throses) or movable ones (diarthroses).
3. The skeleton can be divided into axial and appendicular. The axial skeleton consists of the skull and the vertebral column; the appen-dicular skeleton, of the bones of the girdles and the appendages.
4. The most ancient skeletal element, the notochord, is the axial rod around which the vertebral column develops. The vertebrae develop metamerically around the notochord from the mesenchyme of the scle-rotomes. The principal parts of the vertebrae are the centrum around the notochord and a neural arch which encloses the spinal cord. In the tail region a hemal arch, below the centrum, encloses the caudal blood vessels. Successive vertebrae are yoked together so that while able to move they do not easily become disjointed.

5. Vertebrae arise from the fusion of several skeletal elements formed from the sclerotomes. The arches are formed by four pairs of arcualia: the basidorsals and interdorsals on the dorsal side of the notochord and the basiventrals and interventrals on the ventral side. The basidorsals form the neural arch, the basiventrals, the hemal arch. The interdorsals contribute to the building of the neural arch; the interventrals play a small role in the formation of the understructure of the vertebra.

6. The centrum of vertebrae develops from one or two mesenchymal condensations around the notochord: an anterior hypocentrum and a posterior pleurocentrum. In the tail of the bowfin the two elements form a double centrum, a condition known as diplospondyly. In amphibians only the hypocentrum forms the centrum proper, and in amniotes the pleurocentrum forms the centrum and the hypocentrum, the intervertebral disc. Many minor and major variances occur in the formation of different vertebrae.

7. Cyclostomes have the most primitive vertebrae; they consist only of cartilage plates that correspond to basidorsals and interdorsals. In the sturgeon the vertebrae consist of the four unfused pairs of arcualia around the very large notochord; there is no centrum. In bony fishes the vertebrae are differentiated into those of the trunk with ribs attached to them and those of the tail with a neural arch above the centrum and a hemal arch below. Beginning with Amphibia and progressing to mammals, several regional modifications of the vertebrae occur in the vertebral column.

8. The origin of ribs is confusing. In the sturgeon a bony prong develops from each basidorsal, but in other vertebrates ribs may arise from other sources. Primitively, as in some fishes, two pairs of ribs are found: a dorsal intermuscular pair and a ventral or pleural pair. The ribs of amphibians and amniotes seem to correspond to the ventral pair of ribs.

9. Only tetrapods have a sternum. It consists of a series of midventral skeletal elements to which, except in Amphibia, are attached the ribs and the pectoral girdle. The sternum has a different origin in different classes of vertebrates.

10. The skull arises from a fusion of the chondrocranium, dermatocranium, and splanchnocranium. The chondrocranium forms just anterior to the notochord and underneath the brain by a fusion of two posterior parachordal cartilages and two prechordal cartilages anterior to them and the cartilaginous capsules around the olfactory and otic sensory organs. From the chondrocranium the ethnoid bones develop anteriorly, the sphenoid bones, in the middle, and the occipital bones, posteriorly. A series of dermal bones invests the chondrocranium and forms the walls and the vault of the skull; this is the dermatocranium. The splanchnocranium, a part of the branchial skeleton, also becomes incorporated in the skull. The first branchial, or mandibular, arch forms the jaws of the primitive skull, but beginning with the bony fishes dermal bones invest and gradually replace the mandibular arch. In the mammalian skull the only remnants of the mandibular arch are the incus and malleus of the middle ear. The second, hyoid, arch forms part of the hyoid bones which support the tongue and the columella, or stapes, of the middle ear. The remaining branchial arches largely disappear and leave behind only fragments that contribute to the formation of the larynx and the hyoid. Cartilage and dermal bones, very numerous in fishes, are progressively reduced in number phylogenetically.

11. The teeth of vertebrates below mammals are all alike and are constantly replaced when lost. Teeth may be borne on any of the palatal bones. In Crocodilia and in mammals teeth are borne only by the premaxillae and maxillae in the upper jaw and by the dentary in the lower jaw. The teeth of mammals are differentiated into several kinds; there is a very constant number in each species, and there are, at most, only two dentitions.

12. The appendicular skeleton consists of two pairs of appendages and the bones that support them, called pectoral and pelvic girdles. The original pattern of the pectoral girdles consists of the scapula, precoracoid, and coracoid, whose serially homologous bones in the pelvic girdle are the ilium, pubis, and ischium, respectively. The bones of the anterior and posterior appendages are similarly serially homologous. The three bones of the pelvic girdle remain fairly unchanged, but those of the pectoral girdle undergo some striking modifications. Dermal bones become associated with the pectoral girdle and replace some of them.

13. The pectoral girdle, seldom attached to the vertebral column, is anchored to the sternum; in many mammals it is free. The pelvic girdle of tetrapods is always attached to the sacral vertebrae, the ribs of which are stouter than those of the other vertebrae.

14. The typical tetrapod appendage terminates in a hand or foot. These are composed of series of carpals or tarsals, metacarpals or metatarsals, and five digits. Some of the original carpals and tarsals become fused, and some disappear; even the digits are reduced in number in various vertebrates and undergo various adaptive transformations.

129

SUGGESTED READING

Bourne, H. G. (editor), 1956, *The Biochemistry and Physiology of Bones.* Academic Press Inc., New York.

Murray, P. D. F., 1936, *Bones. A Study of the Development and Structure of the Vertebrate Skeleton. Cambridge University Press*, Cambridge. Both of these volumes are readable and contain a wealth of exciting information.

Romer, A. S., 1955, *The Vertebrate Body.* W. B. Saunders Co., Philadelphia and London.

CHAPTER

6

CHAPTER

6

Figure 1. Striated muscle fibers of the mouse.

THE
MUSCULAR
SYSTEM

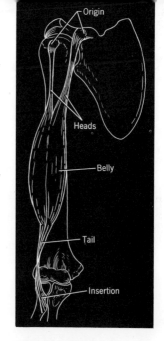

Figure 2.
The characteristic
features of a muscle.

GENERAL INTRODUCTION

All movements, from the contraction and dilatation of blood vessels and viscera to locomotion, are brought about by the alternate contraction and relaxation of **muscle fibers**. The name **muscle** comes from the fancied resemblance of some muscles to mice; the Latin name *musculus* is the diminutive of *mus* or mouse. **Fiber**, used in this sense, is synonymous with cell, and a muscle fiber is a muscle cell. The three types of muscle found in the animal body are (*a*) **visceral, smooth,** or **involuntary,** found in the viscera and in blood vessels, (*b*) **cardiac,** found only in the heart, and (*c*) **skeletal, striated,** or **voluntary,** attached to the skeleton. Only skeletal muscle is under willful nervous control; the other two are innervated by the autonomic nervous system and cannot be controlled voluntarily. Skeletal muscle is called striated because its fibers have parallel cross bands all along their length (Figure 1). One third to one half of the total mass of the body is skeletal muscle. Muscles are attached mostly to bones, and their primary function is to move the skeleton.

The proximal attachment of a muscle is the **origin** or **head** (Figure 2); the distal attachment is the **insertion** or **tail**; the fleshy part is the **belly**.

133

The attachments are fibrous and inelastic; they may be round cords, as tendons, or flat sheets, as aponeuroses. The origin is the relatively stationary attachment; the insertion, the more movable one.

Muscle fibers are covered with sarcolemma, a tough cell membrane. Each muscle fiber is surrounded by loose connective tissue; bundles of muscle fibers are enclosed in larger connective tissue sheets, and the entire muscle in turn is held together by a muscle sheath. This type of connective tissue packing permits the independent action of muscle fibers in an individual muscle and also allows the muscle to be richly supplied with blood vessels. Each muscle fiber is surrounded by a network of capillaries (see Figure 1, Chapter 8).

Muscle fibers contain muscle hemoglobin. Dark, or red, muscle contains a great deal of hemoglobin, white muscle contains less. Red muscle fibers have a smaller diameter than the white ones. The muscles in the hind limbs of birds are composed mostly of red muscle; those in the breast of gallinaceous birds contain mostly white fibers. White and red fibers are mixed in different proportions in the muscles of mammals. The muscles of mastication, those of the diaphragm, and all the more slowly contracting muscles are composed predominantly of red fibers and are relatively indefatigable. The rapidly contracting muscles contain mostly white fibers and are easily fatigued. As a rule the flexor muscles contain more white fibers than the extensors, which are mostly red.

The well-being of a muscle is dependent upon its nerves, which terminate inside the muscle fibers in specialized end-organs called motor end plates (Figure 3). A denervated muscle is paralyzed, atrophies, and perishes in time. Numerous stimuli which originate within the muscle itself, and outside the muscle as well, constantly relay impulses to it by way of the central nervous system. These impulses maintain the muscle in a partial state of contraction known as muscle tonus. Red fibers seem to be largely responsible for muscle tone. Even in resting animals some of the fibers in any one muscle are contracted all the time. The state of contraction of the muscle is proportional to the number of fibers involved and to the frequency of the nervous stimulations they receive.

Animals can perform a number of complicated actions automatically without the intervention of volition. Among these are the postural reflexes; two of the most important are the attitudinal reflexes and the righting reflexes. By means of attitudinal reflexes the displacement of any one part of the body is followed by the appropriate postural changes in the other parts. If an animal is unexpectedly shoved, it performs all

Figure 3. Terminal nerves and motor end plates in skeletal muscle fibers of a rat. (Courtesy of Dr. M. V. Edds, Jr., and the *J. Exp. Zool.*)

of the necessary changes in attitude to keep its balance. These changes require no will and can be performed effectively even by an animal which has had its cerebrum removed. When an animal is knocked off its feet it comes back to a standing position as a consequence of the righting reflexes; but this action is controlled by the cerebrum and cannot be performed by animals from which the cerebrum has been removed.

For the performance of a movement whole series of muscles are put into action. Each principal action is brought about by the contraction of a **prime mover,** whose action is made smooth by the **antagonistic muscles** which relax to about the same degree that the prime mover contracts. Prime movers and antagonist muscles alone, however, could not produce a smooth motion if a large number of **synergistic muscles,** each playing a minor role, did not participate in producing a coordinated action. These are designations of specific actions of any muscle, and the same muscle may in turn be a prime mover, antagonist or synergist. Muscles perform a great many actions. They **abduct,** or draw away from the median axis; they **adduct,** or draw toward the axis; they **depress,** or

135

lower a structure, **elevate,** or raise it; they **extend,** or straighten a joint, **flex,** or bend it; they **pronate,** or turn a structure face down, **supinate,** or turn it face up. In a sphincter they **constrict,** or make an opening smaller, **dilate,** or make it larger. When a muscle contracts it becomes shorter and wider, but its volume remains unchanged.

The nomenclature of muscles is based on a sound plan, and the names usually describe some obvious feature. Some names describe their shape (e.g., serratus, latissimus, vastus, triangularis); others give the number of heads or bellies (e.g., biceps, triceps, quadriceps, digastric); their location (e.g., temporalis, tibialis, and adjectives such as anterior, superior, and supra), or the action they perform (e.g., adductor, abductor, flexor, extensor, levator, and depressor). Many muscles are given the names of the bones to which they are attached, and in such cases the origin is always named first. Discrepancies, such as the **pectoralis major** of the cat being smaller than the **pectoralis minor** and, the **gluteus maximus,** smaller than the **gluteus medius,** occur when muscles are given the same name as their homologous counterparts in man for which the size is accurately described.

Thin layers of skeletal muscle may be found underneath the fatty layer of the skin of amniotes. With the exception of snakes, in which each large ventral scale has some skeletal muscle fibers attached to it, the skin of reptiles has very little cutaneous muscle. In birds the cutaneous muscle is broken up into many slips which raise and move the feathers collectively. The muscles are stronger in the great quills of the wings and tail. It is estimated that over 12,000 muscles may be found in the skin of a goose. Cutaneous musculature, the **panniculus carnosus,** is best developed in mammals. The panniculus carnosus of most rodents extends over almost all of the body. In moles and hedgehogs a heavy cloak of cutaneous muscle covers the entire body. The **platysma,** an apron of thin cutaneous muscle, extends from the mandible to the trunk of most mammals. The facial muscles of mammals are modified slips of cutaneous muscle.

In a number of elasmobranchs and teleosts muscle has given rise to tissue which releases powerful electric discharges. **Electric organs** have arisen independently in each of these groups. The electric organs of the rays are innervated by cranial nerves VII, IX, and X and must have developed from the visceral musculature of the pharynx. In the electric eel the epaxial muscles of the posterior two thirds of the body are differentiated into electric organs. These fishes can discharge over 500 volts, enough electricity to discourage most predators.

136

DEVELOPMENT

Most of the skeletal musculature originates from two sources: the mesenchyme of the myotomes and that of the somatic mesoderm in the body wall. Although it is generally believed that skeletal muscles, except for those in the region of the face and pharynx, are derived from a migration of the mesenchyme from the somites, this is probably true only of the muscles of fishes, particularly the elasmobranchs. Unfortunately, the details of developmental events are known only for some fishes, amphibians, and birds. Little is known for certain about the source or sources of muscles in mammals or in the other classes; it is not possible, therefore, to generalize, since class differences are sure to exist. The brief accounts which follow are sketchy and apply only to the specific vertebrates described.

dilator of pupil - ectoderm

Fishes

In fishes the skeletal musculature is arranged segmentally even in the adult. In the embryo the myotomes of the somites appear to grow ventrally until each meets the one from the opposite side on the midventral line, and the two remain separated by the **ventral septum,** a thin layer of connective tissue. There is an equal number of myotomes and vertebrae which alternate with each other, each muscle mass, or **myomere,** spanning half of each of two adjacent vertebrae. Successive myomeres are separated by **myocommata,** thin layers of connective tissue. A horizontal septum of connective tissue runs anteroposteriorly, parallel to the axis of the embryo. It separates each myomere into a dorsal mass, from which develop the **epaxial muscles** and a ventral mass which gives rise to the **hypaxial muscles.** The muscle fibers in each myomere become arranged in an anteroposterior direction. The origin of the musculature of the fins is not too well understood, probably because it may be different in different orders. In some sharks buds from the myotomes appear to invade the rudiments of the pectoral fins and give rise entirely, or in part, to the fin musculature. It could be assumed that the musculature of the pelvic fins arises in a similar way, but this would be unwarranted. In the salmon, for instance, the musculature of the pectoral fins arises *in situ* from the somatic mesoderm of the limb bud, but that of the pelvic fins is derived both from the mesenchyme of the myotomes and from that of the somatic mesoderm.

Comparative Anatomy

Amphibians

Information about the development of the skeletal musculature of amphibians is also fragmentary. For that matter, most observations have been made on the urodeles. In these animals it appears that the myotomes give rise to the epaxial musculature and probably also to the hypaxial musculature or dorsolateral part of the trunk. The rest of the hypaxial musculature is derived from the somatic mesoderm. The muscles of the limbs develop from the mesoderm of the limb buds, which is somatic mesoderm.

Birds

In birds the development of the musculature is better known. Strauss and Rawles (1953) have elucidated this complex phenomenon with a series of beautifully conceived and executed experiments. After hens' eggs were incubated two and one half to three days, a "window" was cut through the shell over the embryo, and certain regions of the living embryo were marked with fine carbon particles. The embryos were then allowed to develop further, and by tracing the final location of the carbon particles the origin of the different structures could be ascertained. From the myotomes of the somites arise the epaxial muscles, and approximately one third of the body wall musculature in the dorsolateral region. The lower half or two thirds of the body wall musculature is formed from the somatic mesoderm. The musculature of the appendages appears to develop entirely from the limb-bud mesoderm, which consists of somatic mesoderm.

Mammals

In explaining the origin of the musculature of mammals it is usually stated that with the exception of the muscles of the head and neck, which are derived from branchial arches, the skeletal muscles originate from myotomes. Numerous secondary assumptions have been based on this original supposition. As illustrated in Figures 4a and 4b, skeletal muscles are shown arising from segmental bands of mesenchyme derived from the myotomes. These envelop the embryo, and specific ones descend into the limb buds. This would explain the particular innervation of the different muscles of the body; when myotomes grow away from their original position they are supposed to carry with them parts of the nerves which accompanied them when they were first formed. Thus the origin of the muscles of the arm of man has been traced

138

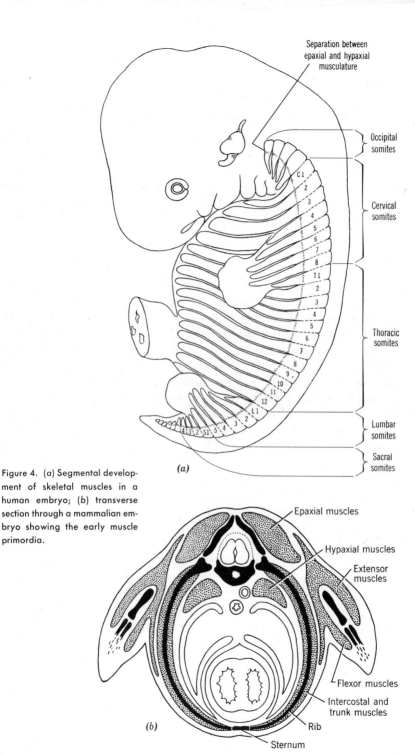

Separation between
epaxial and hypaxial
musculature

Occipital
somites

C 1
2
3
4
5
6
7
8
T 1
2
3
4
5
6
7
8
9
10
11
12
L 1
4 3 2 S 1 5 4 3 2

Cervical
somites

Thoracic
somites

Lumbar
somites

Sacral
somites

(a)

Figure 4. (a) Segmental development of skeletal muscles in a
human embryo; (b) transverse
section through a mammalian embryo showing the early muscle
primordia.

Epaxial muscles

Hypaxial muscles

Extensor
muscles

Flexor muscles

Intercostal and
trunk muscles

(b)

Rib

Sternum

139

to cervical myotomes V to VIII and to thoracic myotome I, since these muscles are innervated by the brachial plexus composed of nerves emerging from these same somites. Much has been made of the neuromuscular relationship in tracing the origin of muscles and in establishing homologies of muscles in different animals. The resemblance in muscular nerve supply, however, seems to reflect similarity in development. One cannot use this basis in homologizing the muscles of animals of different classes. The exact origin of the mammalian skeletal musculature is not known. Since there is some parallelism in the development of muscles in urodele amphibians and birds, one might cautiously assume that in mammals the myotomes give rise only to the epaxial muscles and to the upper part of the muscles of the body wall. The hypaxial muscles in the lower part of the body wall and those of the limbs are probably developed from the somatic mesoderm.

The limbs of tetrapods differentiate from the **limb buds,** which are thickenings of the lateral mesoderm in the pectoral and pelvic regions. The entire skeletal structure of the appendages and their musculature arises from a differentiation of this somatic mesoderm. Two sets of muscles differentiate in the appendages: **extrinsic muscles,** which attach the limbs to their girdles and the trunk and move the entire appendage toward and away from the trunk, and **intrinsic muscles** entirely within the limb, which bend and rotate the limb and move the digits. The intrinsic muscles on the dorsal side of the limbs are extensors and those on the ventral side are largely flexors. The forearm and the leg contain muscles which steady the joints and move the hand or foot and the digits. The greater the movement, strength, and agility of the digits, the greater the muscular development of the forearm and leg. The muscles to the digits terminate in slender, tough tendons which converge at the wrist or ankle. These tendons are enclosed in **tendon sheaths,** which are sleeves of tough connective tissue held together and bound down by a series of connective tissue slings called **retinacula.** The hand and foot also contain a few intrinsic muscles which strengthen and steady the movements of the digits.

The **metameric** arrangement of the myomeres of embryos remains relatively unchanged in the fishes and to some extent in the amphibians. In the amniotes, however, it is changed or masked. Specific changes take place in the myomeres as they establish the adult pattern.

The commonest change is a deviation of the fibers of the myomeres from the original craniocaudal direction. Embryonic muscle masses may also split longitudinally and tangentially into two or more masses. Successive ones, or parts of them, fuse and form single muscles; and parts of muscles may migrate to segmental levels different from those of their origin. In spite of these vicissitudes, some muscles retain their original innervation; for example, the muscle of the diaphragm of mammals, which has migrated a long distance from cervical myotomes V and VI, is innervated by the cervical nerves V and VI. The distribution of the cutaneous nerves over the adult body is a forceful reminder of the segmental origin of muscles and nerves. The surface of the skin is divided into segmental zones called **dermatomes,** each innervated by specific, successive nerves. This term is not to be confused with the dermatome of the paraxial mesoderm which gives rise to the dermis of some of the skin.

The **branchiomeric musculature** arises from the splanchnic mesoderm of the pharyngeal region. In adult fishes branchial muscles elevate and depress the lower jaw (Figure 5). In mammalian embryos the mesenchyme around the pharynx gives rise to the muscles of mastication, the lingual and facial muscles, and the muscles of the pharynx, larynx, and neck (Figure 6a). These muscles are innervated by the cranial nerves found in the pharyngeal arches from which the muscles developed (Figure 6b). From the first pharyngeal arch, innervated by cranial nerve V, the muscles of **mastication** develop. From the second arch, innervated by cranial nerve VII, the **facial muscles** develop. The **stylo-pharyngeus muscles,** innervated by cranial nerve IX, develop from the third arch. The **pharyngeal muscles,** innervated by cranial nerve X, develop from the fourth arch; the mesenchyme behind the fourth arch, innervated by cranial nerve XI, forms the **trapezius series.** In mammals the four occipital myotomes are believed to migrate forward under the pharynx and give rise to the muscles of the tongue, or the **hypoglossal muscles,** which are innervated by cranial nerve XII. This nerve is a relatively recent addition to the group of cranial nerves, and it is believed to have arisen from the anterior spinal nerves. In the pharyngeal regions, in which recognizable somites are absent, the branchial arches and the cranial nerves accompanying them are reference landmarks as good as the specific somites behind the head.

Vertebrates usually have six eye muscles which are innervated by cranial nerves III, IV, and VI. In the embryos of fish, amphibians, reptiles, and birds condensations of mesenchyme, or **head cavities,** in the anterior part of the head give rise to the extrinsic muscles of the eye. Head cavities also develop in the embryos of mammals, including those of man, and the origin and development of the extrinsic muscles follow a pattern which conforms in essential features with that found in other vertebrates (Figure 7). The first head cavity forms the **superior rectus,**

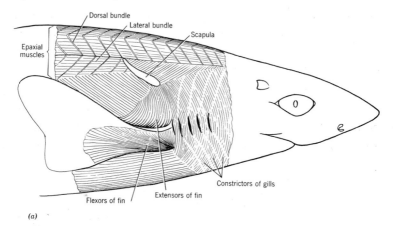

(a)

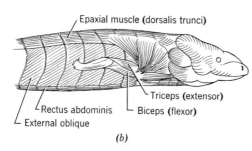

Epaxial muscle (dorsalis trunci)

Triceps (extensor)

Rectus abdominis   Biceps (flexor)
External oblique

(b)

Figure 5. (a) Branchiomeric muscles of the dogfish; (b) superficial muscles of *Necturus*.

inferior rectus, anterior rectus, and the inferior oblique muscles, all of which are innervated by cranial nerve III (oculomotor). The second head cavity gives rise to the superior oblique, innervated by cranial nerve IV (trochlear); from a fusion of parts from the second and third head cavities is formed the posterior (lateral, external) rectus, innervated by cranial nerve VI (abducens).

THE COMPARATIVE ANATOMY OF MUSCLES

Amphioxus

The muscular system of *Amphioxus* is entirely metameric. The myotomes are anchored to the sheath of the notochord; they are roughly V-shaped, with the base of the V pointed anteriorly, and they are separated by myocommata (Figure 8a). The muscle fibers are oriented parallel to the axis. Myotomes on the two sides of the body are arranged alternately; when they contract on one side, they relax on the other.

Cyclostomes

The nearly vertically arranged myotomes resemble a flattened W (Figure 8*b*). The **hypobranchial muscles,** ventral to the gills, have arisen from the myotomes just posterior to the pharynx and are innervated by spinal nerves. The muscular tongue is formed by the hypobranchial myotomes.

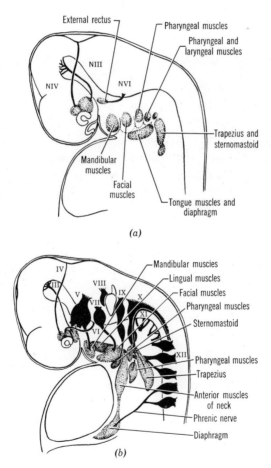

Figure 6. (a) Early development of the branchiomeric musculature in a mammalian embryo; (b) further development of the branchiomeric muscles and their associated cranial nerves.

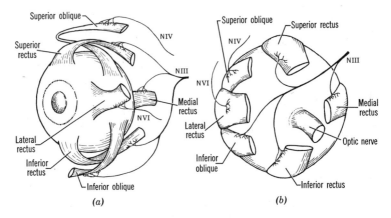

Figure 7. (a) Diagram of the extrinsic muscles of the eye of man; (b) the extrinsic eye muscles seen from behind the eye.

Fishes

A lateral septum separates the myotomes into a dorsal epaxial and a ventral hypaxial mass. The position of the **lateral line** on the surface of fishes corresponds to the lateral septum. The myotomes zigzag down the sides of the trunk, but the fibers are always oriented longitudinally (Figure 8c). Consecutive epaxial muscles form two large dorsal **longitudinal bundles,** continuous from the back of the skull to the tail. These powerful muscles bend the trunk and tail laterally. Below the lateral septum the hypaxial muscles are divided into lateral and ventral longitudinal bundles (Figure 9a). The **linea alba,** a white connective tissue

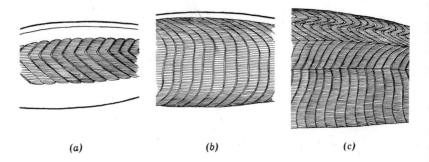

Figure 8. Myotomes in (a) *Amphioxus;* (b) cyclostomes, and (c) elasmobranchs.

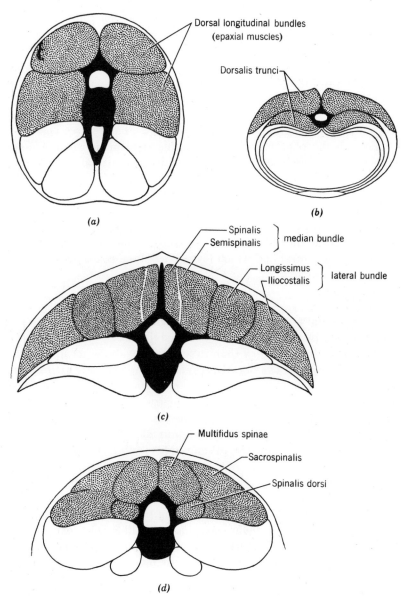

Figure 9. Diagrams of the epaxial muscles, stippled: (a) *Squalus*—through the tail; (b) *Necturus* —through the posterior trunk region; (c) alligator—through the lumbar region; (d) cat—through the lumbar region.

145

ribbon in the ventral midline, separates the ventral longitudinal bundles. Two barely recognizable **rectus abdominis muscles** are found, one on each side of the linea alba of some elasmobranchs. The branchial musculature is differentiated into (*a*) a complex series of **constrictor muscles** which compress the pharynx to force the water out, close the gill slits, and close the mouth; (*b*) a series of **levator muscles** which raise the maxilla and the gill arches; and (*c*) the **interarcual muscles** which draw together the adjacent gill arches and expand the pharynx (see Figure 5). Underneath the pharynx and between the rami of the mandible the hypobranchial muscles elevate the floor of the pharynx, open the mouth, and expand the pharynx.

The fin musculature has a segmented appearance. It is composed of dorsal extensor and ventral flexor muscles. Dorsal and ventral muscles have originated as buds of the same myotomes. Each invading myotome bud divides into a dorsal element which forms part of the extensor muscles and a ventral bud which forms part of the flexor muscles.

Amphibians

The segmental arrangement of myotomes in the epaxial muscles has remained relatively unaltered. The epaxial muscles of the trunk, the **dorsalis trunci**, are less bulky than in fishes; they are larger in urodeles than in salientians. The dorsalis trunci is composed of fibers from all the myotomes (Figure 9*b*). Its fibers are attached to the transverse processes of vertebrae and to adjacent neural spines. In salientians a **longissimus dorsi**, superficial to the dorsalis trunci, extends from the skull to the urostyle. The hypaxial musculature of the urodeles is divided segmentally, but that of salientians is not. In both cases the muscles form four flat layers. On the outside, under the skin, the **external oblique muscle** has fibers running caudoventrally; next, the **internal oblique muscle** has fibers oriented obliquely and ventrodorsally; on the inside is the **transversalis** with fibers running transversely. The two rectus abdominis muscles, one on each side of the linea alba, extend from the sternum to the pubis. They are broad bands of longitudinally oriented fibers segmentally interrupted by myocommata, called **tendinous inscriptions**.

With the development of a closed pharynx, the branchial muscles are no longer like those of fishes. The constrictor muscles of the fishes give rise to the muscles which elevate and depress the jaws and those which elevate the floor of the mouth. The levator muscles of the fishes are modified into the trapezius series and the muscles of the pharynx and larynx. Each of these series is innervated by the cranial nerve of the gill arch where it originated.

The musculature of the paired appendages is still separated into a dorsal extensor and a ventral flexor series. The limbs of amphibians have intrinsic muscles located entirely within them. The muscles of the arm move the forearm, and those of the forearm move the hand and digits. The individual muscles are sturdier and bring about stronger movements than in fishes. Extrinsic muscles attach the limb to the trunk and move the entire limb rather than any part of it.

Reptiles

The epaxial musculature is fairly primitive and is divided into a lateral and a median bundle (Figure 9c). The lateral bundle consists of the iliocostalis, below, originating on the ilium, and the longissimus, above, originating on the ilium, sacrum, and vertebrae. The iliocostalis and longissimus have several divisions; they show metamerism, and both are inserted anteriorly on the rear of the skull. The median bundle has a spinalis, medially, and a semispinalis, laterally; both muscles originate from the neural spines and arches of the vertebrae and are inserted on more anterior ones.

The hypaxial musculature in the abdominal wall is similar to that of amphibians. In the region of the ribs an intercostal muscle, connecting adjacent ribs, is found between the external and internal oblique muscles. The intercostals are split into external and internal layers.

Being more terrestrial than amphibians, reptiles must support more of their body weight with their limbs. Reptilian limbs have greater freedom of movement and a heavier musculature than those of amphibians. Extrinsic and intrinsic muscles are more numerous than in amphibians, and they are stronger. The extrinsic muscles, or those of the shoulders and hips, are elaborate. The muscles of the forearm and those of the leg proper, which move the hand and foot, respectively, and the digits, are better developed than in amphibians and are comparable to those of mammals.

Birds

The musculature of birds has many striking adaptations, but only some of the muscles of the wing and of the hind limb are discussed here.

The largest muscle of the bird, the pectoralis major, can make up as much as one fifth of the total body weight. This is the main muscle of

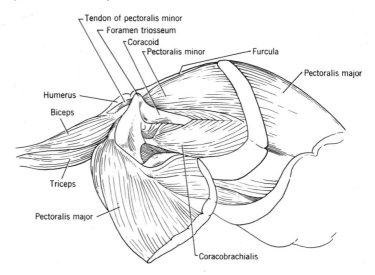

Figure 10. Pectoral muscles of the bird.

flight; it originates on the sternum and furcula and is inserted on the underside of the humerus; its action is to depress the wing. Under the pectoralis major, the smaller **pectoralis secundus,** often referred to as pectoralis minor or **supracoracoideus,** originates on the sternum; its long tendon goes through the foramen triosseum and is inserted on the dorsal side of the humerus (Figure 10); its action is to elevate the wing. The fibers of these two muscles are predominantly red in swifts, terns, and other birds which spend most of their time in the air; in gallinaceous and other birds which have a labored flight they are mostly white. Although the primary movement of the wing is operated by these two muscles, flight consists of more than flapping the wings up and down. Muscles in the shoulder steady the scapula and rotate, abduct, and adduct the humerus. The muscles in the arm proper extend and fold the wing and alter its position during flight. A large triceps helps to keep the wing extended during flight. A small **biceps brachii** is adequate for flexing the wing at the elbow. Large **extensor carpi radialis** and **extensor carpi ulnaris** extend the wing at the wrist. The **flexor carpi ulnaris** folds the wing. A system of muscles controls the rotation of the radius and another controls the movement of the digits. The wing musculature is an excellent example of specialization, and from the size and position of the muscles one can infer their action in flight.

Birds are **bipedal.** To enable them to stand on two feet the axis of the body has been shortened and the center of gravity lowered and moved far back. The legs move mostly back and forth and have little adduction and abduction. The anterior and posterior groups of muscles around the hip joint are well developed, but the lateral and medial ones are not. The major muscles of locomotion are in the **retractor group** behind the hip joint which pulls back the femur. The heavy musculature of the calf (drumstick) is concerned with the movement of the toes. The large **gastrocnemius** and the flexor muscles of the toes are at the back, and the **tibialis anterior** and the extensors of the toes are in front of the tibia. From the muscles of the thigh an intricate system of tendons converges on the tarsometatarsus and goes to the toes enclosed in sleeve-like tendon sheaths. Whether in a flexed or an extended condition, the muscles are arranged to support the joint; the **iliofibularis,** for instance, is particularly adapted for this by passing through a tough connective tissue sling at the knee joint (Figure 11). The flexor muscles of the toes are attached above the knee, and when the knee joint is bent they become tightened. If the leg of a bird is straightened, its toes become extended, and they become flexed if the leg is bent.

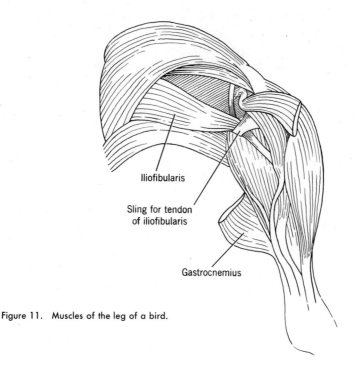

Iliofibularis

Sling for tendon
of iliofibularis

Gastrocnemius

Figure 11.   Muscles of the leg of a bird.

Mammals

The epaxial muscles are not appreciably different from those of reptiles (see Figure 9*d*). They extend as two solid masses on each side of the neural spines, from the sacral and lumbar regions to the neck and head. The largest of these muscle bundles, the **sacrospinalis**, originates from the sacrum and the spinous processes of the posterior vertebrae. In the thoracic region the sacrospinalis divides into three masses: the **spinalis dorsi,** a median, narrow muscle attached to the vertebrae, which extends the length of the vertebral column; a middle longissimus dorsi, which continues all the way to the cervical region and the skull; and a lateral iliocostalis, which extends to the cervical region. Both the longissimus and the iliocostalis give off slips that are inserted to the ribs as they continue anteriorly. In the lumbar region a slender **multifidus spinae** is medial to the large sacrospinalis. The **interspinalis muscles** connect the spinous processes of adjacent vertebrae, and the **intertransversarii** connect the transverse processes.

The hypaxial musculature of the abdomen is similar to that of reptiles. The abdominal wall is composed of the external oblique, internal oblique, and transversalis. These muscles compress and constrict the abdomen, lower the ribs, and force the diaphragm up. In the thoracic region the intercostal muscles are differentiated in three layers and interdigitate with the abdominal muscles. The longitudinally directed rectus abdominis extends from the pubic symphysis to the sternum and lies on each side of the linea alba. In the neck region the **sternothyroid, sternohyoid,** and **thyrohyoid** arise from the rectus abdominis, which originally extended the entire length of the body.

The limbs of mammals can perform nearly every conceivable action. Accordingly, the intrinsic and extrinsic limb musculature has increased in importance and complexity. New intrinsic muscles give the limb greater strength and freedom. The muscles of the shoulders and the hips are so extensive that they grow over most of the trunk musculature. The musculature of the hips and legs, on which locomotion depends, is heavier than that of the shoulders and fore limbs. Except that metamerism has almost disappeared, the musculature of mammals is like that of reptiles. The serratus muscles, the intercostals, the insertion slips of the external oblique, the rectus abdominis, and a few others are the only muscles which still show signs of segmentation.

Many new muscles have developed on the surface of the body. The musculature of the face is very elaborate; the lips are muscular, and the external ears are moved by muscles. All mammals have at least some cutaneous musculature. In the mole, the hedgehog, the armadillo, and the horse the cutaneous muscle forms extensive sheets. Even man has a well-developed cutaneous muscle sheet, the platysma, which extends from the mandible to the clavicles. The diaphragm is peculiar to mammals. Its muscle has arisen from cervical myotomes V and VI and is innervated by the **phrenic nerve,** which arises from cervical nerves V and VI.

SUMMARY

1. Skeletal muscle arises mostly from the myotomes of the paraxial mesoderm. Early in development the primitive myomeres become separated into epaxial and hypaxial by a lateral septum of connective tissue. Fishlike vertebrates, in which the principal locomotion is achieved by a lateral movement of the body, have simple but large epaxial muscles. The epaxial muscles of tetrapods are smaller and more complex than those of fishes. Even in mammals, epaxial muscles remain somewhat primitive and do not show much phylogenetic modification. In contrast, the hypaxial musculature, which is relatively primitive in the fishlike vertebrates, shows great progressive modification in the tetrapods. In the abdomen and thorax the hypaxial muscles split into three main muscle layers.

2. Mammals have the most highly evolved appendicular musculatures. The basic pattern of the muscles of the limbs can be traced to the fishes. The muscles of all limbs, from the fins of fishes to the limbs of mammals, are distributed in a dorsal extensor series and a ventral flexor series. The arrangement of these muscles, their number, and their complexity increases steadily. Intrinsic and extrinsic muscles, which first appear in tetrapods, allow stronger locomotion and greater freedom of movement. The massive musculature of the shoulders and the hips of mammals bears evidence of the progressive development of the extrinsic musculature.

3. The extrinsic muscles of the vertebrate eye arise from head cavities; these have an obscure phylogenetic origin. Differences do occur, but these muscles have remained comparatively unchanged in the vertebrates, and their homology seems to be very clear.

4. A series of striated muscles arises from the splanchnic mesoderm of

151

the pharyngeal region. In fishes these muscles constrict, dilate, elevate, and depress the pharynx. In tetrapods muscles homologous to those in the pharynx develop into the muscles of mastication, the muscles of the neck and the larynx, and some of the muscles of the shoulder.

SUGGESTED READING

Gilbert, P. W., 1957, "The Origin and Development of the Human Extrinsic Ocular Muscles." Contributions to *Embryology*, Vol. XXXVI, pp. 59–78. *Carnegie Inst. Wash. Publ.* **611**, Washington, D. C.

Harrison, R. G., 1894, "The Metamerism of the Dorsal and Ventral Longitudinal Muscles of the Teleosts." *Johns Hopkins Univ. Circulars,* **13**, pp. 62–63.

Romer, A. S., 1949, *The Vertebrate Body.* W. B. Saunders Co., Philadelphia and London.

Strauss, W. L., Jr., 1946, "The Concept of Nerve-Muscle Specificity." *Biol. Revs., Cambridge Phil. Soc.,* **21**, pp. 75–91.

Strauss, W. L., Jr., and M. E. Rawles, 1953, "An Experimental Study of the Origin of the Trunk Musculature and Ribs in the Chick." *Am. J. Anat.,* **92**, pp. 471–509.

CHAPTER

7

Figure 1.
Sparrow hawk pouncing on a mouse.
(Courtesy of Dr. A. A. Allen.)

CHAPTER

7

THE DIGESTIVE SYSTEM

GENERAL INTRODUCTION

All of the physical and psychic attributes of animals are adapted to help them secure food. Animals of prey have sleek bodies, strong sharp claws, beaks, or teeth, keen sight, hearing, and smell, furtiveness, alertness, quickness of response, and an aggressive nature (Figure 1). These are indispensable to animals which must look for, stalk, outwit, outrun, or outfly their prey; a serene hawk or cat would soon starve. Herbivores are more heavy-bodied, and their limbs are adapted for collecting stationary food and for locomotion; they may be alert, have keen sense organs, and be endowed with speed, particularly in flight, but they lack the cunning, boldness, and hostility of the animals of prey. Herbivorous animals need large amounts of food; carnivorous animals need to eat less and less frequently.

Vertebrates cannot synthesize food from raw materials and must eat plant or animal tissues. To absorb these tissues the alimentary tract must first change them to simpler substances. Since flesh is more easily prepared for absorption, the gut of flesh eaters is shorter than that of plant eaters. Tadpoles, which are vegetarian, have a relatively longer gut than adult frogs or toads, which are carnivorous. The digestive systems of grazing animals are fermenting vats designed to convert cellulose into simple substances which can be absorbed through the gut. The more indigestible the material the animal feeds upon, the more complex its digestive apparatus.

The digestive system is divided into compartments, each of which performs specific functions. The **mouth**, including **lips, tongue, teeth,** and **oral** and **buccal glands**, is adapted for procuring food, grinding it, and preparing it for its journey to the gut. The **esophagus** is a pathway for transporting food; the **stomach** is a fermentation vessel in which food is gathered and the major process of digestion begins. The **gut**, or in-**testine**, secretes intestinal juices and, with the aid of the secretion from the **liver** and the **pancreas**, completes the chemical changes of the food. The digested food and water are absorbed through the gut. The indigestible wastes are passed on and are evacuated through the **rectum**. Food is moved along the alimentary canal by **peristalsis**, the rhythmic, alternating contractions and relaxations of the muscle coats of the gut. The purpose of the alimentary tract is to break food into simpler chemical substances and to absorb them.

The basic structure of the gut is remarkably similar throughout its length in all vertebrates. On the outside it is covered by a single layer of mesothelium or visceral peritoneum, similar to and continuous with that which lines the wall of the abdominal cavity. Underneath the peritoneum is a thin layer of connective tissue and a layer of smooth muscle with the fibers oriented longitudinally; this is followed by a layer in which the muscle fibers are oriented circularly (Figure 2). Between the two muscle layers aggregates of nerve cells constitute the **myenteric plexus of Auerbach**. Inside the circular layer of muscle is the **submucosa**, a thick layer of connective tissue which also contains scattered nerve cells, the **plexus of Meissner**. Next is the very thin **muscularis mucosae**, formed on the outside by longitudinal muscle fibers and on the inside by circular fibers. Inside the muscularis mucosae is the **mucosa**, a layer of loose connective tissue which supports the simple columnar epithelium lining the gut (Figure 3). The mucosa is thrown into folds and intestinal villi in the amniotes (Figure 4). In the center of each intestinal villus is the **central lacteal**, a dilated blind pouch which collects the fats absorbed by the intestine. The lacteals drain into collecting lymph vessels; these fuse into larger ones which finally empty into the lymph ducts. Details are discussed later in the chapter on the blood vascular system.

Successive classes of vertebrates add improvements and innovations to increase the absorptive surface of the gut. There may be (*a*) an increase in the length; (*b*) an increase in diameter; (*c*) the formation of longitu-

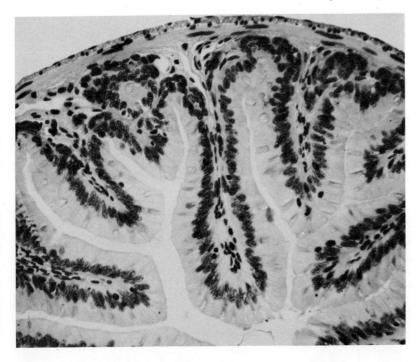

Figure 2.   Transverse section through the intestine of a salamander.

dinal and circular folds; (*d*) the development of villi; and (*e*) the development of outpocketings and recesses.

A number of glands is an integral part of the digestive system. The wall of the entire gastrointestinal tract is peppered with small glands that secrete mucous or serous fluids. Several large glands open into the system by long ducts. Notable among them are the **salivary glands**, which open into the buccal and oral cavities, and the liver and pancreas, which open into the intestine.

DEVELOPMENT

The entodermal lining of the yolk sac is the earliest rudiment of the alimentary tract of the embryo. When the body of the embryo elongates cephalocaudally the primitive gut is pulled into an anterior extension, the **fore-gut,** and a posterior one, the **hind-gut** (Figure 5). At first the fore-gut and the hind-gut are closed to the outside by the **stomodeal**

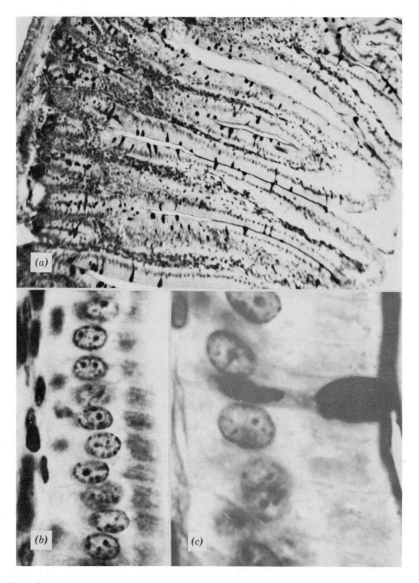

Figure 3. (a) Transverse section through the intestine of a mouse; (b) simple columnar epithelium lining the gut; (c) columnar epithelial cells and one goblet cell from the gut of a mouse.

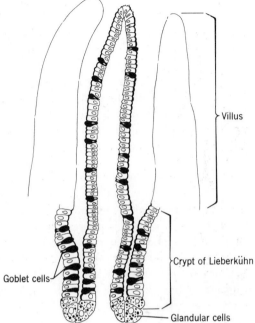

Figure 4.
Diagram of a villus from
the intestine of the mammal.

Villus

Crypt of Lieberkühn

Goblet cells

Glandular cells

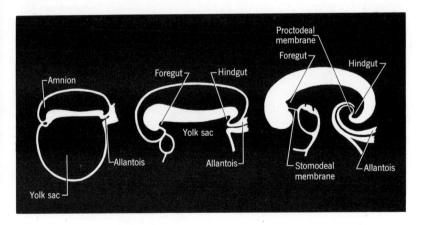

Figure 5.   Diagrams showing the development of the gut from the yolk sac in a mammalian
embryo.

159

membrane and the **proctodeal membrane,** respectively (Figure 5*c*); both are composed of ectoderm on the outside and entoderm on the inside, with no mesoderm between. Later, when these membranes rupture and disappear, the entoderm of the fore-gut and hind-gut becomes confluent with the ectoderm of the **stomodeum** and **proctodeum,** respectively. The splanchnic mesoderm along the sides of the fore-gut forms the pharyngeal arches, a series of dorsoventrally oriented pillars. These bulge laterally and can be seen on the surface of the intact embryo; the depressions or indentations between the pharyngeal arches on the outside are the pharyngeal clefts (Figure 6*a*). The fore-gut expands laterally between the pharyngeal arches and forms the pharyngeal pouches, sacculations which coincide with the pharyngeal clefts on the outside (Figures 6*b* and 7); the entoderm of the pouches comes in contact with the ectoderm of the clefts to form thin layers of tissue, the **pharyngeal membranes** (Figure 8). In fishes the arches give rise to the gills and their skeletal support; the membranes between the arches break, and the pharynx opens laterally through a series of gill slits. In the other classes of vertebrates the pharyngeal clefts remain intact. In amniotes pharyngeal pouch I becomes elongated anteriorly into the **Eustachian tubes** (Figure 8); pouch II disappears, and in its place is

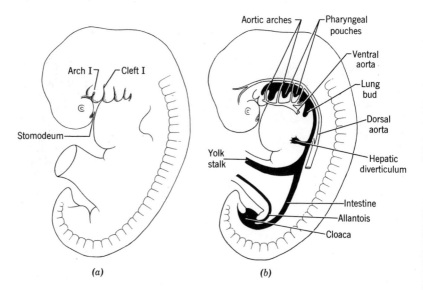

(a)   (b)

Figure 6. (a) Pharyngeal arches and clefts in a mammalian embryo; (b) the same embryo as in (a) showing the pharynx and all of the entodermal derivatives.

160

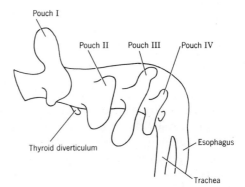

Figure 7. Diagram of the pharyngeal pouches in a mammalian embryo.

formed the **pharyngeal tonsil;** pouches III and IV later give rise to the **thymus** and the **parathyroid glands.** A single **thyroid diverticulum** grows from the floor of the pharynx between pharyngeal pouches I and II and becomes detached from the pharynx; the **foramen caecum,** a shallow pit seen at the back of the adult tongue, is the site of origin of the thyroid diverticulum (see Figure 14). Two other median ventral diverticula are formed from the fore-gut. One immediately posterior to pharyngeal pouch IV gives rise to the **trachea** and **lungs,** and the other, the **hepatic**

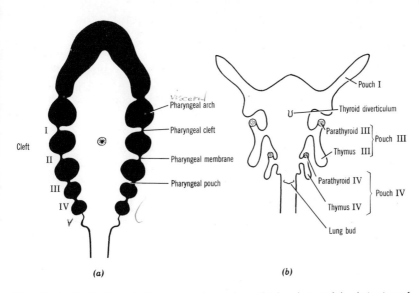

Figure 8. (a) Section through the pharynx of an embryo; (b) dorsal view of the derivatives of the pharyngeal pouches in the mammal.

161

diverticulum, grows into the **transverse septum** and gives rise to the liver. From the hepatic diverticulum grows an additional diverticulum, the **ventral pancreatic diverticulum,** and just opposite, on the dorsal side of the gut, grows the **dorsal pancreatic diverticulum.** The hind-gut forms a dilated cloaca, or passageway, for the reproductive, urinary, and digestive systems (Figure 9). Each of the entodermal diverticula named and figured here gives rise to the **parenchyma** of the major organs of digestion. On the outside the entodermal gut tube is surrounded by splanchnic mesoderm, which gives rise to the smooth muscle and to the connective tissue framework of the gut and other digestive organs.

The stomodeum differentiates into the buccal and oral cavities: the buccal cavity is the space between the cheeks and the gums and teeth; the oral cavity is the space under the palate, bounded by the gums and teeth. Oral glands and salivary glands are formed as outpocketings of the oral and buccal ectoderm. The most important derivative of the ectoderm of the stomodeum is **Rathke's pouch,** a single median diverticulum, which gives rise to the anterior lobe of the pituitary.

COMPARATIVE ANATOMY OF THE DIGESTIVE SYSTEM

The Mouth

Although the anatomy of teeth has been discussed in the chapter on the endoskeleton, the teeth are really a part of the digestive system, having risen from the ectoderm and mesoderm of the stomodeum. Teeth are adapted for many uses, but their main function is to seize, manipulate, tear, or grind food. The dentition of mammals of prey is very different from that of herbivores. The most prominent teeth of carnivores are the canines, but these are nearly always absent in strictly herbivorous mammals. Herbivorous mammals have large, grinding premolars and molars with flat surfaces; carnivores have relatively small molars with pointed crowns. The incisors of rodents and lagomorphs are very long; they are being worn constantly, and they never cease growing. In some mammals teeth have become so modified that they have lost their original function; examples are the tusks of the walrus, sea cow, and elephant. The tusks of hogs are overgrown canines which have lost little of their original shape. The most remarkable oddity in the modification of teeth is found in the male narwhal, whose one single upper left tooth extends straight ahead several feet as a spear with helicoid grooves.

Amphioxus. A funnel-shaped depression at the anterior end of the animal is surrounded by a fringe of ectodermal projections. The true

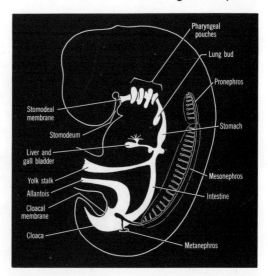

Figure 9. The derivatives of the entoderm.

mouth is at the back of this funnel and is guarded by a series of specialized eminences and cilia.

Cyclostomes. Cyclostomes have no jaws, and the round buccal funnel is surrounded by a thick ectodermal fringe; the inside of the funnel is lined with rows of horny teeth and papillae. A muscular "tongue," also covered with horny teeth, sticks through the mouth at the back of the buccal funnel. A pair of **buccal glands,** which secrete anticoagulating, hemolytic, and cytolytic substances, opens below on either side of the tongue. These animals secure food by attaching themselves to fish and gouging out flesh with their rasplike tongues. When the animals swim upstream to spawn they cease feeding and the buccal glands become much reduced in size.

Fishes. The boundary of the jaws, or **lip,** is a hard ridge. The simple mouth opens directly into the cavernous pharynx. The oral and pharyngeal cavities contain **mucous glands** whose secretions keep these surfaces covered with a layer of slime. The comblike **gill rakers** on the inside of the gill arches strain food particles from the water, which escapes through the gill slits. On the floor of the oral cavity, between the first and second pharyngeal arches, is the primitive tongue, which is a simple fold of tissue. Barbs and teeth may be present on the back of the tongue. Gustatory sensory organs, or **taste buds,** may be present anywhere in the lining of the oral cavity. In the lungfishes the oral cavity communicates with the nasal openings.

163

(a)

Figure 10.   Toad, seizing food with its tongue: (a) The toad's tongue, stretched more than half the length of the animal's body, makes contact with the bait; (b) ⅕₀ second later the tongue is grasping the bait and pulling it away; (c) ⅖₀ second after contact the tongue is being withdrawn, with the tip holding onto the bait.   (Courtesy of Walker Van Riper, Denver museum of Natural History.)

(b)

(c)

Amphibians. The very large oral cavity contains numerous mucus-secreting cells. Terrestrial amphibians also have aggregates of mucous glands in the roof of the mouth near the internal nares, which keep the portals to the alimentary canal covered with mucus; this allows a better grip on the prey and makes swallowing easier. Some of the epithelial cells of the pharynx have cilia. This seems to be a primitive condition; during early development even the embryos of amniotes have a ciliated esophagus. The oral cavity communicates with the external nares by the nasal passageways.

The tongue of some aquatic urodeles is primitive and similar to that of fishes. That of some terrestrial salamanders is long, and its disclike blunt end is rich in mucus-secreting glands; it can be thrust out quickly to seize food. The muscles of the tongue of salamanders are attached to the hyoid arch. The long and muscular tongue of salientians is attached so far forward on the floor of the mouth that it is folded posteriorly; its terminal part is prehensile and glandular. In obtaining food the tongue is flipped out and pulled back rapidly (Figure 10). **Aglossida,** a family of toads, have almost no tongue, but this is an apparent adaptive degeneration.

Reptiles. The mouth has its angle all the way to the articulation of the jaws. A long hard palate separates the nasal passageways from the oral cavity, and the air is channeled directly to the pharynx. The

165

pharynx is separated from the oral cavity by a curtainlike **soft palate** which hangs down just back of the bony palate. The secretion from large mucoid glands in the oral cavity keeps the surfaces moist and makes swallowing easier. **Palatine glands** are found in the upper jaw, **lingual glands** on the tongue, **sublingual glands** at the base of the tongue, and **labial glands** are dispersed along the inner margin of the rigid lip. The sublingual glands of the Gila monster, the only known poisonous

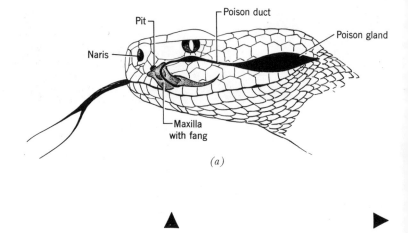

(a)

Figure 11. (a) Head of rattlesnake showing the position of the poison gland and duct and the maxilla and fang; (b) Head of a cottonmouth moccasin, with the poison gland and duct dissected. (Drawn by R. Beach. Courtesy of Drs. J. F. Germaro, Jr., P. J. Squicciarni, and N. J. Rohan, University of Florida.)

lizard, are modified as poison glands. The labial glands of poisonous snakes are variously modified into poison glands (Figure 11). The size and shape of these glands and the way in which the poison is delivered are different in different groups of poisonous snakes. Poison is an effective agent for capturing food. Poisonous snakes strike their prey, and when the prey is paralyzed or dead they swallow it whole. The jaw articulation in snakes is loose, and a joint at the base of the skull allows the mouth to be opened and stretched to astounding sizes. The teeth are pointed posteriorly, and the prey is gradually swallowed as the mandibles are moved backward and forward. All of this is aided by copious secretions of mucus.

The tongue of turtles or crocodiles is small, simple, and not protrusive. That of a snake is bifurcated and surrounded by a tubelike sheath (Figure 11); it can be extruded through a notch in the lower jaw when the mouth is closed. Lizards also have well-developed muscular tongues. The chameleon has a very long tongue with a clublike sticky tip with

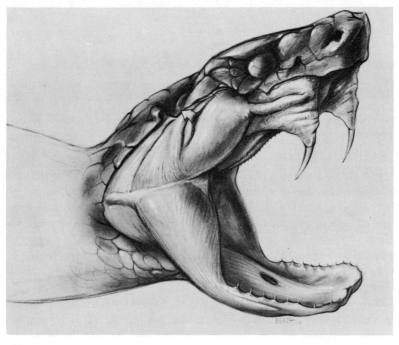

(b)

which it seizes insects (Figure 12). The tongue can be shot out quickly by engorging it with blood and by the action of the hyoid muscles.

Birds. The mouth is bordered by the horny beak, the only fleshy part being at the angle of the beak. Numerous small mucous glands are scattered over the oral cavity. The anterior and posterior sublingual salivary glands and the **angle glands** at the corner of the mouth secrete a mucoid, viscid, acrid-smelling substance which helps in swallowing. Very little is known about the anatomy of the gustatory mechanism of birds, except that it is very discriminating.

167

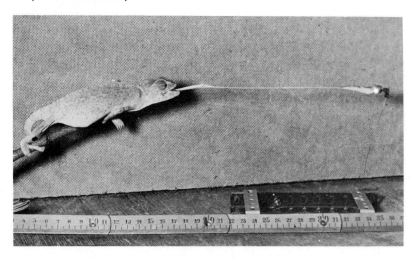

Figure 12. Chameleon, with a body length of ten centimeters, extending its tongue seventeen centimeters to seize food. (Courtesy of Dr. R. Aldevogt, Zool. Inst., Univ. Münster, Germany.)

The peculiar tongue of birds has many forms and sizes. When well developed it is useful in securing food or in moving it in the mouth. In the pelicans, kingfishers, and a few others it is very small and has a limited action. In birds that dabble with their beaks, in parrots, and others the tongue is large and fleshy. The tongue of woodpeckers is reduced to a pointed horny blade with backward projecting barbs, but its base is so long that it has to be coiled around the orbit when it is withdrawn (see Figure 40b in Chapter 5).

Mammals. Movable, fleshy lips and cheeks are the most notable external feature of the mouth of mammals. Even the bill of the platypus is soft and sensitive. The lips are attached anteriorly to the gums by a single median **frenulum.** Lips limit the size of the mouth orifice; they help in grasping food and in keeping it in the mouth when it is being chewed and they make sucking possible. The buccal cavity is the pocket between the outside of the teeth and the cheek. The **cheek pouches** of some mammals are very distensible and are used to carry food or nesting materials. The inside of the lips and cheeks in many mammals is studded with clusters of mucous and serous glands. Cats have mucus-secreting **molar glands** at the corners of the mouth near the molar teeth. From the **parotid gland, Stensen's duct** opens in the buccal cavity at the level of the first and second upper molars. The roof of the oral cavity, or palate, is furrowed by transverse **palatine rugae,** which

168

are particularly deep and rough in carnivores. The hard palate ends posteriorly in a soft palate, which protects the internal nares during swallowing. In man the soft palate hangs down in a soft median pendant called the **uvula**. The entire lining of the buccal and oral cavities contains small mucous and serous glands which keep these linings soft and moist.

Mammals have three pairs of salivary glands (Figure 13). The parotid glands, located in front and below the external ear just underneath the skin, are the largest. They secrete a serous fluid. The **submandibular glands,** just below the angle of the mandible, are large mucoserous glands whose secretion enters the mouth by way of the long **Wharton's duct,** just behind the lower incisors, alongside the frenulum of the tongue. The sublingual glands are smaller than the others and may be absent in some animals. They are mucous and open into the mouth along the sides of the tongue through several **ducts of Rivinus.** A large mucoserous gland is also present in the tongue, just behind the foramen caecum. The serous secretion of the parotid gland contains variable amounts of salivary **amylase** or **ptyalin,** an enzyme that splits starches to maltose. The secretion of saliva is evoked by contact of the food with the mouth; the odor of food or even the thought of it, however, will start secretion.

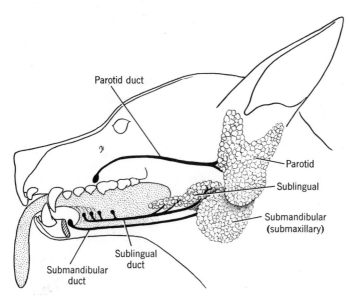

Figure 13. The major salivary glands of a dog.

169

Salivary glands secrete two substances, one viscid and mucinous, the other watery and clear; different foods induce a greater secretion of one or the other. The horse and the ox secrete gallons of saliva daily; they secrete more of it when they eat dry hay than when they eat green grass. Saliva is approximately neutral, but it may be either slightly alkaline or slightly acid. The submandibular gland of *Blarina,* the short-tailed shrew, secretes a poisonous saliva; this is the only known occurrence of poisonous saliva in a mammal.

The very muscular tongue of mammals has many shapes and functions. The foramen caecum is at the base of the V-shaped **sulcus terminalis** (Figures 14, 15), which is the boundary between the body and the root of the tongue. Most of the body of the tongue is lined with epithelium derived from the entoderm of pharyngeal arch I; it has sensory nerves from the mandibular branch of the **trigeminus** and from the **facial nerve** which innervate pharyngeal arch I. The epithelium in the anterior part of the free tongue, however, probably comes from the ectoderm of the stomodeum. The root of the tongue is lined with entoderm from the floor of pharyngeal arches II, III, and IV and is innervated by the **glossopharyngeal nerve** (cranial nerve IX) and the **vagus** (cranial nerve X) which accompany arches III and IV, respectively. The mammalian tongue arises from a number of primordia on the floor of the pharynx. A pair of lateral **lingual folds** grows anteriorly from arch I (Figure 15). Between them, just in front of the foramen caecum, is the **tuberculum impar,** a diamond-shaped single elevation. Another single median swelling, the **copula,** from arches II and III, is just behind the foramen caecum. Folds are also formed laterally from arches III and IV. The two lateral lingual swellings grow dorsally and anteriorly; they meet and fuse in the midline, and the seam of fusion is the **median**

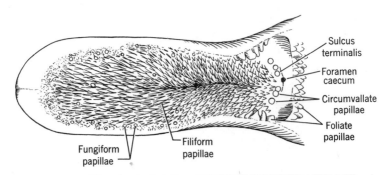

Figure 14. Surface view of the tongue of the cat.

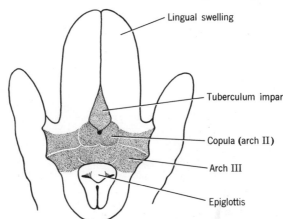

Figure 15.
The primordia of
the tongue of man.

Labels: Lingual swelling, Tuberculum impar, Copula (arch II), Arch III, Epiglottis

sulcus of the adult tongue. The tuberculum impar forms the posterior middle portion of the tongue, just ahead of the foramen caecum; the copula and the swellings from arches III and IV give rise to the root of the tongue and to the **epiglottis,** which forms just behind the tongue. The hyoid bones are the skeletal support of the tongue. The muscles of the tongue are apparently derived from the occipital myotomes and from the oropharyngeal mesenchyme. All of the tongue muscles are innervated by the **hypoglossal nerve** (cranial nerve XII). The tongue contains intrinsic and extrinsic muscles. The intrinsic muscles form a superficial **longitudinal layer,** with fiber bundles alternating with sheets of the **vertical muscle** in the middle layer, and a deep **transverse layer.** There are three pairs of extrinsic muscles; the **genioglossus** from the symphysis of the mandible protrude the tongue; the **styloglossus** from the styloid process withdraw and raise it; and the **hyoglossus** from the hyoid draw its sides downward and backward (Figure 16). In the anteaters the extrinsic musculature of the tongue is so extensive that it is attached to the sternum. The free portion of the tongue is anchored to the floor of the mouth by the **lingual frenulum,** a median fold.

The surface of the tongue is covered with a number of different structures. Numerous conical or spinelike **filiform papillae** are found on the body of the tongue, and interspersed among them are fleshy mushroom-shaped **fungiform papillae.** In the tongues of cats and grazing animals the filiform papillae are cornified, and the tongue is dry and rough. Cats and primates have a row of large flat **circumvallate papillae** just in front of the sulcus terminalis, surrounded by a deep moat at their base (Figure 17); serous glands open at the bottom of the moat. The cat has

171

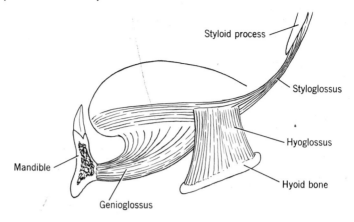

Figure 16. The extrinsic muscles of the mammalian tongue.

five or six circumvallate papillae; man has nine. The horse has two large ones, each about the size of a pea, and the ox may have as many as eighteen. The back of the tongue is covered with large, fleshy, leaflike **foliate papillae**. Rabbits have no circumvallate papillae, but they have rows of parallel foliate papillae on each side of the back of the tongue. Taste buds are concentrated in the sides of the circumvallate papillae and in the foliate papillae. They are scattered throughout the back of the tongue and may also be found on fungiform papillae.

The tongue has many functions. In dogs and cats it is used for lapping; in the ox it is prehensile; in anteaters it can be extended a great length; and in man it is used for the articulation of speech. The tongue of whales, unlike that of other mammals, cannot be protruded.

The Esophagus

The primary function of the esophagus is to convey food from the pharynx to the stomach; it plays no important role in digestion. In the lower vertebrates it does not amount to much, and the pharynx opens almost directly into the stomach.

Fishes. The esophagus is short and has longitudinal folds which allow it to expand to many times its collapsed size. The surface is covered with a number of papillae which are pointed posteriorly to allow easy passage of food but which interfere with its regurgitation. The large J-shaped **esophagus-stomach** of elasmobranchs (see Figure 23) has an anterior esophageal part covered with papillae and a posterior portion, the stomach proper, with longitudinal folds or **rugae**. Mucous cells secrete a layer of slime over the surface of the esophagus.

Amphibians. As in fishes, there is almost no esophagus, and the pharynx opens directly into the stomach. The esophageal region is lined with ciliated epithelium like that of the pharynx. Mucigenous glands secrete slime, and special secretory cells are believed to secrete the enzyme trypsin.

Reptiles. Since the development of the esophagus accompanies that of the cervical region, both assume real importance in reptiles. The esophagus is long, and longitudinal folds allow it to expand. The inner surface of the esophagus of turtles is covered with cornified protuberances.

Birds. At the base of the neck the esophagus is dilated into a **crop**, lodged in the wedge-shaped space between the limbs of the furcula. The crop of birds of prey is an amorphous dilatation in which food is held temporarily before it goes into the stomach; that of grain-eating birds is rounded (Figure 18). The hoactzin, which feeds on tropical leathery leaves and hard fruits, has a large and muscular crop. The wall of the crop of pigeons and doves has glands which secrete a viscid substance called **crop-milk**. Parent birds regurgitate this substance into the beaks of the fledgelings.

Mammals. The esophagus, like that of reptiles and birds, is lined with a stratified squamous epithelium. The epithelium may even be partially

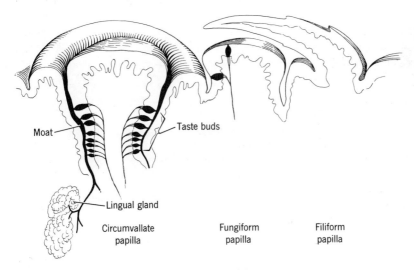

Figure 17. The papillae of the tongue.

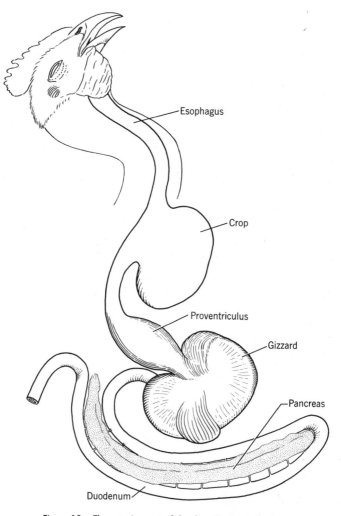

Figure 18. The anterior part of the digestive tract of a hen.

cornified in some mammals.   In the neck the esophagus is surrounded by a bed of loose connective tissue dorsal to the trachea.   Below the diaphragm, where it extends in the peritoneal cavity, it is covered with visceral peritoneum.   Strips of skeletal muscle, particularly numerous in ruminants, are attached to the outer wall of the esophagus.   When not in use the esophagus is collapsed and has longitudinal folds.   It passes through the diaphragm and extends for a short distance in the peritoneal cavity before it opens into the stomach. Some of the marked modifications of the esophagus are associated with the stomach and are mentioned in the next section.

The Stomach

Variable portions of what is normally called stomach in different animals may be parts of the esophagus. The stomach is a dilatation that lies in the upper left of the peritoneal cavity, the corresponding right space being occupied by the right lobe of the liver. In some vertebrates it lies more or less in the center; the identification of the stomach is not based upon shape or location but upon the type of epithelium which lines it and upon the glands that it contains. The separation of stomach and esophagus, therefore, is not an arbitrary one.

Cyclostomes. A slightly enlarged and barely recognizable stomach is lined with a mucigenous type of epithelium. It has no recognizable gastric glands.

Fishes. The stomach has a variety of shapes (see Figures 23, 24). The first part, continuous with and often indistinguishable from the esophagus, is the cardiac region; it is lined with a mucigenous epithelium and contains mucus-secreting glands. The bag-shaped body of the stomach is the **peptic** or **fundic** portion; the glands in its wall secrete **pepsin**, an enzyme which breaks proteins into amino acids. The terminal **pyloric** part of the stomach is attenuated and contains special mucous glands.

Amphibians. The stomach of salamanders is often straight and spindle-shaped. That of salientians has a greatly dilated upper cardiac portion and a short and narrow pyloric part.

Reptiles. Snakes and lizards have a simple spindle-shaped stomach. A part of the stomach of Crocodilia is thick-walled and muscular and resembles the **gizzard** of birds. The gastric juices of snakes have an astounding efficacy; these animals swallow their prey whole, but hardly a trace of bone, fur, or other animal remains can be found in their feces.

Birds. The esophagus opens into the stomach or **proventriculus**, which in seed-eating birds has a thicker and more muscular wall than in birds of prey. The proventriculus opens into the gizzard (Figure 18). This is very thick-walled in seed-eating birds, but flabby and distensible in flesh eaters. The glands on the inside of the gizzard of seed-eating birds secrete a substance which congeals into a protective horny pellicle. Pebbles swallowed by these birds are lodged in the gizzard and, like millstones, help to grind the food. In birds which change their diets seasonally from seeds to insects the gizzard becomes alternately thick- and thin-walled.

Mammals. The shape of the stomach is varied. Although not exactly like that of any other mammal, the stomach of man is generalized enough to serve as a standard type. It is saclike, bent, and placed transversely in the abdomen (Figure 19). The largest part is on the left side of the body, tucked alongside the liver. The anterior, concave side is the **lesser curvature;** the posterior, convex part is the **greater curvature.** Just around the opening of the esophagus is the cardiac portion, and the bulge on the left is the body or fundus. The distal, attenuated part on the right is the pyloric portion. Each division of the stomach contains characteristic glands. The peptic glands in the fundus secrete gastric juices and hydrochloric acid.

The extent of the different regions varies in different animals. Almost one half of the stomach of the horse, the **cardia,** is the expanded aglandular distal part of the esophagus, which is lined with stratified squamous epithelium. The word **cardia** is not to be confused with **cardiac stomach** or that region of the stomach which contains special mucous glands around the opening of the esophagus. The larger part of the stomach of the pig and the hippopotamus contains mucus-secreting glands and is, therefore, cardiac stomach (Figure 20). The "stomach" of artiodactyls consists of a series of pouches, the **rumen, reticulum, omasum,** and **abomasum** (Figure 21). The rumen is covered with short conical processes; in the ox it occupies more than the entire left half of the abdominal

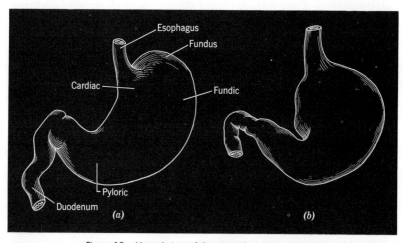

Figure 19. Ventral view of the stomach: (a) man; (b) cat.

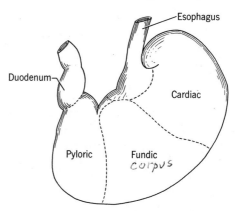

Figure 20.
Stomach of the pig.

cavity and may have a capacity of sixty gallons or more. The reticulum makes up five per cent of the total bulk of the stomach in the ox; it has raised folds which outline a honeycomb pattern (Figure 22). The reticulum of the camel has complicated diverticula, or **water cells,** which can store water. The omasum, or **manyplies,** has a series of muscular sheets and folds protruding from its wall and comprises about eight per cent of the total bulk of the stomach. Camels and certain other ruminants have no omasum. These three compartments of the ruminant's

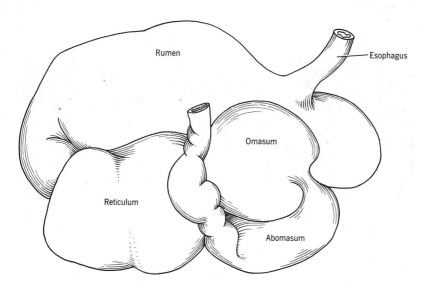

Figure 21. Stomach of the ox.

177

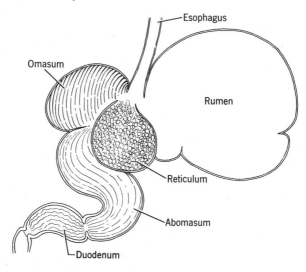

Figure 22. Diagram of the sacs in the stomach of a ruminant.

stomach are aglandular and are lined with a stratified epithelium. The last segment, the abomasum, is about the size of the omasum, and its wall contains gastric glands. Anything swallowed goes to the anterior part of the rumen and reticulum. The partially triturated food in these two chambers is regurgitated into the mouth, rechewed, and swallowed again. Food finally passes from these chambers to the omasum. The rumen, reticulum, and omasum store, soak, and churn plant food. There are no cellulose-splitting enzymes in the stomach; special types of bacteria, however, ferment cellulose into glucose and organic acids. Some of these substances are absorbed directly through the walls of these pouches, and others pass on to the abomasum and eventually to the intestine.

Gastric juices contain pepsin, which splits proteins; gastric lipase, which splits fat; rennin, in the young stomach, which coagulates milk; and hydrochloric acid, which provides the optimal acidity for the action of enzymes.

The Intestine

The narrow, pyloric end of the stomach opens into the intestine through a poorly closed **pyloric sphincter**. The breakdown of food is completed in the intestine and absorption takes place. The secretion from the large number of intestinal glands, bile from the liver, and the juices of the pancreas all work toward changing the chemical composition of the food to make it fit for absorption. Rhythmic, **peristaltic contractions** of the muscular walls of the intestine carry or push the food onward and churn it. In each class of vertebrates the intestine has taken a step forward in increasing its absorptive surface.

Cyclostomes. The intestine is a short straight tube enlarged near its posterior end into a **rectum.** A single longitudinal fold, the **typhlosole,** projects into the lumen in a spiral fashion to form a rudimentary **spiral valve.**

Fishes. Fish which feed on vegetable matter have a much longer intestine than those which feed on animal food. In all fish, except teleosts, the first part of the intestine forms a spiral valve; this is best, and most characteristically developed in the elasmobranchs (Figure 23). The valvular intestine opens into the short **large intestine.** The last segment of the large intestine is the rectum. In reality, the large intestine has a smaller diameter than the small intestine. In sharks **rectal glands** open into the gut at the separation of the small and large intestine. This separation is always marked by a **circular valve** or ridge. The ganoid, *Polypterus,* has a single **pyloric caecum** or diverticulum at the junction of the stomach with the intestine. Most teleosts have numerous pyloric caecae (Figure 24). The lungfishes have a **cloacal caecum** protruding from the posterior part of the intestine. The spiral valve and the pyloric and cloacal caecae are means of enlarging the total absorptive surface of the intestine. The liver and the pancreas open into the anterior por-

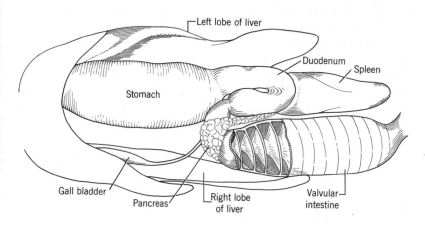

Figure 23. The digestive system of *squalus.*

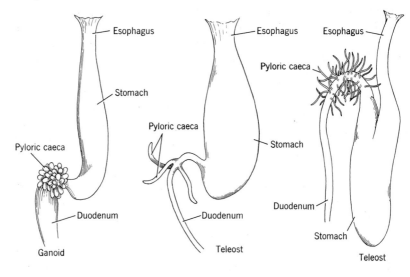

Figure 24. Pyloric caeca in fishes.

tion of the small intestine, or **duodenum,** by way of a **common bile duct** and the pancreatic duct. The large intestine of most fishes opens into the cloaca, an enlarged common passageway for the digestive and the urogenital systems. In some fishes the large intestine opens to the outside separately, through the anus.

Amphibians. Transverse folds project into the lumen of the intestine. In some salientians the gut is lined with villi. The small intestine is longer than that of fishes, and it is coiled; it changes abruptly at a ridge called the **iliocolic valve** to a short, straight large intestine which opens into a cloaca.

Reptiles. The intestine is longer than in the preceding classes. Its inner surface has numerous folds and is covered with conical villi. The large intestine has a wider bore than the small intestine, a **colic caecum** arises at the junction of the two segments, and an iliocolic valve separates the two segments. The large intestine opens into the cloaca.

Birds. The inner surface of the long and tightly coiled small intestine is covered with villi. The large intestine is short and straight and has a smaller diameter than the small intestine. A pair of colic caeca grows out of the posterior part of the large intestine before it empties into the cloaca (Figure 25). Some birds, however, have no colic caeca.

180

Mammals. The gut is clearly divided into a long and narrow small intestine and a shorter and wider large intestine. The first part of the small intestine, the duodenum, is continuous with the pyloric stomach and receives the common bile duct and the pancreatic duct through an elevation called the **ampulla of Vater.** Numerous mucus-secreting **glands of Brünner,** embedded in the submucosa, and large, leaflike villi distinguish the duodenum from the other segments. The duodenum is shorter than the other parts; in the mouse and the rat it is only a few millimeters long. The second division of the small intestine, the **jejunum,** is recognized by the absence of Brünner's glands. The last division, the ileum, is the longest and can be recognized by the presence in its wall of aggregated or singly scattered lymphoid nodules which make up **Peyer's patches.** When very large Peyer's patches can be seen as concrescences on the wall of the gut, but usually they are very small and are not visible to the naked eye. The total length of the intestine varies in different animals; in man it is about 21 feet, in the horse, 70 feet, in the ox, about 130 feet, and in the blue whale, over 500 feet. There are numerous villi on the surface of the small intestine, and the mucosa is thrown into longitudinal and transverse folds. The villi become progressively smaller in the ileum and disappear in the large intestine.

The ileum enters the **colon** through the iliocolic valve. The colon has a dilatation known as the caecum. In the horse the caecum has a capacity of several gallons (Figure 26) and contains a bacterial flora that splits cellulose into simple, absorbable substances. The caecum of marsupials and rodents is long and narrow; it is conical in the cat, and in man it looks like a pouch. The caecum of man and the anthropoid

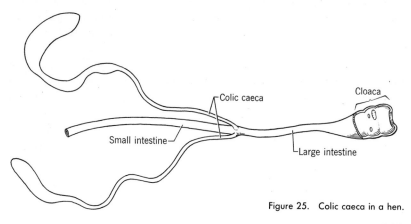

Figure 25. Colic caeca in a hen.

181

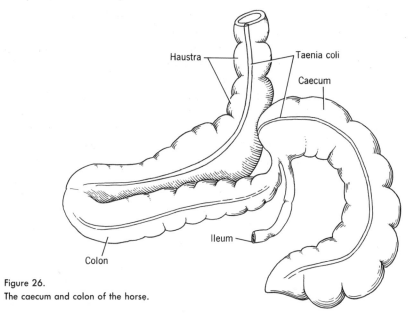

Figure 26.
The caecum and colon of the horse.

apes has a narrow diverticulum, the **vermiform appendix.** The colon is bent into the ascending limb on the right side, the **transverse colon,** and the **descending** colon on the left side. The last segment of the large intestine, the rectum, is attached to the pelvis by loose connective tissue. In most mammals the colon is sacculated into pocketlike dilatations called haustra (Figure 26). The outer, longitudinal muscle layer of the colon is often concentrated in bands known as **taenia coli.** The inner surface of the colon has no villi, and many of the cells of the epithelium secrete mucus. Almost all of the epithelial cells of the rectum produce mucus.

The wall of the intestine is pock-marked with **crypts of Lieberkühn,** or intestinal glands (Figures 4, 27). These glands are lined with primitive cells, which proliferate by mitosis and repopulate the cells of the lining of the villi; with goblet cells, which secrete mucus; and with glandular cells which secrete the intestinal juice, or **succus entericus.** This contains **enterokinase,** which activates trypsin; **peptidase,** which converts peptides to amino acids; **maltase,** which converts maltose to dextrose; **lactase,** which splits lactose into galactose and glucose; **sucrase,** which hydrolyses sucrose to dextrose and levulose; **amylase,** which splits starches; **lipase,** which splits fats; and **nucleotidase,** which splits phosphoric acid from nucleotides, leaving nucleosides. There is an interaction between the

182

enzymes secreted by the gastric glands, those secreted by the pancreas, and those in the succus entericus. These enzymes, and the special bacterial flora in the gut of most herbivorous animals, break down complex foodstuffs into simpler substances which can be absorbed through the lining cells of the intestine. This is the sole function of the gut. The breakdown of cellulose without the action of microorganisms would be minimal. In addition to this function, microorganisms help synthesize vitamins B and K.

In the colon some absorption of food still takes place. The colon also absorbs water from the waste products. Excreta, if forced to remain a long time in the colon, become dry and impacted.

With the exception of monotremes, mammals have no cloaca. The rectum opens to the outside separately as the anus and is lined with stratified squamous epithelium like that of the skin. Numerous glands open around the anus. Nearly all carnivores have glands near the anus which secrete fetid substances.

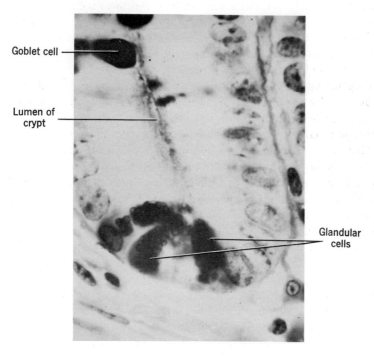

Figure 27. A crypt of Lieberkühn in the intestine of the mouse.

183

The Liver

All vertebrates have remarkably similar livers. Whether in fishes or mammals, the liver is the largest single organ of the body. It develops as a median diverticulum of the gut which grows in the **septum transversum** and expands behind, encroaching on the peritoneal cavity. In the adult the liver is suspended from the transverse septum by the **coronary ligament,** which is the connection between the visceral peritoneum covering the liver and parietal peritoneum lining the body cavity. The common bile duct, **ductus choledochus,** conveys bile to the duodenum; bile is manufactured by the liver from the breakdown of red blood corpuscles. In the liver bile is collected in bile capillaries; these converge toward larger and larger bile ducts, and finally one main **hepatic duct** drains the bile from each lobe of the liver and conveys it to a common **cystic duct** which opens into the **gall bladder** (Figure 28).

Cyclostomes. The liver is small and single-lobed in the lampreys; it has two lobes in all the other cyclostomes. Ammocoetes of lampreys have both a bile duct and a gall bladder, but these seem to degenerate in the adult.

Fishes. The liver is very large and is divided into two major lobes which may have minor subdivisions (see Figure 23). A bile duct drains each lobe, and a gall bladder is present.

Amphibians and Reptiles. All have very large livers and a gall bladder.

Birds. The liver has two or more lobes. A gall bladder is present in some birds; when it is absent, as in the pigeon, two hepatic ducts, one from each major lobe, empty separately into the duodenum.

Mammals. The liver is divided into two major lobes, each of which is further subdivided (Figure 29). The right lobe is larger than the left. Not all mammals have a gall bladder: the horse, deer, rat, the striped gopher, and others have none. In the giraffe it is present in some individuals, but not in others. The liver is a pliable organ which takes the shape of the space that houses it.

The **hepatic portal vein** drains the blood of the intestines, and conveys it to the liver. This is the life line of the animal because it carries most of the absorbed foodstuffs. Fats, which are emulsified by the bile and split by lipase into glycerol and fatty acids, are transported by the **lymph.** Proteins and carbohydrates are brought directly to the liver from the gut so that they may be worked over immediately. The liver synthesizes glycogen from the glucose in the blood and stores it; when the concentration of blood glucose falls below a certain level the liver splits glyco-

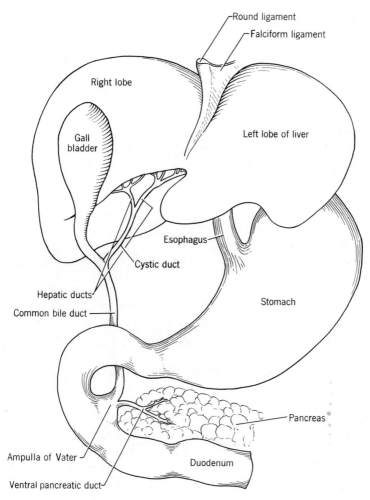

Figure 28.   Liver and gall bladder of man.

gen into glucose again. The liver also guides the metabolism of fats and proteins. It synthesizes vitamin A from precursors absorbed in the gut and stores it. It is an important organ in controlling the metabolism of iron. It destroys aged red blood corpuscles and forms bile. It detoxifies noxious substances transported by the blood, and it performs an untold number of functions.

185

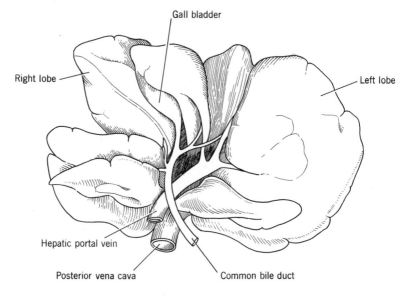

Gall bladder

Right lobe

Left lobe

Hepatic portal vein

Posterior vena cava

Common bile duct

Figure 29.   Ventral view of the liver of a dog.

The Pancreas

The pancreas arises from two diverticula of the entoderm; the ventral pancreatic diverticulum grows as an appendage of the hepatic diverticulum and the dorsal pancreatic diverticulum forms in the dorsal mesentery opposite the hepatic diverticulum (Figure 30).   During development the stomach grows disproportionately to the left and seems to turn to the right to bring the dorsal and ventral pancreatic elements either close to each other or actually in contact so that they fuse.   The point of origin of each pancreas can be traced by finding the place of entrance of the duct into the gut.   Usually, only one of the two ducts, the ventral or **duct of Wirsung**, remains.   This either opens into the last part of the **ductus choledochus** or directly into the duodenum very near the ductus choledochus (see Figures 28, 30).   In some animals the dorsal pancreatic duct persists, and in others both ducts can be found.

The pancreas embodies two distinct organs, both derived from the entoderm.   One part of the pancreas is concerned directly with digestion and secretes its products into the intestine; the other part, diffused throughout the rest of the organ in small aggregates of cells called **islets of Langerhans**, is an endocrine gland.   These cells secrete **insulin**, a hormone indispensable in the metabolism of sugars.

186

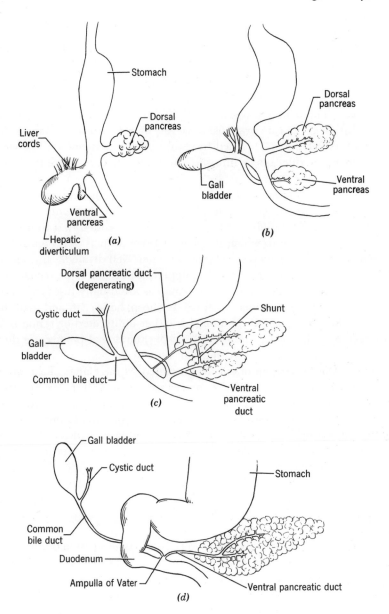

Figure 30. Progressive stages in the development of the pancreas in a mammalian embryo: (a) (b) and (c) show the gradual rotation of the stomach to the right and the coming together and fusion of the pancreatic elements; (d) the adult pattern.

Amphioxus. There is no defined pancreas, but cells resembling pancreatic cells are scattered in the anterior wall of the gut.

Cyclostomes. In the lampreys clusters of pancreatic cells occur with the liver tissue and in the typhlosole of the gut underneath the liver. Hagfishes have a small pancreas located near the place where the bile duct enters the gut.

Fishes. The pancreas is scattered diffusely in the mesenteries and is difficult to see. Elasmobranchs, however, have two distinct pancreatic elements (see Figure 23) joined by a thin bridge or **isthmus.** The ventral pancreatic duct opens into the intestine a short distance from the ductus choledochus.

Amphibians, Reptiles, and Birds. The pancreas of amphibians usually has one lobe and one duct; that of reptiles has more than one duct. In birds the long single lobe of the pancreas is embedded in a tight loop of the duodenum, into which it opens by several ducts (see Figure 18).

Mammals. The pancreas is large and often well defined. In rodents it is diffuse in the mesentery and sometimes can scarcely be recognized from the fat. The two lobes of the pancreas are usually fused, and one or the other of the two ducts persists. In sheep, horse, cat, and man the ventral duct persists and the dorsal is either obliterated or remains as an accessory duct. In the ox and the pig the dorsal pancreatic duct persists and the ventral one is small or absent.

There is a duplication of enzymes secreted by the glands of the stomach and by the pancreas. The pancreas secretes several major enzymes, among them amylase, trypsin, and lipase. Amylase, like that from the salivary glands, splits starches into sugars. Trypsin breaks proteins into peptides, and lipase splits fats into glycerid and fatty acids.

SUMMARY

1. The entire digestive system of vertebrates is adapted in every detail to the feeding behavior of an animal and to the type of food it eats. The digestive tract is longer and more complex in higher than in lower vertebrates, and it is longer in herbivorous than in carnivorous animals.

2. The mouth and associated structures are adapted for procuring food and preparing it for swallowing. Glands in the lining of the mouth and tongue keep the surfaces moist and slimy so that food can be tasted and easily swallowed. Salivary glands in the higher vertebrates provide lubricants and in some mammals secrete amylase for the digestion of starches.

3. The tongue of fishes is small and of little use. That of some amphibians is large and important in gathering food. In other vertebrates it plays various roles in gathering food, in revolving it in the mouth, and in swallowing it. The tongue can be remarkably different even in the same classes of vertebrates. In the mammal it is muscular and glandular and has a complex embryonic history.

4. Animals with a distinct cervical region also have an esophagus. The esophagus is relatively aglandular; in birds the lower part is dilated into a crop.

5. The stomach has great varieties of shapes, but its basic structure and function are similar in most vertebrates. Birds have a glandular proventriculus that secretes the gastric juices and a muscular gizzard that churns and grinds the food.

6. The intestine becomes increasingly long and its surface more extensive in each class of vertebrate. The absorptive surface is greatest in the mammals.

7. A clear-cut separation of large and small intestines occurs, particularly in mammals.

8. All vertebrates have a large liver, which is little changed among the different classes. The liver develops from a diverticulum of the entodermal tube of the primitive gut.

9. The pancreas arises from two separate diverticula from the entoderm of the gut. It is diffuse in *Amphioxus*, cyclostomes, and most fishes but distinct in elasmobranchs and in tetrapods. The two pancreatic elements may fuse with each other or remain separate.

SUGGESTED READING

Dukes, H. H., 1942, *The Physiology of Domestic Animals*. Comstock Publishing Company, Ithaca, N. Y.

Kingsbury, B. F., 1915, "The Development of the Human Pharynx." *Am. J. Anat.,* **18,** pp. 609–627.

Maximow, A. A., and W. Bloom, 1948, *A Textbook of Histology*. W. B. Saunders Company, Philadelphia and London.

Witschi, E., 1956, *Development of Vertebrates*. W. B. Saunders Company, Philadelphia and London.

Young, J. Z., 1950, *The Life of Vertebrates*. Oxford, Clarendon Press.

Figure 1. Skeletal muscle of a mouse showing each fiber surrounded by networks of capillaries.

THE CIRCULATORY SYSTEM

GENERAL INTRODUCTION

The metabolic activity of any tissue is related to its blood supply, and the more active the organs, the more extensive their circulatory system. One cannot imagine the number of blood vessels in a piece of skeletal muscle until, with appropriate methods, one can see that each muscle fiber is surrounded by networks of small vessels (Figure 1).

Vertebrate tissues have a staggering number of blood capillaries. A transverse section of muscle with an area of about 0.5 square millimeters contains about 500 muscle fibers and 700 capillaries. If all the capillaries in the skeletal muscles of the human body were put end to end, they would form a tube that would go about two and a half times around the world. The blood vessels of a kidney are so numerous that when they are injected with a plastic and the kidney tissue is macerated and washed away the rigid complex of blood vessels maintains the shape and bulk of the kidney virtually unchanged (Figure 2). Every cell of the endocrine glands is more or less in contact with the lining of blood vessels, making the exchange of food, oxygen, and waste products very intimate and efficient. In contrast, cartilage has no blood vessels, and the exchange in the cartilage cells must take place slowly by a diffusion through the matrix.

Figure 2. The blood vessels in the kidney of a lamb injected with a plastic. The kidney tissue has been macerated and washed away.

Fluid media circulate through the intricate networks of tubes of the blood vascular and the lymphatic systems. Blood is pumped by the heart to the arteries and from there to many arterioles and to the countless branching blood capillaries; these come together to form venules, which converge into veins that flow into bigger veins and finally into the major venous trunks that bring the blood back to the heart. The venous system can be likened to the formation of a river from smaller streams, and since smaller veins flow into larger ones veins are called tributaries. In contrast, arteries diverge and are called branches. The blood fluid seeps out of blood vessels into the tissues; a large portion of this fluid returns to the blood capillaries, but some of it is gathered by a very delicate extensive network of **lymphatic capillaries,** from which lymph flows slowly into larger and larger **lymph vessels.** The major lymph trunks return it to the blood vascular system.

Blood vessels are the tunnels for the transport of blood. Arteries carry the blood away from the heart; veins carry it toward the heart. Arteries and veins are found together and have the same treelike arrangement. The aorta and its main branches make up the **conducting arteries;** **distributing arteries** carry blood to the tissues, and the small arterioles terminate in capillaries.

The basic structure of arteries and veins is similar; they differ only in the relative thickness of their walls (Figure 3). Blood vessels have three layers. On the outside the **tunica externa,** or **adventitia,** consists of connective tissue fibers oriented parallel to the long axis of the vessel, and loose disoriented fibers anchor the vessel to the surrounding tissue. The **tunica media,** or middle layer, is composed of circularly arranged elastic fibers and smooth muscle fibers. The **tunica intima,** or inner layer,

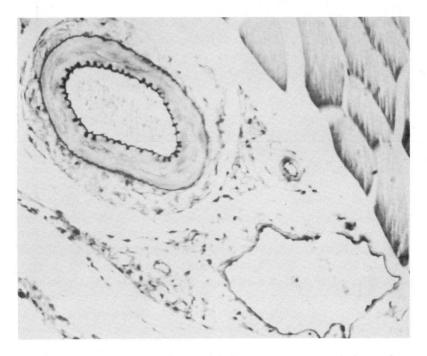

Figure 3. Artery of the mouse in the upper left; the accompanying vein in the lower right.

consists of areolar connective tissue and a single layer of flat epithelial cells called collectively the **endothelium**. In the arteries a thick **tunica elastica interna** separates the tunica intima from the tunica media (Figure 3). Conducting arteries are also called **elastic arteries** because their tunica media abounds in elastic fibers; the tunica media of the distributing arteries is rich in smooth muscle fibers, and these vessels are called **muscular arteries**. The walls of veins are very thin, and the three layers are indistinct. Veins, but not arteries, have numerous valves formed by foldings of the tunica intima. The large venous trunks which return the blood from the body to the heart are called **systemic;** those that return blood from the lungs to the heart are the **pulmonary veins**. Veins that are interrupted by venous capillaries are called **portal veins** or **portal systems;** when such venous capillaries are very wide, tortuous, and irregular they are called **sinusoids**. The sinusoids in **erectile** or **cavernous tissue**, in the penis and clitoris, are separated by connective tissue partitions and smooth muscle; this tissue becomes turgid when the sinusoids are filled with blood. Blood vessels, like other organs, are supplied with blood vessels of their own, called **vasa vasorum**. Capillaries consist of tubes of endothelium surrounded by wisps of connective tissue and occasional smooth muscle fibers. The diameter of capillaries is approximately the same as that of the red blood corpuscles or **erythrocytes** and is, therefore, constant in the same species.

Blood does not always go through capillary beds to pass from the arterioles to the veins. In the finger tips and under the nail bed of man, in the toes of mammals and birds, in the ears of mammals, etc., **arteriovenous anastomoses** shunt the blood from the arterial system directly to the venous system. These short vessels have a very thick wall with a lumen not much larger than that of capillaries and are innervated by nerve fibers from the parasympathetic division of the autonomic nervous system. Arteriovenous anastomoses constrict and dilate, causing changes in the flow of blood through the skin, and help to regulate the temperature of the body. During exposures to cold arteriovenous anastomoses constrict and dilate cyclically, preserving the viability of the surface tissues. This mechanism makes it possible for a bird to swim in icy water or for rabbits to live in subzero temperatures without the danger of either freezing the exposed appendages or lowering the body temperature.

The pumping action of the heart keeps blood in motion. The heart is housed in an extension of the celom called **pericardial cavity**. Except where the blood vessels enter it and leave it, the heart can expand and contract freely in the pericardial cavity. The relation of the heart to the pericardial cavity is the same as that of the viscera to the peritoneal cavity; it is slung in the **dorsal mesocardium** and is covered with a layer of **visceral pericardium** or **epicardium;** the pericardial cavity is covered with **parietal pericardium.** The inside of the heart is lined with **endocardium** or endothelium similar to that of other blood vessels. Cardiac muscle is peculiar to the heart; it is striated, like skeletal muscle, but the muscle fibers are branched and the branches seem to be continuous and form a **syncytium.** The vertebrate heart consists of four primary regions: (1) Posteriorly, the **sinus venosus** is the portal of venous blood from the body; (2) next is the **atrium;** (3) then the **ventricle;** and finally, (4) the **bulboconus arteriosus** (see Figure 6). The heart of most vertebrates is richly vascularized with blood vessels that comprise the **coronary circulation** (see Figure 9).

Lymph from the lymphatic capillaries passes into larger and larger lymph vessels. Spaced along the path of lymph vessels are the **lymph nodes,** which filter the lymph and remove from it cell debris or microorganisms. These are well developed only in mammals. **Lymphocytes** formed in the nodes are added to the lymph as it emerges from the nodes. Lymph nodes may be barely visible or they may be as large as chestnuts. Aggregates of them are usually found in regions in which large numbers of lymph vessels converge toward the main lymphatic ducts. The mesenteries of the posterior parts of the intestine are studded with lymph nodes of various sizes. Lymph channels enter the nodes as **afferent vessels** on the convex side; lymph percolates through a spongework of sinuses crisscrossed by strands of phagocytic cells which can engulf extraneous materials and is drained at the concave side of the node in the **efferent vessels.** Although their normal color is grayish, the lymph nodes in the lungs of modern man are dark gray, blue, or black due to particles of carbon and dust engulfed by the phagocytic cells. All lymph vessels converge toward the main lymphatic ducts, which return lymph and lymphocytes to the blood vascular system. The flow of lymph toward the heart is very slow; valves along the path of the vessels prevent a backflow (Figure 4).

Lymph capillaries occur with blood capillaries and are similar to them. Lymph vessels accompany veins but are more numerous, thinner walled, and translucent. The bulging of the valves gives lymph vessels a beaded appearance (Figure 4). After a fatty meal the lymph vessels from the intestine are full of emulsified fat or **chyle,** which is whitish.

Lymphoid tissue is an accumulation of lymphocytes; it can be dense or diffuse. Dense lymphoid tissue consists of compact nodules of lymphocytes; lymph nodes are composed of both dense and diffuse lymphoid tissue. Tonsils are aggregates of lymph nodules associated with an

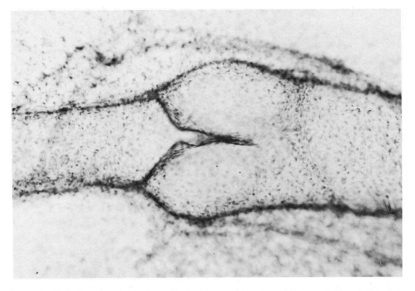

Figure 4. Valve in a lymphatic channel. In this vessel lymph could flow only from left to right. (Courtesy of General Biological Supply House, Inc., Chicago.)

epithelium; they are found around the pharynx, although even Peyer's patches in the ileum or any lymphoid accumulation in the wall of the gut constitutes a tonsil. Tonsils have only efferent lymph vessels.

Blood is composed of cells, the **corpuscles,** and **plasma,** a fluid intercellular substance. Blood contains red corpuscles or **erythrocytes,** white corpuscles, or **leucocytes,** and **platelets.** The red color of blood is due to the erythrocytes; plasma is colorless or strawcolored. The erythrocytes are oval or round. In mammals they are smaller than those of the lower classes; they are round, except in the camel, in which they are oval, and roughly biconcave. The most striking feature of mammalian erythrocytes is that they are nucleated while being formed but lose the nucleus when they become mature; the erythrocytes of mammalian embryos, and those of all adult nonmammalian vertebrates, are nucleated. The erythrocytes are large in fish and Amphibia, and their size varies in each species; in mammals, for instance, they range from 4.1 microns in the goat to 7.5 microns in man. The number of erythrocytes per cubic millimeter of mammalian blood ranges from about 5.5 million in man to 14 million in the goat. It has been estimated that the total surface of erythrocytes in man is about 3000 square yards and about 19,150 square yards in the ox. The red color of erythrocytes is due to hemoglobin. This is a respiratory pigment; it has the property of combining with oxygen in the gills or lungs. When the blood travels through the capillaries hemoglobin gives up oxygen to the tissues. The two main groups of leucocytes are the granular and the agranular. **Neutrophils** make up the largest number of granular leucocytes; **eosinophils** and **basophils** make up a very small proportion of the total number of leucocytes. The agranular leucocytes are the lymphocytes, which are very numerous, and the **monocytes,** which are not. The number of leucocytes is different in different vertebrates. Birds have about 20,000 leucocytes per cubic millimeter of blood; mammals have from about 5500 in man to about 17,000 in the pig. The number of different leucocytes is variable. The blood of birds and mammals has a preponderance of neutrophils and lymphocytes; monocytes average from 1 per cent in the rabbit to 10 per cent in the ox. The percentage of eosinophils ranges from 1.5 in the goat to 10 in the dog. In most mammals basophils make up less than 1 per cent of the total leucocyte count, but in birds it is about 2 or 3 per cent. Blood platelets have the property of initiating the coagulation of blood when tissues are injured. They are believed to arise from the fragmented cytoplasmic processes of giant cells called **megakaryocytes,** found in blood-forming organs and in the spleen and lungs. The number of blood platelets ranges from about 155,000 per cubic millimeter in the dog to 250,000 in man.

Plasma has innumerable properties: (1) It carries nutrients from the gut to the liver and from the liver to the tissues of the body; (2) it transports the waste products of metabolism from the tissues to the organs of excretion; (3) it transports the hormones from the endocrine glands to the tissues; (4) it regulates hydrogen ion concentration; and (5) it helps defend the body against the invasion of microorganisms.

DEVELOPMENT

The patterns of development which follow pertain mostly to the embryos of amniotes; these must serve only as examples of developmental history, since in other vertebrates these events are different.

Blood cells and blood vessels arise together first outside the embryo in the splanchnic mesoderm of the wall of the yolk sac, where mesenchymal cells proliferate and become heaped up in clusters called **blood islands** (Figure 5). The cells at the periphery of the blood islands differentiate into endothelial cells that form connecting tubes, and those nearer the center differentiate into the first blood cells. Adjacent blood

197

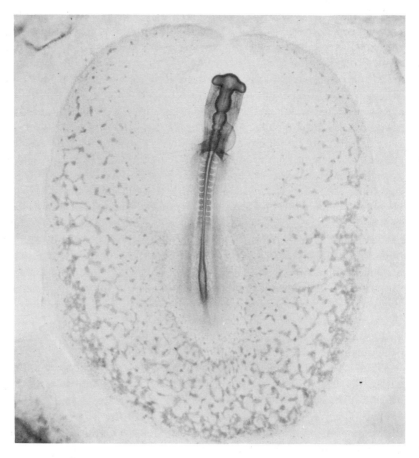

Figure 5. Surface view of a thirty-three hour chick embryo. The reticulated markings in the germinal disc are the blood islands. The primary divisions of the brain and of the mesodermal somites are very clear. (Courtesy of Wards Natural Science Establishment, Inc., Rochester 9, New York.)

islands become continuous until the entire wall of the yolk sac has a continuous network of capillaries.

When the first somite is differentiated in the embryo differentiation of blood islands takes place also in the splanchnic mesoderm dorsal to the gut. Clefts appear there which become confluent and form a maze of interconnecting channels. The main blood vessels are formed through the enlargement and differentiation of certain paths of these early networks and the atrophy of side branches. Arteries and veins develop in the same way, and it is not known what agencies determine the differentiation of one or the other. The first recognizable blood vessels in the body of the embryo are the **paired dorsal aortae**. During early stages two separate vascular systems develop, one on each side of the embryo. Each dorsal aorta bends ventrally around the anterior end of the pharynx and continues ventrally under the pharynx in the wall of the pericardial cavity to become attached on each side to a **vitelline vein** from the yolk sac. The two vitelline veins collect the blood from the wall of the yolk sac and bring it to the embryo, passing through a **primitive heart tube** in the wall of the pericardial cavity; from there, through the short **ventral aorta,** blood passes dorsally through the aortic arch and down each dorsal aorta (Figure 6*a*). From each aorta blood returns to the yolk sac by way of **vitelline arteries**. In early embryos, then, the only union between the vascular system of the two sides of the body is in the yolk sac. In animals which develop from eggs rich in yolk the vitelline circulation lasts until the embryos hatch. In mammals which are dependent on the placenta for subsistence the vitelline circulation is relatively short-lived. An **umbilical artery** branches off each dorsal aorta and brings blood to the **chorioallantoic membranes** in oviparous animals and to the placenta in mammals. Exchange of gases and the elimination of wastes takes place in the extraembryonic membranes; in mammals food and other essential materials are obtained through the placenta. **Umbilical veins** from the extraembryonic membranes bring blood back to each heart tube. The first union of the vascular system of the two sides of the embryo takes place in the pericardial cavity when the two heart tubes encroach upon each other and their medial walls fuse and break down; the heart, now a single tube, begins to expand in the pericardial cavity (Figure 6*b*). Venous channels, or **anterior cardinal veins,** on each side of the head and pharynx (Figure 6*b*), develop from the large sinusoidal spaces in the head region of the embryo; these channels open on each side of the posterior part of the heart with the vitelline and umbilical veins. When the embryo attains a second pharyngeal arch a **second aortic arch** develops with it. The two dorsal aortae fuse in the middle of the embryo and form a single vessel for a distance; but they remain doubled anteriorly as the two roots of the aorta and posteriorly continuous with the two umbilical arteries (Figure 6*c*). One **posterior cardinal vein** develops from each side in the posterior part of the embryo; each of these unites with the corresponding anterior cardinal, and the two systems open into the heart as the **common cardinal vein** or **duct of Cuvier** (Figure 6*c*). More aortic arches, joining the ventral and dorsal aortae, are subsequently formed. Six is the usual number of aortic arches formed

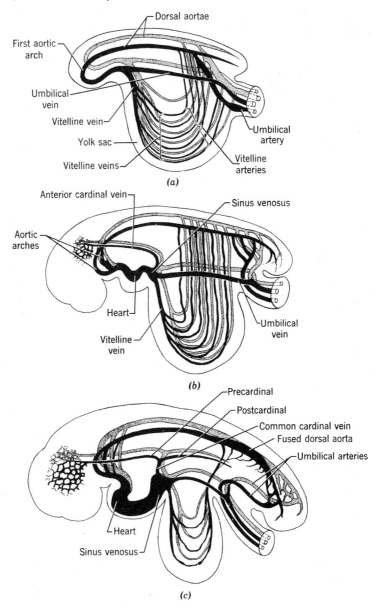

Figure 6. The progressive development of the vascular systems in a mammalian embryo: (a) only the vitelline and umbilical circulation are present; (b) the anterior cardinal vein has developed; (c) the anterior and posterior cardinal veins are present, and the dorsal aortae are fused posteriorly as the vitelline circulation atrophies.

in most of the classes of vertebrates. Mammals attain five aortic arches and a rudiment of a sixth one.

When all of the basic elements of the circulatory system are formed and ready to differentiate further the embryo has (1) a single tubular heart which extends in an anteroposterior direction, (2) aortic arches which connect the ventral with the dorsal aortae, (3) a single dorsal aorta doubled at both ends, and (4) a system of cardinal veins which drains the systemic blood and returns it to the heart. Further details in the development of each of these systems are given under separate headings.

The heart primordia extend cephalocaudally in the pericardial cavity (Figure 7a,aa); when they enlarge their medial walls come in contact and fuse and the fused walls disintegrate. The single heart primordium remains doubled posteriorly and anteriorly (Figure 7b,bb). The two posterior parts comprise the sinus venosus; each receives a vitelline, umbilical, and common cardinal vein. The heart soon overgrows the pericardial space and doubles up on itself to form a loop that swings to the right side of the cavity (Figure 7c,cc). Four regional differentiations can be recognized in the heart: the two horns of the very thin-walled sinus venosus; anterior to it, the single dilatated atrium, and anterior to the atrium, the thick, muscular-walled ventricle; the most cephalic part of the heart is the **conus arteriosus**. The boundaries of the adjacent segments are marked by muscular constrictions. *The adult heart, whether it is that of a fish or that of an amniote, evolves from this simple basic pattern* (Figure 7d,e,f). Differential growth of certain parts, fusion of adjacent segments, disappearance of original partitions, and the formation of folds, walls, cushions, and partitions give the heart its definitive adult form. For details of these events the student should consult textbooks of embryology.

The heart of the early mammalian embryo, like that of adult fishes and urodeles, is located just under the pharynx between the rami of the developing mandible. When the cervical region differentiates the heart of amniote embryos comes to lie caudal to the head.

COMPARATIVE ANATOMY OF THE HEART

The size of the heart varies, but it is fairly consistent in each class. The relative size of the heart of birds is greater than that of any other class. Among the mammals the smaller species have relatively larger hearts. Naturally, the largest heart is found in whales, among which

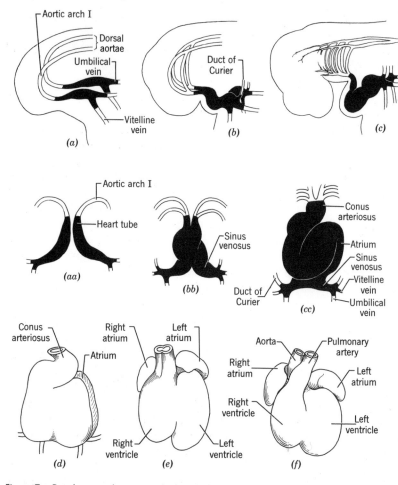

Figure 7. Developmental stages in the heart of the mammal: (a) side view, (aa) ventral view; (b) side view, (bb) ventral view; (c) side view, (cc) ventral view; (d) ventral view; (e) ventral view; (f) ventral view.

an animal weighing over 60 tons may have a heart weighing 800 pounds or more. The normal heart rate is variable, but it is usually very high in small animals with relatively large hearts. In small birds it may be close to 500 per minute. In small mammals it may be as high as in birds, but in large mammals it is much slower. The horse has a heart rate of 32 to 45 per minute, and the rate of the elephant is about 25; that of man varies from 60 to 90.

Amphioxus

A single-chambered, undifferentiated heart tube underneath the pharynx slowly pumps the blood into the arteries of the gills.

Cyclostomes

The heart, located just posterior to the last pair of gills, is surprisingly complicated. The sinus venosus receives a single, large, common cardinal vein on the dorsal side, one internal jugular vein, anteriorly, and one hepatic vein, posteriorly. The sinus venosus opens into a broad, thin-walled atrium which communicates with the thick-walled ventricle by a narrow atrioventricular valve. The free edges of this valve are attached to tough fibrous chordae tendineae anchored to the inner wall of the ventricle. The single ventricle opens into the bulbus where a semilunar valve prevents a backflow of blood into the ventricle. Venous blood passes linearly through the heart from the sinus venosus, the atrium, the ventricle, and the bulbus on to the ventral aorta and the gills. The heart handles only venous blood, and has a single type of circulatory system.

Fishes

The large sinus venosus receives the common cardinal veins from each side and the hepatic veins from the liver. The single-chambered atrium balloons out dorsally on each side of the muscular ventricle. The ventricle opens into the conus arteriosus where a series of semilunar valves prevents backflow. The regions of the heart are no longer arranged linearly, but the bulbus, ventricle, and atrium form an S-shaped loop (Figure 8a,b). The heart of fishes is completely venous like that of cyclostomes and has a single circulation.

In the heart of lungfishes the atrium is partially divided into right and left auricles; the sinus venosus opens into the right auricle, and the vessels from the lunglike swim bladder return oxygenated blood to the left atrium. The conus arteriosus is divided; a branch carrying oxygenated blood from the left side of the ventricle goes to the anterior gills, and the other branch, carrying unoxygenated blood from the left side of the atrium, goes to the posterior gills and to the swim bladder. This is the beginning of a double circulatory system; the heart has three chambers, and the ventricle is partially separated by an incomplete interventricular septum.

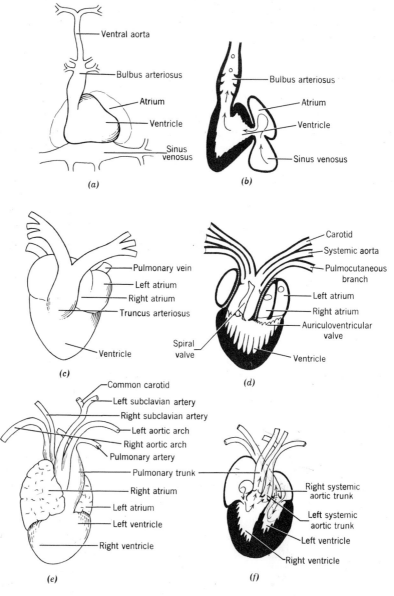

Figure 8. (a) and (b), the heart of elasmobranchs; (c) and (d), the heart of the frog; (e) and (f), the heart of the alligator.

In most fishes arteries from the second efferent branchial arterial arches carrying oxygenated blood go directly to the heart and form the coronary circulation, or intrinsic circulation of the heart. Coronary veins drain the walls of the heart and return the blood to the sinus venosus.

Amphibians

The sinus venosus has shifted to the right and opens into the right atrium. The two atria are separated by a thin interatrial septum. From the right atrium the blood goes into the single large muscular ventricle (Figure 8*c*,*d*). Although the ventricle has one chamber, bundles of muscular folds keep the blood in the right side from spilling into the left side. The two atrioventricular apertures are guarded by valves; fibrous chordae tendineae are attached to the free flaps of the valves and keep them from becoming everted into the atria when the ventricle contracts. The venous blood from the right side of the ventricle is forced into the bulbus without mixing with that in the left side; the bulbus itself then contracts and semilunar valves prevent a backflow of blood into the ventricle. A spiral valve through the middle of the bulbus separates the bulbus into two channels; the venous blood from the right side of the ventricle passes on one side of the spiral valve and flows through the pulmocutaneous arches to the lungs and skin or to the gills. Pulmonary veins return oxygenated blood to the left atrium; from there it flows to the left side of the ventricle. When this contracts blood is forced into the bulbus on the other side of the spiral valve, and from there it flows into the carotid systemic arteries.

Reptiles

The heart is four-chambered, but blood spills from one chamber into the other through a gap at the anterior part of the interventricular septum; in the Crocodilia the gap is closed. The sinus venosus of turtles is still a separate chamber attached to the right atrium, but that of other reptiles has disappeared. In all reptiles the conus is split into a pulmonary trunk, which conveys blood from the right ventricle to the lungs, and two aortic trunks (Figure 8*e*,*f*). The left aortic trunk emerges from the right ventricle and the right one from the left ventricle. The two aortic trunks cross over each other, and at the point where they cross a small foramen Panizzae allows the blood from the two trunks to mix. Pulmonary veins return oxygenated blood to the left atrium; it passes to the left ventricle, and from there it goes into the right aortic arch.

Comparative Anatomy

The left ventricle is much larger and thicker walled than the right. The coronary circulatory system is only moderately developed.

Birds

The heart has four chambers. The sinus venosus is completely incorporated into the wall of the right atrium and cannot be seen as a separate structure. Three large venous trunks, two **precavae** and one **postcava**, return systemic blood to the right atrium. Blood passes from the right atrium to the small right ventricle and from there to the pulmonary trunk. Pulmonary veins return arterial blood to the left atrium. Blood passes from the left atrium into the large, very thick-walled left ventricle, which conveys the fluid to the single arch of the aorta. Many details in the heart of the bird are similar to those in the heart of mammals.

Mammals

The sinus venosus is completely incorporated into the wall of the right atrium. One posterior and usually one anterior vena cava return systemic blood to the right atrium; some mammals have two anterior venae cavae. Blood is forced into the right ventricle, from which it goes to the pulmonary trunk and the lungs. Pulmonary veins return oxygenated blood to the left atrium, and from there it passes to the left ventricle, which propels blood to the single arch of the aorta (Figure 9a,b). The right ventricle is smaller and thinner walled than the left ventricle. A complete interventricular septum separates the two ventricles, and an interatrial septum separates the atria. A thin region in the cephalic part of the interatrial septum, the **fossa ovalis**, represents the site of the **foramen ovale**. During development the foramen ovale has a valvelike flap which allows blood from the right atrium to pass to the left atrium, bypassing the pulmonary circulation. The inside walls of the ventricles are thrown into many fleshy columns, **trabeculae carnae**, and pockets (Figure 9b). The orifices of all the vessels entering or leaving the heart are guarded by efficient valves which prevent a backflow. The right atrioventricular canal has the **tricuspid valve;** the left one, the **bicuspid** or **mitral valve** (Figure 9d). The valves are connective tissue flaps with the free edges attached on the ventricular side to the chordae tendineae; these are anchored to fleshy fingerlike projections called **papillary muscles** (Figure 9c). When the heart muscle contracts the papillary muscles do also and the chordae tendineae do not slacken; if they did, the flaps of the valves would be everted into the atria. Blood, then, can pass

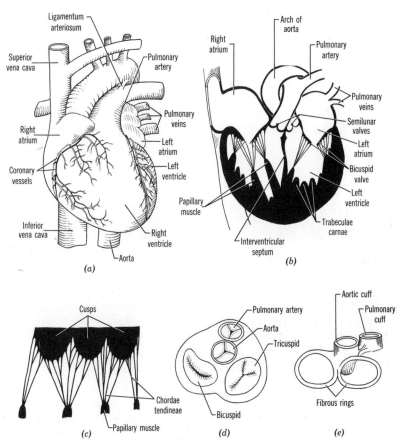

Figure 9. (a) Surface anatomy of the heart of man; (b) diagram of the internal anatomy of the mammalian heart; (c) tricuspid valve; (d) dorsal surface of the atrioventricular wall showing the valves; (e) skeleton of the human heart.

from the atria to the ventricles but cannot be forced back into the atria without tearing the valves and the inelastic chordae tendineae. Each of the aortic and the pulmonary trunks is protected by a semilunar valve (Figure 9d). Each valve consists of three cusps, with the free edge bordered by a tough fibrous lip (Figure 10a,b). When the blood flows from the ventricles to the arterial trunks the flaps are eased out of the way; but when the trunks of these vessels contract the cusps fill with blood, become distended by the back pressure, and their free edges meet and close the passage (Figure 10c,d).

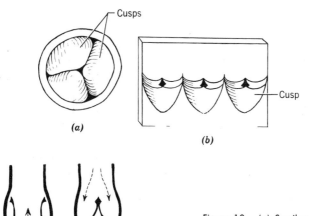

Figure 10. (a) Semilunar valve of the aorta seen from above; (b) aorta spread out, showing the three cusps; (c) and (d) cusps open and closed.

The heart has a very extensive **intrinsic** or **coronary circulation.** The main coronary arteries come directly from the base of the dorsal aorta and run into the atrioventricular and interventricular sulci (see Figure 9a). The great coronary veins that accompany the arteries drain into the coronary sinus in the posterior wall of the right atrium, at the base of the entrance of the posterior vena cava. Some of the blood, instead of progressing from coronary arteries to the capillary networks and to veins, is drained from the arterioles directly into the lumen of the ventricles by straight venous shunts called **Thebesian veins.** Since this is a direct drainage, the Thebesian veins keep the supply of blood to the heart muscle fresh and eliminate stagnation. The phylogeny of the coronary circulation is interesting. The heart of cyclostomes and amphibia is nonvascular, but blood percolates through the cavernous recesses of its spongy walls. Coronary circulation begins in fishes, becomes more nearly complete in reptiles, and reaches its greatest development in birds and mammals, with the formation of Thebesian veins.

A fibrous ring surrounds each of the passageways of the heart. An atrioventricular ring separates each atrioventricular canal, and strong rings are at the base of the pulmonary and aortic trunks; the one at the base of the aorta is a stout cuff (see Figure 9e). All four of these structures are joined. A bone, the **os cordis,** is attached to the right side of the aortic cuff of the sheep. In many other mammals this side of the cuff is reinforced by a cartilage plate.

CONTRACTION OF THE HEART

Numerous nerves go to the heart from the **sympathetic** and the **parasympathetic** divisions of the **autonomic nervous system**. Yet rhythmic contractions can go on even after these nerves have been cut off; the nerves regulate and guide the rhythm of the pulsations, but do not initiate it. In cyclostomes and in fishes the contraction of the heart is a wavelike movement which begins in the sinus venosus and ends in the bulbus. In higher vertebrates the right atrium contracts first; the exact origin of the contraction is the **sino-atrial node** (S-A node). This is the part of the atrium into which the sinus venosus has become incorporated. Since contraction impulses originate in this node, it is called the **pacemaker**. Impulses generated in the pacemaker spread through the walls of both atria; they are picked up by the **atrioventricular node** and are conveyed to the walls of the ventricles by the **atrioventricular bundle** (Figure 11). Since the conduction of the impulse over the walls of the atria is faster than that over the atrioventricular bundles, the atria contract before the ventricles.

DEVELOPMENT AND FATE OF THE AORTIC ARCHES

The dorsal and ventral aortae of the embryo are a continuous vessel bent anteriorly to form **aortic arch I** (see Figures 6 and 7). When additional pharyngeal arches develop, cross links are formed between the

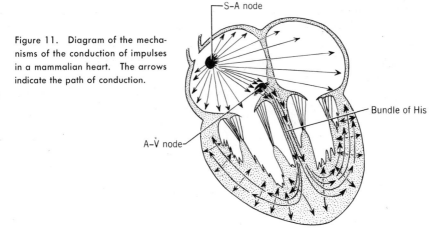

Figure 11. Diagram of the mechanisms of the conduction of impulses in a mammalian heart. The arrows indicate the path of conduction.

S–A node

A–V node

Bundle of His

209

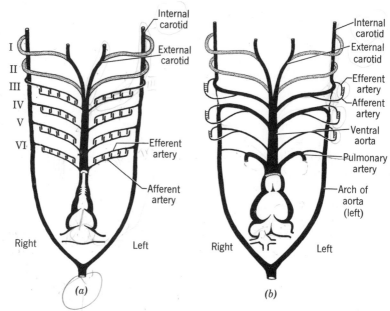

Figure 12. Fate of the aortic arches: (*a*) fish; (*b*) urodele; (*c*) salientian;

dorsal and ventral aortae, one for each pharyngeal arch. The cyclostomes may have as many as fifteen arches and some primitive elasmobranchs, seven; the fishes and the embryos of all other vertebrates develop only six aortic arches. Since the adults of all vertebrates above fishes lack gills and the fishlike pharynx, the primitive pattern of their aortic arches is greatly modified. The descriptions which follow pertain mostly to the fate of the individual six pairs of aortic arches laid down in the embryos of each class. The sixty odd pairs of aortic arches in *Amphioxus* are so specialized that it would serve little purpose to describe them here. The basic pattern of the aortic arches of cyclostomes and the circulation in their gills can be illustrated by those of the fish. In the cyclostomes the number of aortic arches varies in different species.

Fishes

Several very important modifications take place within this group, and what happens in the different fishes foretells the trends of differentiation in the other vertebrates. The aortic arches of gill-bearing vertebrates are primarily devices for bringing venous blood from the heart to

210

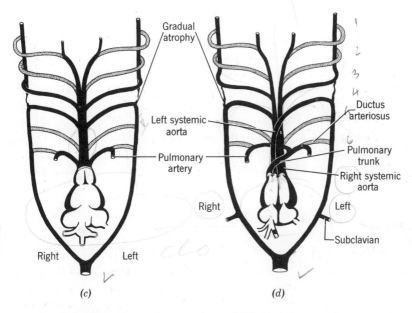

(*d*) reptile.   The stippled structures disappear; those solid black remain.

the gills, where the blood is oxygenated and drained into the dorsal aorta as arterial blood.   The ventral incoming limbs of the aortic arches, or afferent branchial arteries, convey venous blood to the gill filaments, and the dorsal outgoing branches, the efferent branchial arteries, drain them (Figure 12*a*).   Although all fish embryos have six arches, arch I is always lost or modified in the adult; aortic arch II is present in elasmobranchs but largely disappears in the other fishes.   African lungfishes, which depend mainly on lungs for breathing, have lost the capillary networks of the gills of arches III and IV, and the corresponding aortic arches are uninterrupted vessels.   When aortic arches I and II drop out the anterior extensions of the dorsal aortae from arch III continue to the head as the **internal carotid arteries;** the extensions from the ventral part of arch III continue to the jaws as the **external carotid arteries** (Figure 12A*a*).   Blood flowing in arch III passes forward to the head, and this tendency becomes more pronounced in the other classes.   Arch III forms the major part of the internal carotid artery.   *The pulmonary arteries arise as vessels from arch VI to the swim bladder of Latimeria and the lungfishes; this is one of the most important steps in the evolution of the circulatory system.*

211

Amphibia

Arches I and II disappear during development. Arch V disappears in some urodeles and in all salientians, leaving intact only arches III, IV, and VI. The dorsal link between arches III and IV becomes very thin in urodeles and almost disappears in salientians. Blood from the ventral aorta flows to arch III, which is now the internal carotid artery (Figure 12*b,c*). The right and left aortic arches IV are now the systemic aortae. The vessels to the gill filaments of larval or adult gilled urodeles spring as side branches of aortic arches III, IV, VI, and a much reduced V. The original aortic arches are continuous unbroken tubes (see Figure 11B*b*).

Reptiles

Aortic arches I, II, and V disappear in most reptiles. In certain lizards and snakes a very thin aortic arch V may persist, and the dorsal connecting link between arch III and IV may not disappear completely. Arch III gives rise to the internal carotid artery, and the forward extensions of the ventral aortae form the external carotid arteries (Figure 12*d*). Instead of a single bulbus arteriosus, three vessels emerge from the ventricles of the heart: one pulmonary trunk, which branches to the pulmonary arteries formed from aortic arch VI, and right and left systemic aortic arches derived from arch IV. The right arch emerges from the left side of the ventricle and is larger than the left; a single common carotid artery emerges from the ventral side of the right arch. One subclavian artery is attached to each aortic arch.

Birds

Arches I, II, and V disappear. Arch III forms the internal carotids on each side, and the forward extension of the ventral aorta gives rise to the external carotids. Aortic arch IV forms the systemic aorta on the right side and the first part of the subclavian artery on the left. The left root of the dorsal aorta disappears, and the one on the right side, continuous only with arch IV, remains as the permanent aortic arch (Figure 13*a*). All of the systemic arterial trunks are attached to the single right arch of the aorta. The pulmonary arteries come from arch VI; the ductus arteriosus, a connection between the right pulmonary artery and the aorta in the embryo, is reduced in the adult to a cord of connective tissue called ligamentum arteriosus.

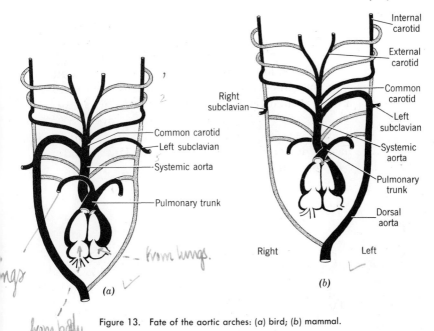

Figure 13. Fate of the aortic arches: (*a*) bird; (*b*) mammal.

Mammals

The aortic arches of mammals have the same developmental history and fate as those of the birds. Aortic arch V does not even make a transitory appearance in most mammalian embryos; it may be found in the embryos of pigs. The outstanding difference between the bird and the mammal is that the arch of the aorta of the bird comes from the right aortic arch IV, but that of mammals is from the left aortic arch IV. The ligamentum arteriosus of adult mammals is, naturally, on the left side (Figure 13*b*). The systemic aorta emerges from the left ventricle and arches sharply to the left. The right aortic arch IV forms the first part of the right subclavian artery, from which emerges the **right common carotid artery** to the head and neck. The common trunk of subclavian and carotid arteries is called, collectively, the **right innominate artery** or **brachiocephalic artery** (Figure 14). The left subclavian artery and the left carotid artery may emerge together from the aorta, as in the carnivores, or separately, as in primates. In the horse a single brachiocephalic artery divides into right and left subclavian arteries, and a single common carotid artery divides into right and left. Other combinations occur in mammals.

213

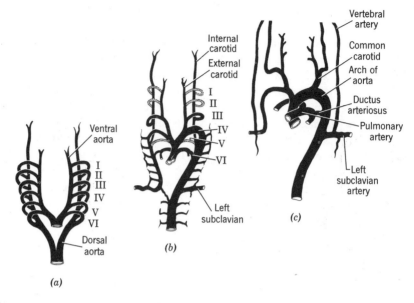

Figure 14. Development and fate of the aortic arches in a mammalian embryo: (a) full complement of aortic arches; (b) disappearance of arches I, II, and V; (c) the adult pattern.

THE AORTA AND ITS BRANCHES

From its single or double arches the aorta swings to approximately the middorsal line and extends to the caudal artery. The aorta gives off paired **segmental arteries** to the dorsal muscles and to the vertebrae over its entire length. A fusion of several of these segmental arteries, or a local enlargement of one of them, gives rise to the distal part of the subclavian arteries. The aorta sends paired arteries to the paired organs of the body, the largest of these being the **renal arteries** to the kidneys, and three large unpaired **visceral arteries** to the alimentary tract. The first unpaired artery is the **coeliac**, which sends large branches to the liver, stomach, pancreas, and duodenum. The second is the **superior mesenteric**, which goes to the small intestine below the duodenum and to the upper part of the large intestine. The third visceral artery is the **inferior mesenteric** to the large intestine. In sharks a fourth unpaired artery, the **gastrosplenic**, emerges from the aorta posterior to the coeliac artery and supplies the spleen and the greater curvature of the stomach. In amphibians a single large **coeliacomesenteric artery** to most of the digestive viscera may represent a fusion of coeliac and superior mesen-

214

teric arteries. Although differences occur in most vertebrates, the un-paired visceral arteries just described are relatively similar. The superior mesenteric artery has arisen from a fusion of the proximal parts of vitel-line arteries; these return blood from the aorta to the yolk sac of the embryo. The two umbilical arteries of amniote embryos give rise to the paired iliac arteries of the adult (see Figure 6). Umbilical arteries re-turn blood from the aorta to the chorioallantoic membranes of the embryos of reptiles and birds and to the placenta of the embryos of mammals. Each umbilical artery gives off a large **external iliac artery** to the hind limb and a smaller **internal iliac artery** to the terminal part of the alimentary tract, the urinary bladder, and the pelvis. The parts of the umbilical arteries distal to the bladder atrophy after birth. The bases or roots of the umbilical arteries, where they branch from the dorsal aorta, remain as the **common iliac arteries.**

The basic patterns of blood vessels discussed here will suffice to illus-trate the principles of the distribution of blood to the vertebrate body. These vessels are similar and unchanged even in different classes. Many arteries branch from the distributing arteries and go to the organs, where innumerable terminal arteries vascularize the tissues. The de-tails of these will be studied in the laboratory.

DEVELOPMENT OF THE MAMMALIAN VENOUS SYSTEM

A great deal can be learned about the phylogeny of the major venous pathways by studying their development in the mammalian embryo.

The systemic veins collect the blood from the body. In young em-bryos the anterior cardinal veins drain the body anterior to the heart and the posterior cardinal veins drain it posterior to it. These veins are first established as communicating networks, blood spaces, and sinuses. Later, vessels acquire a more constant diameter, but they never possess so specific a gauge as the arteries.

The system of cardinal veins gives rise to the anterior and posterior caval systems. We follow first the changes in the posterior system of cardinal veins and then those in the anterior system.

The Posterior Cardinal Veins

These extend from the sinus venosus to the tail and are mainly asso-ciated with the dorsolateral border of the transitory mesonephric kidney of the embryo. In older embryos the middle segment of the posterior cardinal veins degenerates, leaving intact the anterior segment, which empties into the sinus venosus, and the posterior segment coming from the tail and the posterior limbs (Figure 15). In the meantime, another set of venous channels, the **subcardinal veins,** forms on the medial border of the mesonephric kidney, parallel to the posterior cardinals. Consequently, in order for blood to be drained from the posterior segment of the posterior cardinal veins, it must percolate through venous capillaries in the mesonephric kidney and be drained by the subcardinal vein, which returns it to the sinus venosus. This series of events shows two important changes: (1) the establishment of the renal portal system, and (2) the deviation of blood into a different channel. Shunts form across the two subcardinals, fuse, and give rise to a large sinus called the **intersubcardinal anastomosis.** Other changes soon take place: the most anterior part of the right subcardinal vein lies very near the liver, and a fold of dorsal body wall, the **caval mesentery,** develops as a bridge between the liver and right subcardinal. The numerous venous channels through this fold establish a connection between the liver and the right mesonephros. The blood from the intersubcardinal anastomosis takes a direct route to the sinus venosus by way of this new shunt which is called the **caval** or **mesenteric segment.** The left subcardinal vein largely disappears, as does also the proximal segment of the right subcardinal bypassed by the caval segment. As the circulation of blood through the liver increases, the caval segment is pushed posteriorly. Another pair of veins, the **supracardinals,** appears dorsomedially late in development and drains the dorsal body wall (Figure 15). The supracardinal veins become fused with the subcardinal anastomosis. The right supracardinal posterior to the anastomosis becomes very large; the left one disappears. The anterior parts of the supracardinals become the **azygous veins.** Thus three pairs of venous channels appear, and segments from each of them are used to establish a single median posterior vena cava. In the final diagram of Figure 15 the origin of each segment of the posterior vena cava is clearly marked (see also Figure 18*b*). This type of development becomes particularly significant when one compares it with the venous patterns existing in the different classes of vertebrates. Not all mammals have a single posterior vena cava; in aquatic mammals it is doubled and may have cross links (Figure 16).

The Anterior Vena Cava

A pair of large anterior cardinal veins drains the part of the embryo anterior to the sinus venosus; these veins open into their respective ducts of Cuvier. In very young embryos a subclavian vein carries the blood from each anterior limb to the posterior cardinal vein. Gradually, however, the subclavian veins shift position and become tributaries of the anterior cardinal veins. As in the system of the posterior cardinal veins, the anterior cardinal veins also aim at channeling the blood to the right side of the heart. A new vessel forms across the two cardinal veins, which shunts the blood from the left side to the right. The segment of the left cardinal from the shunt to the heart drops out. Thus the anterior cardinal veins become the internal jugular veins; more superficial tributaries, the external jugular veins, are also formed. Internal and external jugulars from each side join the innominate vein together with the subclavian veins. The two innominate veins are usually joined into a single anterior vena cava, which opens into the right atrium just cephalic to the entrance of the posterior vena cava (see Figure 15).

The Hepatic Portal Vein

The single hepatic portal vein, which brings the blood from the intestine to the liver, arises from the two vitelline veins. In young embryos these convey blood from the yolk sac to the sinus venosus. In older embryos, when the yolk sac and its blood vessels atrophy, remnants of the vitelline veins bring blood from the intestine to the liver. Shunts form across the two trunks of the vitelline veins. The right or the left segment between the successive shunts drops out leaving a single, tortuous venous trunk, which is the adult hepatic portal vein.

COMPARATIVE ANATOMY OF THE VENOUS SYSTEM

Cyclostomes

Paired jugular, or the anterior cardinal veins anterior to the heart, open into a single trunk of the fused common cardinal veins; this trunk has shifted to the right side of the sinus venosus. The two posterior cardinal veins are also fused before they reach the single common cardinal. The posterior cardinal veins are located slightly lateral to the dorsal aorta; they skirt around the cloaca, and posteriorly they are fused in a single caudal vein. Lateral segmental veins from the kidney enter the posterior cardinal vein, and there is no renal portal system.

The hepatic portal vein develops from the vitelline veins. An odd contractile **portal heart** is found in the portal vein. A single hepatic vein returns the hepatic blood to the sinus venosus.

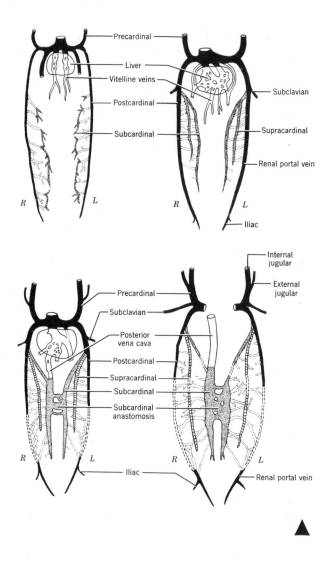

Figure 15. Progressive steps in the ontogenetic development of the venous system in a mammalian embryo. The posterior and anterior cardinal veins are indicated as solid lines, the subcardinals stippled, and supracardinals are cross-hatched. R represents the right side, L the left side.

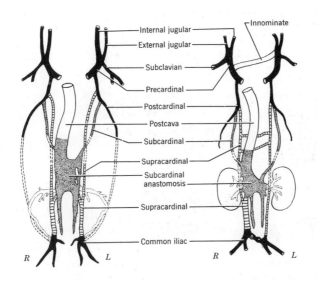

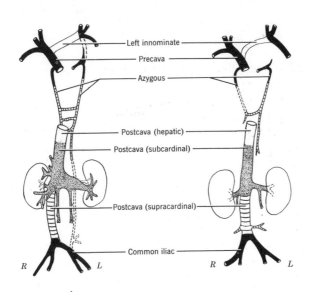

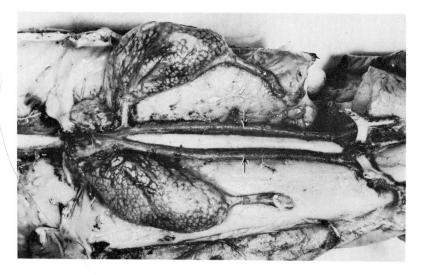

Figure 16. Photograph of the kidneys and *doubled* postcava in a whale embryo. (Courtesy of Prof. R. J. Harrison, London Hospital Medical College.)

Fishes

The venous system shows several evolutionary trends within this class. The anterior cardinal veins from the dorsal side of the head give rise to the jugular veins, and the venous sinuses in the ventral side of the head form the inferior jugular veins. The jugular veins open into the ducts of Cuvier. The posterior cardinal veins draining the blood from the posterior part of the body also open into the ducts of Cuvier. The subclavian vein of young fish opens into the posterior cardinal, but that of adults opens into the duct of Cuvier with the lateral abdominal vein from the body wall (Figure 17a); the iliac vein from the posterior fin empties into the lateral abdominal vein. The posterior cardinal veins are joined by the single caudal vein; they rise laterally along the kidney, but the proximal segment of the veins atrophies, and the blood coming up the posterior cardinals has to pass through the kidneys and is drained by a new pair of median subcardinal veins. Since the incoming venous blood goes through a venous capillary system and is drained by an efferent venous channel, this is a renal portal system, and the posterior cardinal veins, or the afferent venous vessels, are the renal portal veins. Teleosts have no lateral abdominal veins; lungfishes have a single median anterior abdominal vein, continuous posteriorly with the pelvic veins

220

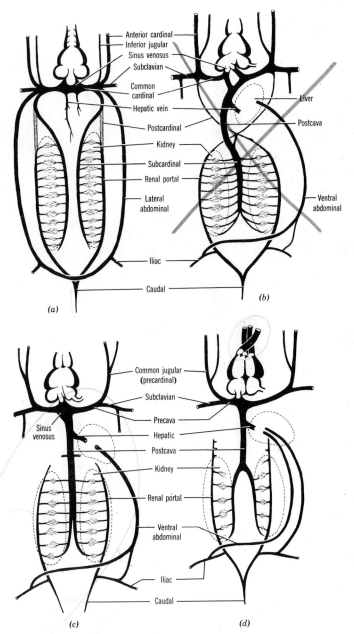

Figure 17. Comparison of the posterior system of cardinal veins and the gradual appearance of the precava and postcava: (a) fish; (b) urodele; (c) salientians; (d) reptile.

221

from the iliacs. The iliac veins of both teleosts and lungfishes have a shunt that connects them with the renal portal veins. In lungfishes two subcardinal veins are fused from about the middle of the kidney to the caudal vein. Above this point the subcardinals remain separated. The right subcardinal vein of lungfishes is much larger than the left one and may now be called the postcaval vein.

Amphibians

The basic venous pattern of the amphibians is similar to that of lungfishes. The jugular veins, with the subclavian from each side, form two precaval veins that open separately into the sinus venosus. The renal portal veins arise from the caudal vein, and the iliac veins, from the pelvic limb. Pelvic veins from the iliacs also join the anterior abdominal vein; this opens into the hepatic portal vein instead of emptying into the sinus venosus. The single postcaval vein extends from the posterior edge of the kidneys to the sinus venosus and has arisen from the right subcardinal vein. In urodeles a thin anterior remnant of the posterior cardinal veins extends from the renal portal vein to the sinus venosus, but in salientians these segments have completely disappeared (Figure 17*b,c*).

Reptiles

Two precaval veins and one postcava enter the right sinus venosus. The precavals have arisen directly from the ducts of Cuvier, and each receives the jugular, subclavian, and the vertebral veins. Snakes, having no limbs, have no subclavians. The renal portal veins of reptiles lie very near the renal veins from the kidneys to the postcava (Figure 17*d*). This is almost the last vestige of the renal portal system. When the renal portal veins and the renal veins become confluent the renal portal system disappears. The postcava has developed largely from the intersubcardinal anastomosis and anteriorly from the vitelline veins. Reptiles have lateral abdominal veins which come from the iliac veins and empty into the hepatic portal vein.

Birds

The sinus venosus is completely incorporated into the wall of the right atrium, and the two precavae and the postcava open into the right

222

atrium. Each precava receives the jugular and the subclavian veins. Since the single postcava receives blood directly from the posterior cardinals, it is no longer correct to speak of these veins as the renal portals. Birds have a single median **caudal mesenteric vein** that connects the short caudal vein with the hepatic portal vein (Figure 18*a*). This vein has been considered homologous with the anterior abdominal vein of amphibians.

Mammals

The major events in the development of the venous system are described in the beginning of this section (Figure 18*b*).

THE LYMPHATIC SYSTEM

There is a continuous transudation of plasma from the capillaries into the tissues. Much of this fluid is reabsorbed into the blood vascular sys-

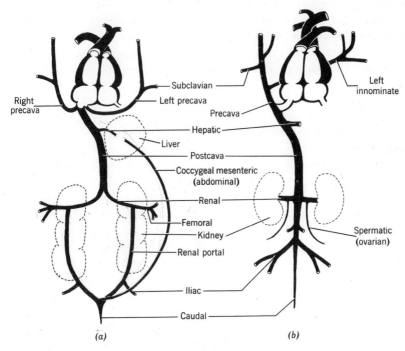

Figure 18. The principal venous systems in (a) bird and (b) mammal.

tem, but the remaining fraction is taken up into the myriads of inter-lacing lymph capillaries in the tissues. When tissues are injured or infected they become swollen as a result of the blocking of the lymph channels which drain them. Lymph capillaries occur with blood capillaries; they have a larger lumen, but otherwise they resemble blood capillaries. They are very delicate, and they need a soft and fatty loose connective tissue bed to support them. Lymph vessels always accompany veins but are more numerous than veins. The path of most lymph channels is interrupted by lymph nodes, which strain debris from the lymph. All along their course valves prevent the backflow of the slowly moving lymph in lymph vessels. Lymph flows toward the heart in the same direction as venous blood. The flow is probably made possible by the rhythmic contraction of the arteries and the pressure caused by the contraction of skeletal muscle. In mammals the negative pressure in the thorax and the positive pressure in the abdomen during inspiration also help to massage the lymph toward the heart. In the lower vertebrates some of the large lymph vessels acquire muscular walls that contract rhythmically; these are called lymph hearts, which are found in places where lymph channels enter veins. The larger lymph vessels have the same general structure as the veins, but their walls are very thin. The most conspicuous elements of the lymphatic system are the central lacteals in the villi of the intestine (Figure 19). Lacteals are bulbous blind sacs which occupy the axial part of each villus with a lumen broader than capillaries. The leaflike villi in the duodenum contain several lacteals that are connected at the base. They are composed almost entirely of endothelial cells, with a few smooth muscle fibers arranged longitudinally. The lacteals are constricted at the base and are attached to a complex network of lymph capillaries in the mucosa. These networks go across the muscularis mucosae and flow into similar capillaries in the submucosa. All of the numerous lymph capillaries converge toward larger channels in the mesenteries. These drain into lymph nodes and finally converge again into larger channels that empty into the thoracic duct. This extensive system of lymph channels conveys fats to the venous system. After a fatty meal the lymphatic channels are swollen with chyle, an emulsified fat which is white and makes the lymph channels visible. A system of lymph lacteals underneath the epidermis of the skin drains into lymph capillaries like the lymphatic system in the intestine.

Fishes

The peripheral lymph plexuses converge toward the larger channels that accompany the venous trunks. Lymph vessels empty into the ve-

224

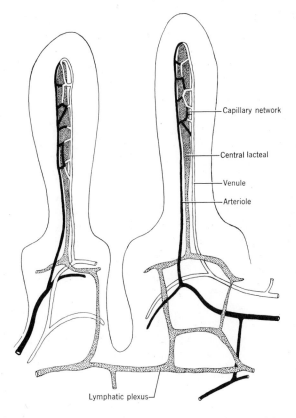

Capillary network

Central lacteal

Venule

Arteriole

Lymphatic plexus

Figure 19.   Central lacteals and surrounding blood vessels in the villi of the intestine.

nous system in the anterior, middle, and posterior parts.   Fishes have no lymph nodes.

Amphibia

In coecelians and urodeles lymph vessels under the skin carry lymph to the posterior cardinal venous system.   There is a pair of lymph hearts for each segment of the body.   Lymph channels along the dorsal aorta converge toward the subclavian veins and empty there.   Salientians have large lymph sinuses under the skin, and a lymph heart is located at each junction of the limbs and the body.   The posterior pair at the base of the iliac veins, near the end of the urostyle, can be seen pulsating under the skin of a live animal.   Amphibians have no lymph nodes.

225

Reptiles

A rich lymphatic system returns lymph into the precaval and iliac veins. Only one posterior pair of lymph hearts is present near the entrance of the posterior lymph channels into the iliac veins. There are no lymph nodes.

Birds

All lymph channels converge toward two **thoracic ducts.** They collect the lymph from the entire body and each empties into one of the pre-caval veins. Birds have no lymph hearts, and they have vestigial lymph nodes.

Mammals

Two large lymph channels, the **thoracic duct** and the **right lymphatic duct,** return the lymph to the left and right subclavian veins, respectively, near the junction with the jugular veins (Figure 20). The main collecting trunk, the thoracic duct, extends from the lumbar region to the subclavian vein. It is located left of the aorta in a bed of loose connective tissue and fat. It receives all of the lymphatic channels below the diaphragm and from the left half of the body above the diaphragm. At its origin in the lumbar and lower thoracic regions the thoracic duct is dilated into a collecting pool called the **cisterna chyli** (Figure 20). The jugular, subclavian, and other lymph trunks from the right side may open separately or in various combinations into the subclavian vein. When the jugular and the subclavian trunks unite the common trunk they form is the right lymphatic duct. Mammals have highly developed lymph nodes.

THE HEMOPOIETIC ORGANS

The formation of blood is called **hemopoiesis.** During early embryonic life the first blood is formed in the wall of the yolk sac. Later, however, intraembryonic blood formation replaces the yolk sac. Several organs have hemopoietic property in the embryo. When the wall of the yolk sac is no longer active the mesonephric kidney, the liver, the spleen, and finally the bone marrow take on the function of making blood corpuscles. In adult mammals the bone marrow assumes the function of forming erythrocytes and granular leucocytes. In many of the lower

226

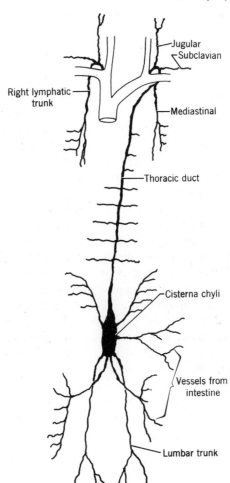

Figure 20.
Schematic diagram of the
lymphatic system of man.

vertebrates and in some mammals the liver and the spleen normally carry on hemopoietic activity. The agranular leucocytes are formed in the lymph nodes, the spleen, and the thymus.

SUMMARY

1. Veins carry blood toward the heart, and arteries carry it away. The basic structure of veins and arteries is the same, but arteries have thicker walls than veins, and only veins have valves which prevent the backflow of blood. Capillaries, with a diameter approximately that of red blood corpuscles, form an intricate network between the arteries and veins.

2. The circulatory system arises from the splanchnic mesoderm. The first blood and blood vessels, the vitelline vessels, are formed in the wall of the yolk sac. One vitelline venous trunk from each side of the embryo drains the wall of the yolk sac and empties into the ventral extension of the aorta. These two vessels lie in the wall of the pericardial cavity; they later fuse on the midline and form the heart tube. Three pairs of venous trunks open into the posterior part of the simple heart tube: the vitelline veins from the yolk sac, the umbilical veins from the extraembryonic membranes, and the common cardinal veins from the embryo itself. The sinus venosus is the common receptacle of venous blood. The heart of fishes conveys only venous blood to the gill filaments and, therefore, has a single circulation. Venous blood from the sinus venosus progresses anteriorly to the atrium, the ventricle, and finally the conus arteriosus. The sinus venosus shifts toward the right side of the atrium in the heart of lungfishes. In amphibians the atrium is divided into two chambers. The right atrium receives the systemic venous blood, and the left atrium, the arterial blood from the skin, lungs, and gills. Even though the ventricle of amphibians is single-chambered, the dynamics of the heart of salientians are such that little mixture of venous and arterial blood takes place. From the single ventricle blood is pumped into the conus arteriosus, which is divided by the spiral valve, so that venous and arterial blood are forced into separate channels.

3. In the heart of amniotes atria and ventricles are separated and the conus is divided into separate arterial trunks that spring directly from the ventricles. The heart of reptiles has four chambers, and three arterial trunks emerge from the ventricles. In Crocodilia an interventricular septum completely separates the two ventricles, but in the heart of all other reptiles a gap in the anterior part of the septum allows some mixture of blood from the two ventricles. In the reptilian heart the sinus venosus is almost completely incorporated in the right atrium.

4. The heart of birds and mammals has no sinus venosus, and the systemic veins open directly into the right atrium. The two atria and ventricles are separate chambers. The right ventricle opens into the pulmonary trunk, and the left ventricle, into the aorta. Thus the right side of the heart contains venous blood, the left side, arterial blood. The wall of the left ventricle is much thicker than that of the right.

5. The primitive arterial system consists of two dorsal aortae, continuous with two ventral aortae by way of aortic arches. Aortic arches are arterial shunts which connect the ventral and dorsal aortae in the region of the pharynx, one aortic arch for each pharyngeal arch. Posterior to the pharynx the two dorsal aortae become fused. The fate of the aortic arches in the region of the pharynx is different in each class of vertebrates. Six aortic arches appear during development in nearly all vertebrates. The first two disappear even in fishes. In urodeles arches III, V, and VI remain intact, arch V is very thin, and arches I and II disappear during development. In all other tetrapods arches I, II, and V disappear. In Salientia, reptiles, birds, and mammals, the segment of the root of the aorta between arch III and arch IV disappears, arch III forms the common carotid artery, and arch IV remains as the arch of the aorta. In Salientia and reptiles the right and left limbs of arch IV persist, and there are two arches of the aorta. In birds the left arch IV forms the left subclavian and the right arch IV, the arch of the dorsal aorta. In mammals the opposite takes place. Arch VI gives rise on each side to the pulmonary arteries.

6. Paired vessels branch off from the dorsal aorta to the organs and tissues; several large unpaired ones vascularize the organs of the digestive system. The paired vessels have arisen from the original segmental vessels; the unpaired ones have either developed from a fusion of segmental vessels or from the enlargement of one of them. The pattern of the branches of the aorta is remarkably similar in most vertebrates.

7. The most primitive venous system is composed of anterior and posterior cardinal veins on each side of the body; these open together into the sinus venosus by the common cardinal vein. When the subcardinals, a new system of veins, arise the anterior part of the posterior cardinal becomes detached from the posterior part. Blood from the posterior cardinal veins has to pass through the kidneys and is then drained by the subcardinal veins which return it to the sinus venosus. Since the postcardinals are afferent venous trunks and the subcardinals, efferent trunks, they form a portal system, and the postcardinals are the renal portal veins. This is the principal posterior systemic venous return of fishes. In a few fishes and in all tetrapods the systemic venous return is by a single median posterior vena cava. This vein is formed from the posterior system of cardinal veins and from the hepatic veins. A single median hepatic portal vein brings the blood from the intestine to the liver. This vein has arisen from the two vitelline veins, and its phylogenetic history is similar in all vertebrates. The anterior system of cardinal veins persists in all vertebrates as the internal jugular veins and the anterior venae cavae; these veins receive all the venous return of the anterior parts of the body.

8. In the progression of phylogenetic ascension the most noteworthy characteristic of the systemic venous system is its original bilateral symmetry. Paired structures, however, fuse into single vessels in some cases, and in other cases one of the pairs drops out. Shunts also form across pairs of vessels, and some of the segments disappear, leaving only one vessel. Each of these events rechannels blood toward the right side of the heart. The developmental history of the circulatory system can be followed clearly in phylogeny and in ontogeny.

9. Extravascular fluids are collected by very intricate systems of lymph capillaries. These converge toward large vessels, which in turn drain lymph into the venous system. Pulsating lymph hearts in lower vertebrates help in propelling lymph toward the heart. Lymph nodes, interposed along the path of lymph vessels, strain debris from lymph and produce lymphocytes; these are essentially peculiar to mammals.

10. Erythrocytes and granular leucocytes are formed in the hemopoietic organs. The first hemopoietic organ of the embryo is the yolk sac. The liver, spleen, and bone marrow later take over these functions. In adult mammals bone marrow is the principal blood-forming organ, but in many species the liver and spleen continue to perform this function.

SUGGESTED READING

Foxon, G. E. H., 1952, "The Mode of Action of the Heart in the Frog," from *New Biology*, **12**, pp. 113–127. Penquin Books Ltd., Harmondsworth, Middlesex, The Campfield Press, St Albans.

Franklin, K. J., 1937, *A Monograph on Veins*. C. C. Thomas, Springfield, Ill.

Harrison, R. J., 1955, "Adaptations in Diving Mammals." *Science News,* No. 35, pp. 74–90. Penquin Books Ltd., The Campfield Press, St Albans.

O'Donoghue, C. H., and E. Abbott, 1928, "The Blood Vascular System of the Spiny Dogfish, *Squalus acanthias* and *Squalus sucklii.*" *Trans. Roy. Soc. Edinburgh,* **55**, Part III.

Patten, B. M., 1925, *The Early Embryology of the Chick*. The Blakiston Company, Philadelphia and London.

Witschi, E., 1956, *Development of Vertebrates*. W. B. Saunders Company, Philadelphia and London.

Figure 1. Western toad singing, with its gular pouch inflated. (Courtesy of Dr. A. A. Allen, Cornell University.)

Figure 2. Two types of internal gills of fish, the one on the right showing its blood vascular system.

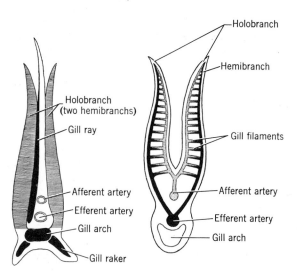

9

THE RESPIRATORY SYSTEM

INTRODUCTION

Respiration is the release of energy by cells through the oxidation of carbon-containing molecules which form carbon dioxide. Cells can exist only when they have an adequate supply of oxygen and can eliminate carbon dioxide. The problem of supplying the organism with oxygen and eliminating carbon dioxide has been resolved in many different ways by different animals, but in spite of great evolutionary diversity in the respiratory systems of living things the basic physiological principle in each system is the same. Broadly speaking, respiration can be **external**, when concerned with gaseous exchange between blood and the external environment, and **internal**, when it takes place between the blood in the capillaries and the tissues. This chapter considers only some of the anatomical mechanisms devised by vertebrates for external respiration. All of the details of structure are tailored to bring about a speedy and efficient gaseous exchange between the blood and the environment. The respiratory organs of aquatic and terrestrial vertebrates have great structural differences, but the working principles are

233

identical; in one the oxygen is obtained from the water, in the other from the air.

Vertebrates have two types of respiratory organs, **gills** and **lungs**. These are the airing devices of the blood and adjuncts of the circulatory system. The gills of fishes are probably more ancient organs than the lungs of tetrapods, and in changing from an aquatic to a terrestrial type of life the gills gave way to lungs; this transition came about very gradually, and fishes acquired lunglike organs even before they abandoned the water. The living Choanichthyes and *Polypterus* have "lungs" as well-developed as those of amphibians. Many vertebrates have unique respiratory mechanisms. The skin of most Amphibia is an important respiratory organ, and the lungless salamander has no other. The African hairy frog has hairlike projections in the skin of the posterior limbs which have a respiratory function. Some fish swallow air, and respiration takes place through the stomach or the intestine. A fish from the Indian regions can emerge from water for hours, as long as it keeps its extremely vascular respiratory tail submerged. Some turtles have a cloacal diverticulum which also serves as an accessory respiratory organ.

Gills are featherlike structures composed mostly of arterial capillary loops covered with a very thin layer of epithelium; they are designed to make up as large a surface area as possible for the exchange of gases. Venous blood from the heart is brought to the gill by an afferent artery; the blood runs through arterial capillaries, where it is oxygenated, and is drained by the efferent artery. Gills may be external, as in larval fish and amphibians, or internal, as in adult fishes. Internal gills consist of **gill filaments** that spring from both sides of an interbranchial septum like the barbs from the vane of a feather. All of the filaments on one side of a septum make up a **hemibranch;** the filaments on the two sides make up the **holobranch** or complete gill. The skeletal support of the gills consists of **gill bars** and **gill rays** (Figure 2).

External gills are found only in the larvae of some bony fishes and amphibians and are lost at metamorphosis. Most amphibians lose their gills, but some completely aquatic salamanders, the **perennibranchiates,** retain large external gills even as adults. In a sense these animals remain larval throughout their life. The gills of young tadpoles are large when the water they live in is poor in oxygen and rudimentary when the water is saturated with the gas. This is an excellent demonstration of structural adaptation to supply and demand.

Bony fishes have a swim bladder, on the dorsal side, which is a sac connected by a duct with the anterior part of the gut (Figure 3). The

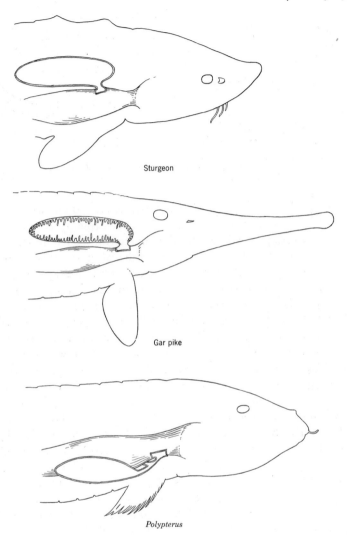

Sturgeon

Gar pike

Polypterus

Figure 3. Types of swim bladders with a duct connected with the gut.

Ganoidea have a swim bladder which communicates with the digestive tube through a patent duct, but the ducts of most Teleostei are blocked (Figure 4). The Ganoidea fill their swim bladders by gulping air. The swim bladder of fishes with a blocked duct has an anterior chamber with a rich capillary plexus in its wall, called **red gland, red body,** or

235

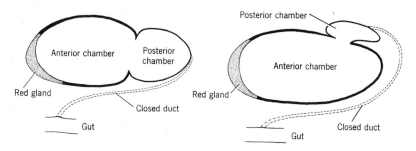

Figure 4. Two types of swim bladder without a duct.

rete mirabile; this plexus secretes oxygen and various amounts of nitrogen and carbon dioxide (Figure 4). Another capillary network in the posterior part of the chamber absorbs these gases, which are then eliminated through the gills. The swim bladder of most teleosts functions as a hydrostatic organ, but that of ganoids and lungfishes is a respiratory organ. *Polypterus,* one of the most primitive ganoids, has a swim bladder divided into two ventral lateral lobes extending posteriorly on either side of the esophagus (see Figure 3). The common duct of these sacs opens into the esophagus. The wall of the swim bladder, or bladders, of lungfishes is thrown into folds that greatly increase its surface; these organs are spongy and are actually better developed respiratory organs than the lungs of many amphibians. It would be convenient to conclude that lungs of land vertebrates have evolved from the apparently more primitive swim bladder. However, since the more primitive fishes have the best developed lunglike swim bladder, it is likely that lungs are the more ancient organs, the swim bladder having arisen from the lungs. In any case, the swim bladder of the most advanced teleosts is a hydrostatic organ, and if it were located on the ventral side of the body the fish would be top-heavy and would have to swim belly up. When the air is withdrawn with a hypodermic needle from the swim bladder of the surface-feeding sea minnow *Fundulus* the fish cannot remain at the surface and sinks to the bottom; later, when the gases are restored in the swim bladder, the fish is able to rise to the surface again.

Vertebrates with lungs can breathe air through the nostrils, or nares, which communicate with the roof of the mouth. The nares of most fishes have no connection with the pharynx; in elasmobranchs external grooves extend from the corners of the mouth to the separate nasal sacs. In the Choanichthyes an open air passageway exists between the nares and the pharynx. The inner openings of these passages are the

choanae or internal nares. The nasal passage of amphibians is short
and direct, like that of air-breathing fishes, with the choanae found just
inside the tip of the maxilla. The opening of the external nares of
Amphibia can be regulated by muscular action. With the formation
of a false palate in reptiles the air passage is elongated, and the choanae
are located far back in the pharynx. The nasal passages of most birds
are short because the external nares are placed at the base of the mandible and the palate has a median cleft. Kiwis, with external nares at
the tip of the long beak, have much longer air ducts. The outer part of
the nasal canal of birds has two or three turbinated bones, the most
posterior of which is covered with olfactory epithelium and contains the
receptor cells of smell. The nasal passages of mammals are large and
long. Just inside the external nares the **vestibular region** is lined with
an epithelium like that of skin. The vestibule opens into a maze of
turbinated bones, which comprise the respiratory region in front, and
an olfactory region behind (Figure 5). The turbinated bones of the
respiratory region are covered with a ciliated epithelium that contains
numerous mucus-secreting cells; those of the olfactory region contain
olfactory sensory cells. The choanae open into the pharynx at the back
of the oral cavity, behind the soft palate. The long, tortuous nasal passages provide means to warm the air before it reaches the pharynx, to
strain out dust particles, and to pick up olfactory sensations.

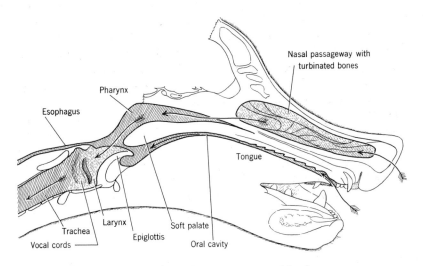

Figure 5. The respiratory passageway of the dog.

The posterior part of the pharynx of tetrapods has two openings: an anterior **glottis** and a posterior **esophageal orifice**. An elevation, the **epiglottis**, is erected in front of the glottis (Figure 5). During the act of swallowing the larynx is automatically raised and the epiglottis, with the root of the tongue, prevents food particles and fluid from entering the glottis.

The glottis opens into an enlarged recess called the larynx or voice box; this is best developed in mammals. It is composed of a series of cartilages closely associated with the hyoid apparatus; muscular bands stretched on the lateral walls of the larynx make up the **vocal cords** (see Figure 9). Air expelled from the respiratory passageways makes the vocal cords vibrate and produce sound.

The larynx opens into the tubular trachea whose skeleton of cartilaginous rings keeps it from collapsing. In most mammals the rings are incomplete on the dorsal side where the trachea is in contact with the esophagus (see Figure 9). The trachea of aquatic mammals that dive to great depths has broad and stout cartilage rings often arranged in spirals. The length of the trachea is variable and is usually, but not always, related to the length of the neck. At its distal end the trachea forks into right and left **bronchi** which enter the **lungs**, the principal respiratory organs of tetrapods (see Figure 10). Lungs consist of conducting passageways for the air and air spaces, the alveoli, through which the exchange of gases takes place. The lungs of some amphibians are simple sacs with a vascular wall, but those of higher vertebrates become increasingly complex.

DEVELOPMENT

The development of the respiratory system is intimately associated with that of the pharynx and the pharyngeal arches and pouches; these are among the most characteristic features of all vertebrate development. The development and fate of the pharynx has already been described in the chapter on the digestive system. The pharynx is the expanded anterior part of the digestive tube, or foregut; it is lined completely with entoderm, and all the structures that arise from it are derived from the entoderm. A series of sacculations, or pharyngeal pouches, evaginate from each side of the pharynx. The fate of these pouches in amphibians and amniotes has already been described and has nothing to do directly with the respiratory system.

Before sketching the development of the gills of fishes from the pha-

238

ryngeal pouches of the embryo, it must be remembered that the mass of the gill consists of blood vessels formed from the aortic arches and a skeletal framework, both of which are formed from the mesoderm. The inner covering of the gill slits is the entoderm which lined the original gill pouches, and the outer covering is the ectoderm continuous with that of the skin. The lining of the gills of Chondrichthyes and Osteichthyes is probably derived from the ectoderm on the outside of the gill slits. The passage of the gill slits is mostly lined with entoderm and some ectoderm, the two being indistinguishable.

In early embryos a single diverticulum grows from the middle of the floor of the pharynx just posterior to the last pair of pharyngeal pouches; this entodermal diverticulum gives rise to the swim bladder of fishes and the trachea and lungs of tetrapods. In most fishes the swim bladder becomes displaced dorsally, but in *Polypterus* it remains ventral and becomes divided, one lobe resting on each side of the esophagus (see Figure 3). The pharyngeal diverticulum of tetrapods is called the **lung bud**; it grows and elongates posteriorly and splits into two at its dorsal end, each part representing a **primary bronchus**. Each primary bronchus divides many times until the entire bronchial tree and the respiratory elements of the lungs are formed. The epithelial lining of the larynx, trachea, bronchial trees, and alveoli of the lungs is derived from entoderm. The bulk of the lung tissue is composed of blood vessels and connective tissue derived from the mesoderm.

THE COMPARATIVE ANATOMY OF THE RESPIRATORY SYSTEM

Cyclostomes

In the ammocoetes eight pairs of gill clefts develop on the sides of the pharynx, but the first pair is lost. During metamorphosis the pharynx becomes separated from the esophagus. The pharynx of adult lampreys is a blind sac underneath the esophagus; the two communicate anteriorly in a short gullet at the bottom of the oral sucker. From each side of the pharynx seven gill slits lead into seven rounded gill pouches. The first pouch contains a hemibranch; the remaining six, holobranchs. Each pouch opens to the outside through a separate external gill slit. The current of water to the gills can come either through the oral funnel or directly through the external gill slits. Direct intake of water through the outer gill slits is an admirable adaptation in animals which attach themselves firmly to their victims, engaging the entire oral funnel.

239

The pharynx of the hagfishes communicates directly with the esophagus; their gill pouches, however, do not open directly to the outside. From each pouch a tube extends posteriorly; all the tubes come together and open to the outside as a single canal.

Fishes

The pharynx is a relatively long and broad passage that constricts posteriorly into the opening of the short esophagus. The pharynx opens laterally to the outside by gill slits, through which water drawn into the mouth is expelled. The gaping of fishes is concerned with respiration: with the mouth opened and the gill slits closed the pharynx expands and the water is drawn in; when the mouth is closed the gill slits are opened and the pharynx is constricted to expel the water that ventilates the gills.

The gill passages of the different classes of fishes are different in details but not in basic structure. Both the elasmobranchs and the bony fishes have five gill slits, but there are some aberrant patterns. The lungfishes have the fewest gills. In many fishes the anterior hemibranch of the first gill is lost. The first gill slit of elasmobranchs is reduced in size and is called the **spiracle**. This is small or absent in fast-swimming forms but large in the bottom-dwelling skates and rays. The gill within the spiracular opening is smaller than the others and is peculiar in that its afferent artery, instead of coming from an aortic arch, comes from the gill behind it; for this reason the spiracular gill is called **pseudobranch**.

The Osteichthyes characteristically have a swim bladder. Chondrichthyes have none, but during development a small rudiment of it makes a transitory appearance. Bottom-dwelling forms, such as flounders, have no swim bladder, having lost it through adaptation. The swim bladder of Choanichthyes and most Ganoidea is **physostomous;** a **pneumatic duct** communicates with the gut (see Figure 3). The bladder of the more primitive teleosts is also physostomous, but that of higher ones is **physoclistous,** with the duct closed (see Figure 4). The lining of the swim bladder of lungfishes and some ganoids is thrown into folds and resembles that of the lungs of tetrapods (Figure 6). Simple or complex, one- or two-chambered, the swim bladder has several functions. In some cases it is an accessory respiratory organ. Lungfishes can live for months encased in dried clay during the periods of estivation, using only their lungs to breath. The swim bladder is a hydrostatic mechanism; by controlling its gas content the fish automatically changes its own specific gravity and can remain with comfort at any level of the

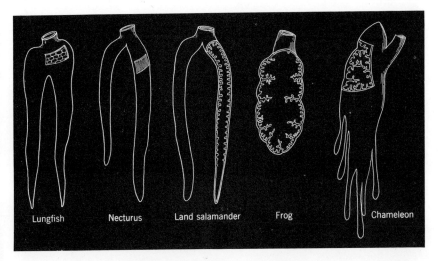

Figure 6. Comparison of vertebrate lungs.

water. The physostomous bladder of some fishes produces character-istic sounds when bubbles of gas escape through the duct. In some teleosts the swim bladder has a narrow anterior extension which ends close to the hearing mechanism and is probably associated with the re-ception of sound vibrations.

In attempting to derive the phylogenetic history of the lungs of tetra-pods, it has been thought that either the swim bladder is an ancestral type of lung or that it is a modified lung. Evidence, however, favors the view that lungs are more ancient than the swim bladder. The shift in position of the swim bladder from the ventral to the dorsal side of the fish is an adaptation of the bladder which serves as a hydrostatic mechanism.

Amphibians

The pharynx of amphibians is very broad and except in a few uro-deles has no lateral gill slits in the adult. In its most primitive form, in the urodeles, the glottis is a narrow slit bounded by a pair of cartilages. More advanced amphibians have a larynx composed of a pair of **arytenoid cartilages** around the glottis and one **cricoid cartilage** below them; these cartilages form the framework of the simple larynx. Frogs and toads even have vestigial vocal cords. Accessory vocal pouches, found in male salientians, when inflated give vocal sounds great resonance (Figures 1, 7).

241

Figure 7. Male leopard frog croaking, with its lateral air pouches inflated. (Courtesy of Dr. A. A. Allen, Cornell University.)

Salientians have almost no trachea, and the glottis opens directly into the lungs. The trachea is longer in the larger urodeles and is supported by incomplete cartilage rings. It divides into bronchi at its posterior end, and each bronchus opens into a saclike lung.

The lungs of urodeles have smooth walls, but those of salientians have a wall that is thrown into partitions (see Figure 6). The lungs of toads are spongy and contain partitions and respiratory chambers called alveoli. The more completely terrestrial the amphibians, the greater the respiratory surface of their lungs. This makes up for the deficit of respiration through the skin in the terrestrial salientians, such as toads. Some adult salamanders have neither gills nor lungs, and their respiration must take place mostly through the moist skin.

The lungs of amphibians lie in the common pleuroperitoneal cavity in contact with the other viscera. Breathing in and out of air is accomplished mostly by lowering and raising the floor of the mouth, causing a pumping action synchronized with the opening and closing of the external nares. These animals, however, must swallow air. Urodeles with poorly developed lungs gulp air and force it into the lungs by opening the glottis, closing the nares, and raising the floor of the mouth.

242

Reptiles

A small fold of tissue in front of the glottis may be a vestigial epiglottis. The glottis is surrounded by a pair of arytenoid cartilages. The primitive larynx consists of a cricoid cartilage, and the two arytenoid cartilages supported by the hyoid apparatus. Some lizards and alligators, the only reptiles that produce vocal sounds, have small vocal cords. All other reptiles are mute.

The trachea, short in lizards but long in alligators and turtles, is supported by incomplete cartilage rings. It branches into two bronchi, except in those snakes which have only one lung.

The lungs of reptiles show a considerable advance over those of amphibians, but they are still primitive. The lung or lungs of snakes have respiratory epithelium only at the base; the rest is a simple sac. The lungs of lizards and turtles are progressively spongier, and those of alligators resemble those of mammals. Long narrow pouches in the lungs of chameleons project from the posterior surface and become insinuated among the viscera (see Figure 6). These odd structures may be the forerunners of the air sacs of birds described next.

Reptilian lungs are located anteriorly in the pleuroperitoneal cavity. In some a fold of body wall partially separates the cavity into an anterior chamber which contains the lungs and a posterior one which houses the viscera. Movements of the floor of the throat cause a bellows action and bring about breathing. Raising and lowering the ribs by muscle action accomplishes the same thing. In turtles breathing is accomplished by a contraction and relaxation of peculiar muscle bands along the viscera.

Birds

The wide, but shallow, pharynx opens into a slitlike glottis which is supported by the two arytenoid cartilages. The small shallow larynx is supported by two small cricoid cartilages, and there are no vocal cords; the larynx of birds is not a sound-producing mechanism. Birds have long necks and the trachea is necessarily long; in many cases it is considerably longer than the neck and forms loops under the skin or between the muscles. In swans and some cranes a long loop of trachea is embedded in the sternum, and in the penguins the trachea is doubled. The trachea branches into bronchi, and both structures are supported by complete cartilaginous or bony rings. The place where the trachea forks into bronchi is modified into a voice-producing **syrinx,** found only

243

in birds. The syrinx assumes many different shapes and is particularly noteworthy in ducks and geese. The sound-producing mechanisms are vibratile membranes. Some of these are at the sides of the bronchi, but the principal one, the semilunar membrane, is stretched across a median skeletal element, called pessulus, at the junction of the bronchi. The semilunar membrane vibrates like a reed in a wood-wind musical instrument. A variable number of syringeal muscles is attached to the outside of the syrinx, making variations in sound possible.

The bronchi enter the small compact lungs and extend to the distal end, gradually losing the supporting bronchial rings. The intrapulmonary part of the bronchus, called mesobronchus, gives off many lateral secondary bronchi that break up into parabronchi. These loop around the lung and converge toward other secondary bronchi. The walls of the parabronchi are like sieves, and each opening leads into an air capillary, large numbers of which make up the respiratory part of the lungs. The air-conducting system of the avian lungs is a complete intercommunicating system. The lungs of birds are not only peculiar but also very efficient. The two mesobronchi and some secondary bronchi continue posteriorly past the boundary of the lung, become insinuated among the viscera, penetrate the bones, and expand at characteristic places of the bird's body to form air sacs (Figure 8). The air in the air sacs has not gone through the respiratory part of the lungs and is not vitiated. These spaces are reservoirs of air which, through muscle action and movements and compression of the viscera, is forced back into the lungs. The most important function of the air sacs is that of decreasing the specific gravity of the body and is analogous with that of the swim bladder of fishes. The best developed air sacs are found in the best flying birds; Ratitae have poorly developed ones.

The small and compact lungs adhere firmly to the ribs, and some are actually embedded in them. The lungs are enclosed in the pleural cavities, separated from the rest of the coelom by a thin membrane called the oblique septum. Muscles attached to this membrane and to the ribs cause an expansion and contraction of the lungs, or inspiration and expiration. During flight compression and relaxation of the air sacs brings about a circulation of air.

Mammals

Only mammals have a lidlike epiglottis guarding the glottis, and only mammals have a well-developed larynx. In spite of the variety of sounds that it can produce, the larynx is an unpretentious mechanical

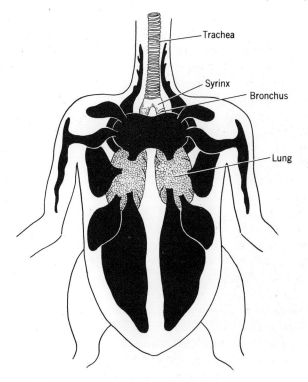

Figure 8. The air sacs of a bird.

device. Two arytenoid cartilages on the posterior surface, and the cricoid cartilage caudal to them, are covered over on the ventral side by a shieldlike **thyroid cartilage** (Figure 9). The larynx articulates with the hyoid apparatus. Folds of tissue extending between the thyroid cartilage and the arytenoid cartilages form the true vocal cords. Secondary folds, or false vocal cords, are found in the space in front of the true vocal cords. Intrinsic and extrinsic laryngeal muscles change the shape and size of the larynx and stretch or slacken the vocal cords to vary the pitch and resonance of vocal sounds.

Depending on the length of the neck, the trachea is short or long. It is supported by cartilage rings that are incomplete on the dorsal part resting against the esophagus (Figure 9). In diving mammals the rings are complete or they are arranged in spirals. The trachea branches into two main bronchi whose walls also contain cartilage rings (Figure 10). Pigs have one bronchus going to the left lung and two to the

245

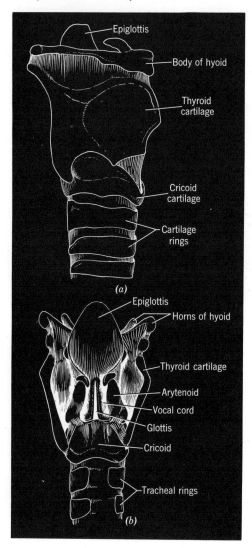

Figure 9. The human larynx: (a) lateral view; (b) dorsal view.

right. Once within the lungs, the bronchi divide several times, each successive division having a narrower lumen than the preceding one. Finally, the small bronchi divide into bronchioles which have no cartilage supports in their walls. The terminal conduits of air are the respiratory bronchioles from which arise the alveolar ducts and clusters of alveoli (Figure 10). The alveoli are true respiratory mechanisms lined with an epithelium so delicate and so closely adherent to the endothelium of the capillaries that it escapes even careful microscopic detection.

The lungs are spongy organs, pink or gray in appearance. In human beings the lungs of heavy smokers or those of miners may be virtually black, due to the collection of dust and carbon particles accumulated in the **phagocytic cells.** Each lung is lobated (Figure 10), the number of lobes of the right lung being larger than those of the left. The cat, for instance, has four lobes on the right side and three on the left. The number of lobes corresponds to the second division of the bronchi. A few mammals, such as the sloths and the orangutan, have lungs that show no gross lobation in the adult.

The lungs are entirely within the pleural cavities, or, rather, they protrude within the pleural cavity, being covered by the visceral pleura, which is continuous with the parietal pleura which lines the cavity. On the midventral line, underneath the sternum, the parietal pleurae of the pleural cavities come together to form a septum called the **mediastinum.** This extends from the dorsal body wall to the sternum and is attached to the diaphragm. The mediastinum encloses the esophagus, aorta, posterior vena cava, and the entire pericardial cavity.

Breathing, or the intake and the expulsion of air, is dependent on increasing and decreasing the size of the airtight pleural cavities; the elastic lungs expand or contract alternately like bellows. When the

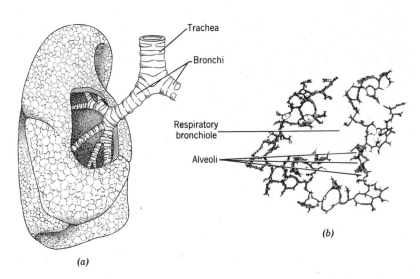

(a)

(b)

Figure 10. Mammalian lung: (a) dorsal view; (b) microscopic detail of lung.

247

muscles of the diaphragm contract the dome is flattened and the pleural cavities are elongated, causing inspiration of air; when the muscles relax the diaphragm becomes arched, again contracting the lungs and causing expiration. Contraction and relaxation of the muscles of the abdominal walls achieve the same results, as does also the alternate contraction and relaxation of the intercostal muscles which raise and depress the thoracic rib cage. All of these agents are at work to some extent in normal breathing.

SUMMARY

1. The principal organs of respiration in the fishes are the gills; those of the tetrapods are the lungs. However different structurally, gills and lungs share the function of oxygenating the red blood corpuscles and eliminating carbon dioxide.

2. The development of the primary respiratory organs is intimately associated with that of the pharynx. A series of pouches develops on each side of the pharynx of all vertebrate embryos. The entoderm of the pouches pushes outward to meet the ectoderm covering them on the outside and fuses with it to form thin plates. In all fishes these plates rupture, and the canals are the gill slits, separated by bars of mesoderm, the gill arches, which contain skeletal elements, and the major blood vessels of the gills. The internal gills are feathery sheets of capillary loops attached to the gill arch and are developed largely from the ectoderm of the gill slit. They are covered by a protective shield called operculum. External gills protrude laterally from the gill arches.

3. Amphibians have only external gills and only during the larval stage. With the exception of those of the Perennibrachiata, all gills are lost at metamorphosis, and respiration takes place through the lungs. The skin of most amphibians is also an important respiratory organ.

4. In the Teleostomi a midventral diverticulum of the embryonic pharynx gives rise to a sac or swim bladder, which in the ganoids and Choanichthyes remains connected with the pharynx through an open duct; in most teleosts the duct is obliterated. In lungfishes the swim bladder is a functional lung. During the months in which these fishes live encapsulated in dry mud on the river banks the gills are ineffective, and the lungs are the only effective respiratory organs. In other fishes the swim bladder is largely a hydrostatic organ.

5. The transition from the fishes to the amphibians must take place

somewhere near the Choanichthyes. Although complete evidence is lacking, the swim bladder and lungs are homologous structures, both having originated as diverticula from the floor of the pharynx. In spite of the greater complexity of the lungs, the swim bladder of modern fishes is probably a modification of a more ancient lunglike structure.

6. The lungs of amphibians show an instructive evolutionary trend from the simple sacs in most aquatic salamanders to the spongy lungs of terrestrial toads.

7. Whereas in all other fishes the nares terminate in blind sacs, those of Choanichthyes open through the roof of the oral cavity, as do also those of amphibians. In reptiles, birds and mammals the hard palate, a bony shelf, separates the nasal passages from the oral cavity, and the internal nares open far back in the pharynx near the entrance to the respiratory organs.

8. The portal of the respiratory system of tetrapods is the glottis. In mammals this is guarded by a cartilaginous epiglottis. The glottis opens into the larynx, or voice box, which is very simple in amphibians and more highly developed in mammals. The larynx of mammals is supported by several cartilages; folds and muscles form true and false vocal cords. Birds have no true larynx.

9. The larynx opens into the tubular trachea. This is almost non-existent in amphibians but very long in birds and mammals. The trachea is supported by complete or incomplete cartilage rings. The trachea branches into bronchi, usually one going to each lung. At the bifurcation of the trachea birds have the syrinx, a voice apparatus not found in other vertebrates. The syrinx has supporting cartilaginous plates and rings, several sound-producing vibratile membranes, and numerous extrinsic muscles.

10. The lungs of amphibians and reptiles rest in the pleuroperitoneal cavity, just anterior to and touching the abdominal viscera. In birds the oblique septum separates the pleuroperitoneal cavity into an anterior pleural and a posterior peritoneal cavity. The lungs of mammals lie in the pleural cavity, completely separated from the peritoneal cavity by the muscular diaphragm. Contraction and relaxation of the diaphragm provide the main movements for the mechanism of inspiration and expiration of air in mammals.

11. The lungs of amphibians, even those of toads, are moderately simple saccular devices; they increase in complexity in reptiles and achieve incredible complexity in birds and mammals. The lungs of birds are very different from those of all other vertebrates. They have a complicated system of connecting tubes between the various bronchioles and respiratory air capillaries. Bronchioles extend beyond the lungs and form dilated air pockets throughout the body and in the skeleton. The air from the bronchi can be swept through the lungs and into the air sacs without its being vitiated; it oxygenates the blood on its way out of the air sacs. The air sacs have the dual function of being air reservoirs and reducing the specific gravity. Structures resembling air sacs are first encountered in the reptiles.

12. The lungs of mammals have an intricate system of bronchi and bronchioles which conducts the air to and from the terminal respiratory alveoli.

SUGGESTED READING

Graham, J. D. P., 1939, The Air Stream in the Lungs of the Fowl. *J. Physiol.*, **97,** pp. 133–137.

Harrison, R. J., 1955, Adaptations in Diving Mammals. *Science News,* No. 35, pp. 74–90. Penquin Books Ltd., The Campfield Press, St Albans. An excellent account of the problems of circulation and respiration in these mammals.

Jones, F. R. H., 1957, The Swim Bladder in the *Physiology of Fishes* (M. E. Brown, ed.). Vol. II. Academic Press Inc., New York.

Jones, F. R. H., and N. B. Marshall, 1953, The Structure and Function of the Swim Bladder. *Biol. Rev.* Cambridge, **28,** pp. 16–83. This is a comprehensive review of the swim bladder and includes the most important references to original work.

Krogh, A., 1941, *The Comparative Physiology of Respiratory Mechanisms.* University of Pennsylvania Press, Philadelphia, Pa. An authoritative account of the problem.

Scholander, P. F., and Laurence Irving, 1941, Experimental Investigations on the Respiration and Diving of the Florida Manatee. *J. Cellular Comp. Physiol.,* **71,** pp. 169–191. A very informative and interesting article.

CHAPTER

10

Figure 1. Photograph of the lobated kidneys of the seal and the *doubled* posterior vena cava. (Courtesy of Prof. R. J. Harrison, The London Hospital Medical College, London.)

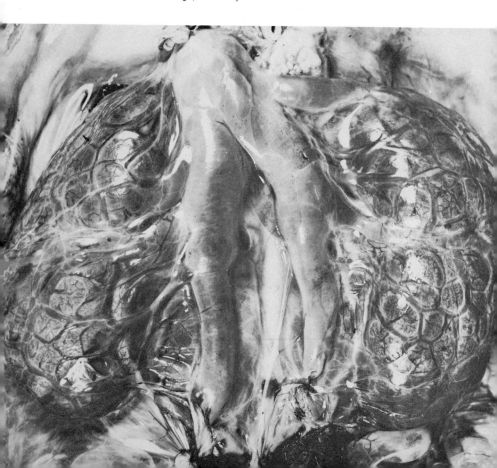

THE EXCRETORY SYSTEM

GENERAL INTRODUCTION

The urinary and reproductive systems of most adult vertebrates are separate but their developmental history is so intimately related that they comprise the **urogenital system.** Without a knowledge of comparative anatomy, the development of the urogenital system in higher vertebrates would be puzzling.

The **kidneys** are the filters of the circulatory system. They keep the composition of blood plasma constant by removing urea and other nitrogenous wastes, inorganic salts, nonvolatile foreign substances, and water.

All vertebrates have, at least during early development, a **pronephric** type of kidney (Figure 2); in adult forms this is found only in hagfishes, some Chondrostei and teleosts, and lungfishes. Ammocoetes and tadpoles have large functional pronephric kidneys which degenerate at metamorphosis. The second type of kidney, the **mesonephros,** is found in most adult cyclostomes, nearly all fishes, and amphibians; all of these animals acquire first a functional pronephros, which later degenerates as the mesonephros differentiates. The mesonephros is transitory in amniotes. All adult amniotes have a **metanephros,** which develops

253

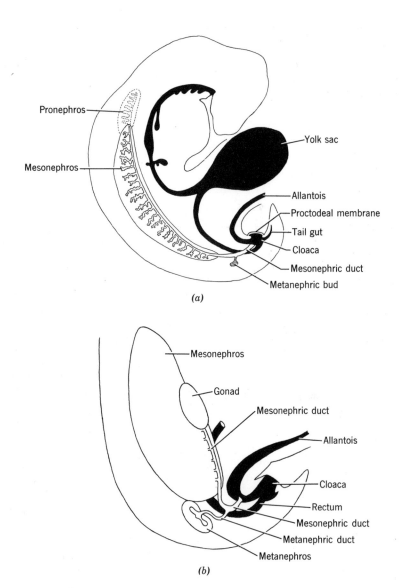

Figure 2. (a) Outline of a mammalian embryo, with the entodermal derivatives drawn black; (b) an older embryo with a larger metanephric kidney.

caudal to the mesonephros (Figure 2). All three types of kidney consist of tubules with a similar basic structure and function.

The anatomical and functional unit of the kidney is the **uriniferous tubule** or **nephron** (Figure 3). This is a single tubule, intimately associated with a tuft of arterial capillaries called **glomerulus**. Substances filter out of the glomerulus into a thin-walled **Bowman's capsule** and travel through the tubule (Figure 4); useful substances are selectively reabsorbed

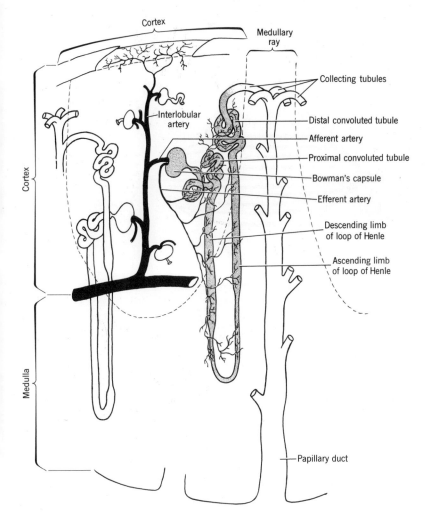

Figure 3. The relation of nephrons to the interlobular artery and to the cortex and medulla.

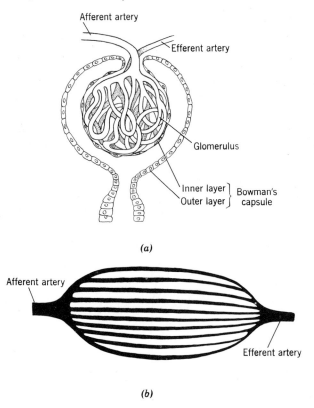

Figure 4. (a) Glomerulus surrounded by Bowman's capsule;
(b) glomerulus stretched out.

and put back in circulation; the wastes, known collectively as **urine,** are excreted. The uriniferous tubules of the pronephros have a relatively simple vascular pattern, but the mesonephros and metanephros have increasingly complex ones. Excretory ducts of the pronephros and mesonephros are the **pronephric** and **mesonephric ducts;** those of the metanephros are the **ureters.** In many vertebrates urine is collected into a **urinary bladder** before it is voided.

The nephrons of the pronephros are short and only slightly coiled. They open into the coelomic cavity by the **nephrostome,** which is lined with cells that bear cilia (Figure 5*b,c*); the waving of these cilia causes a current that directs the fluids from the peritoneal cavity into the tubules. The other end of the tubule is connected to the pronephric duct. Short arteries from the dorsal aorta form glomeruli near the nephrostomes. Some of the blood wastes filtering out of the glomeruli ooze into the peritoneal cavity, enter the pronephric tubules through the nephrostomes, and are then eliminated through the pronephric ducts. The presence of **external glomeruli** and a ciliated nephrostome are characteristic features of the pronephros. The tubules of the mesonephros generally have no nephrostome, and they are longer and more tortuous than those of the pronephros. At one end each tubule encapsulates the glomerulus, and at the other end it opens into the mesonephric duct (Figure 5*d*). The nephron of the mesonephros is not appreciably different from that of the metanephros.

For the purpose of orientation, the adult urinary system of the mammal is described briefly. These details are applicable to all metanephric kidneys and are particularly useful in understanding the developmental events which are described later.

The two oval rectroperitoneal kidneys of the mammal are located in

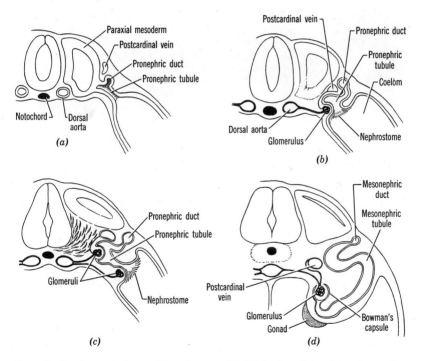

Figure 5. Development of pronephric and mesonephric tubules from the nephrogenic mesoderm: (a) early pronephric kidney; (b) later pronephric kidney; (c) fully developed pronephros; (d) mesonephros.

the lumbar region. They are covered by a **renal capsule** of tough connective tissue. A convex border faces laterally, and a concave side, the **hilum,** faces medially. In a cut made exactly through a median dorsoventral plane may be seen an outer dark band, the **cortex,** and a middle lighter, longitudinally striated zone, the **medulla** (Figure 6). The cortex makes up about one third of the kidney, and the medulla, two thirds. The cortex and medulla are united by **medullary rays** which penetrate the cortex. The medulla is arranged into one or more triangular areas, called **renal pyramids,** whose apices are the **renal papillae.** In kidneys with more than one pyramid **cortical** or **renal columns** are pushed between the pyramids. In the hilum a deep cleft called the **renal sinus** contains loose connective tissue and fat that surround and support renal arteries, veins, and nerves (Figure 7). The **renal pelvis,** the dilated proximal portion of the ureter, occupies the major portion of the renal sinus. The renal pelvis is expanded into anterior and pos-

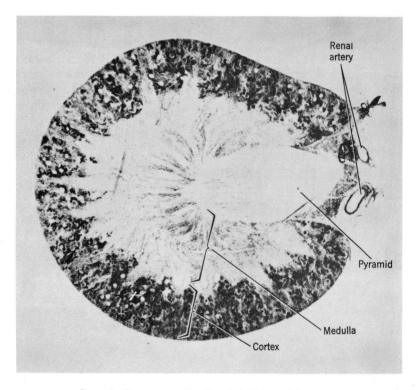

Figure 6. Transverse section through the kidney of the mouse.

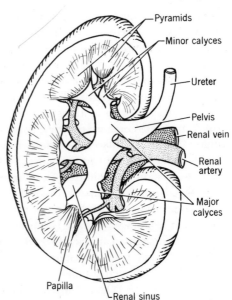

Pyramids
Minor calyces
Ureter
Pelvis
Renal vein
Renal artery
Major calyces
Papilla
Renal sinus

Figure 7.
The gross anatomy of
the kidney of a mammal.

terior stalks called the **major calyces,** each of which is divided into three
or more goblet-shaped **minor calyces.** The wall of the minor calyces is
reflected over one or two renal papillae and is perforated to allow the
passage of urine from the pyramid. The two ureters travel posteriorly
underneath the parietal peritoneum and empty directly into the urinary
bladder. A single duct, the **urethra,** drains the bladder.

Different segments of the nephron rest consistently in the cortex and
the medulla. To have a clear idea of this the student should first study
Figure 3, in which the details described here are represented graphically.
Mammalian nephrons, if stretched out, have a length of two to four centimeters, and they are 100 to 200 microns in diameter. The kidneys of
an ox contain about 4 million nephrons each; those of a cat about 200,-
000, and those of man about 1.5 million.

A nephron is a tube open only at its distal end. The closed proximal
end is invaginated into a double-walled Bowman's capsule around the
glomerulus (see Figure 4). The capsule opens into the tortuous **proximal convoluted tubule;** both the capsule and the proximal convoluted
tubule rest within the cortex. The proximal convoluted tubule emerges
from the cortex and enters a medullary ray, continues as **the loop of
Henle,** and re-enters the cortex to form the **distal convoluted tubule;** the
terminal segment of the nephron, the **collecting tubule,** is in the medul-

259

lary ray. In the medulla several collecting tubules form collecting ducts, and all of the collecting ducts in one pyramid converge toward its renal papilla. The nephrons are arranged in a circle around the interlobular arteries which traverse the cortex perpendicular to the surface of the kidney. Afferent arterioles, radiating from the interlobular arteries, form at their ends a glomerulus which is enclosed in a Bowman's capsule. Malpighi, who first described the microscopic structure of the kidney in the seventeenth century, likened the interlobular artery to the trunk of a tree, the afferent arterioles to its branches, and the glomeruli, to fruit hanging from the branches. The glomerulus is formed by a brushlike system of capillaries (see Figure 4b); each capillary remains single throughout its course, and all the capillaries come together in the single efferent artery, smaller than the afferent artery. The capillary systems of the glomerulus have two peculiarities: they do not anastomose, and they connect two arteries instead of an artery and a vein. Branches from the efferent artery vascularize the rest of the nephron and, in particular, the convoluted tubules.

Urine is the concentrated filtrate of the glomeruli. Water and many of the dialyzable plasma constituents of glomerular blood are filtered into Bowman's capsule; there is normally no protein because the molecules of blood protein are too large to pass through cell membranes. During its journey through the renal tubule a process of selective reabsorption of glucose, electrolytes, and water makes the waste filtrate more concentrated. Although about twenty-five gallons of fluid per day pass through the glomeruli of human kidneys, the daily output of urine is a little over one quart.

DEVELOPMENT

The urinary and the reproductive systems have an intimate embryonic history. The excretory organs develop early in the embryo; the gonads appear much later and convert for their own use structures formerly belonging to the excretory system. Because the development of the mammalian urogenital system reviews the apparent evolutionary history of these systems it is described briefly here.

The tubules of the pronephros are formed from the intermediate mesoderm of the cervical somites. One tubule develops from each somite, the most anterior forming first; by the time the caudal tubules differentiate the anterior ones have usually begun to regress. Each pronephric tubule sends a dorsal extension to meet and fuse with the one from the tubule behind it and establish a continuous duct (see Figure 5a). The two ducts keep on growing posteriorly beyond the last pronephric tubules, plowing their way between the ectoderm and the intermediate mesoderm of other somites, until they reach the posterior dilatation of the hind gut; this they penetrate one on each side to convert this part of the gut into a cloaca (see Figure 2). The formation of a pronephros in amniotes is an oddity, since it soon disappears; its ducts, however, are essential structures.

From the intermediate mesoderm behind the pronephros differentiate a large number of mesonephric tubules; these do not form ducts of their own but tap the already formed pronephric ducts, which thenceforth are called the mesonephric or **wolffian** ducts. The formation of mesonephric tubules begins anteriorly and progresses posteriorly; the most anterior part begins to degenerate even before the posterior parts differentiate, and the mesonephros seems to "migrate" posteriorly during development. The mesonephros is particularly large in the embryo of the pig and the rabbit and relatively small in that of the cat and man.

From each mesonephric duct grows a **metanephric bud** (Figure 8). This extends dorsally into the undifferentiated intermediate mesoderm caudal to the mesonephros, called **metanephric blastema**. The blind end of the metanephric bud in contact with the blastema becomes dilated into the primordial renal pelvis, from which anterior and posterior extensions form the major calyces (see Figure 2). The ends of these split several times and give rise to minor calyces. Straight, collecting tubules radiate from the minor calyces into the blastema, and the blastema differentiates into nephrons. The metanephros, then, has a dual origin: the conducting mechanism, including the ureter, renal pelvis, calyces, and collecting tubules, arises from the mesonephric duct; the nephrons are formed directly from the metanephric blastema. During this time certain other changes have taken place.

When the metanephros begins to form a groove nearly parallel to the wolffian duct appears on the surface of the mesonephros. The sides of this groove fold over, fuse, and form the **müllerian duct;** the anterior part of this duct remains open. The two müllerian ducts converge posteriorly and open very close together into the cloaca. The cloaca can now be separated into a urogenital sinus on the ventral side, which receives the mesonephric, metanephric, and müllerian ducts, and a rectum on the dorsal side (Figure 9c,d). The müllerian ducts are the primordial structures of the ducts of the female reproductive system, and the wolffian ducts, those of the male reproductive system. Each embryo is equipped with the materials for the development of both the male and

261

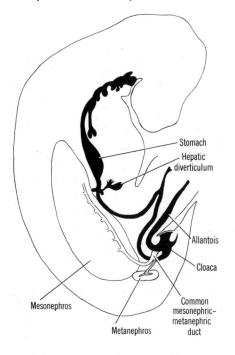

Stomach

Hepatic diverticulum

Allantois

Cloaca

Mesonephros

Common mesonephric–metanephric duct

Metanephros

Figure 8. Mammalian embryo, with the entodermal structures drawn black.

the female reproductive systems. The fate of this indifferent pattern is described in Chapter 11.

The cloaca is continuous dorsally with the rectum and ventrally with the allantois. The common mesonephric and metanephric ducts open through each lateral wall, and the fused müllerian ducts open posteriorly (Figure 9a,b,c). The early cloaca is walled off from the outside by the cloacal membrane, which later disappears. The rectum becomes separated dorsally. The urogenital sinus expands and stretches out the common duct of the mesonephros and metanephros, incorporating mesoderm in its wall, and mesonephric and metanephric ducts open separately into the urogenital sinus (Figure 9d). Through differential growth, the metanephric ducts are shifted cephalad and laterally, whereas the mesonephric ducts remain more or less stationary, the four ducts outlining the **trigone,** a triangle of mesoderm on the wall of the otherwise entodermal lining (see Figure 11, Chapter 11). The urogenital sinus forms the urinary bladder into which the two metanephric ducts open. The allantois becomes the **urachus,** a solid cord, and the

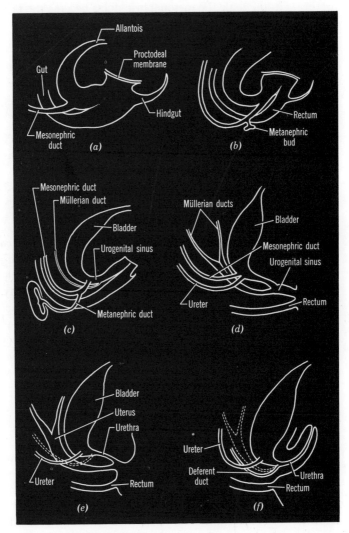

Figure 9. Progressive differentiation of the cloaca in mammalian embryos: (a) primitive pattern; (b) beginning of separation of cloaca into ventral and dorsal portions; (c) fully separated cloaca and the development of metanephric duct; (d) separation of mesonephric and metanephric ducts; (e) female urogenital system; (f) male urogenital system.

263

mesonephric ducts retain their opening into the neck of the bladder or urethra. In the male the mesonephric ducts become the principal ducts of the gonads; in the female they atrophy.

COMPARATIVE ANATOMY OF THE EXCRETORY SYSTEM

Amphioxus

The urinary system in *Amphioxus* is so primitive that its closest parallel is that of some annelids. The system is so different from that of vertebrates that it is not described here.

Cyclostomes

The two suborders, Myxinoidea and Petromyzontidae, can be separated on the basis of their kidneys. The myxines have a large modified pronephros located so far anteriorly that it bulges on each side of the esophagus and nephrostomes open into the pericardial cavity. Posterior to the pronephros, and extending along the entire peritoneal cavity, is a mesonephros so primitive that it has retained its original segmentation. In contrast, the adult Petromyzontidae have no pronephros; their two mesonephroi are long and narrow. The mesonephric ducts unite posteriorly just before they open into the urogenital sinus, which opens to the outside through a urogenital papilla.

Fishes

A few fishes have pronephroi, but most have mesonephroi. Sharks have long and narrow mesonephroi; many teleosts have short, bulky ones, located in the posterior part of the peritoneal cavity. The mesonephroi of the males are larger than those of females; some of the mesonephric tubules are attached to the testes and become efferent ducts. In many fishes mesonephric tubules and efferent ducts open into the mesonephric ducts, which have the dual function of excretory and sex ducts. The two mesonephric ducts fuse to form the urogenital sinus in the male and the urinary sinus in the female; the sinuses open into the cloaca through the urogenital or urinary papilla, respectively. In some species the posterior extension of the mesonephric ducts balloons into a urinary bladder.

264

Amphibians

All adult amphibians have mesonephroi. In urodeles the mesonephroi have a narrow anterior extension from which, in the males, some
of the mesonephric tubules become attached to the testes to form the
efferent ducts. At spaced intervals collecting ducts from the mesonephric tubules drain into the mesonephric ducts (see Figure 6, Chapter 11). The collecting ducts from the posterior part of the kidney converge into a separate duct of the male. The mesonephric ducts of the
male carry both urine and spermatozoa to the cloaca.

The kidneys of salientians are far apart and are located back in the
peritoneal cavity. They are large, roughly oval bodies, larger at the
posterior than at the anterior end. In males a few mesonephric tubules
are differentiated into the efferent ducts of the testes, and the mesonephric ducts carry both urine and spermatozoa. The two ducts open separately into the cloaca. A recess of the cloaca forms a urinary bladder,
which is not directly connected with the mesonephric ducts (see Figure
7, Chapter 11). As the urine trickles from the ducts into the closed
cloaca it backs up into the bladder.

Reptiles

Adult reptiles have a metanephric kidney and variable remnants of a
mesonephros. The gross appearance of the kidneys of reptiles is as
varied as the body forms of the orders and suborders of the class. The
kidneys are far back in the peritoneal cavity. They are long, strikingly
lobulated and, in snakes and lizards, occasionally fused with each other.
The kidneys of crocodilians and turtles are short and are located in the
pelvis. The ureters, long in snakes and lizards but short in crocodilians
and turtles (see Figure 8, Chapter 11), open separately into the cloaca.
Lizards and turtles, but not snakes and crocodilians, have urinary bladders, developed partly from the embryonic cloaca and partly from the
allantois. The bladder seems to be an accessory organ of respiration.
Female turtles have accessory bladders which they fill with water to
moisten the ground when digging holes in which they deposit their eggs.

Birds

The paired, deeply lobated, elongated kidneys of birds are lodged in the
synsacrum. The ureters are attached to the midventral part of each
kidney and extend directly to the **urodeum** of the cloaca (see Figure 10).

265

Comparative Anatomy

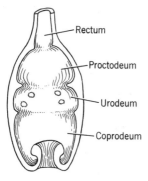

Figure 10. Cloaca of a bird.

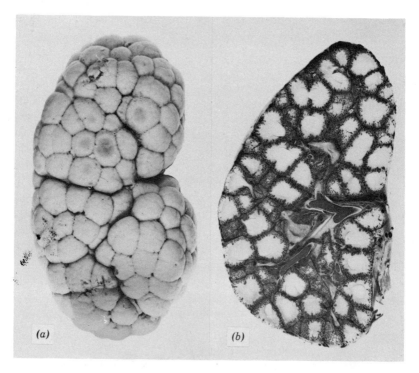

Figure 11. The lobated kidney of a seal: (a) surface view; (b) tangential section.

An adaptation for flying is the absence of a urinary bladder. The urine of birds is whitish and semisolid.

Mammals

The kidneys are firmly anchored in a rectroperitoneal space by a padding of fat. They are covered with a renal capsule of tough connective tissue. The surface is smooth in the cat, sheep, man, etc., and deeply furrowed and lobated in the seal, ox, and bear (Figures 1, 11). Lobation is always apparent in the embryos of animals with multipyramidal kidneys, but it is lost late in development, in some but not in others.

In monotremes urine collected in the renal pelvis is conveyed by the ureters to the cloaca; a longitudinal fold partially separates the cloaca into the urogenital sinus, ventrally, and the rectum, dorsally. In metatherian and eutherian mammals urine is collected in the urinary bladder. The proximal part of the urethra is surrounded by an involuntary sphincter, which the animal educates to respond to volition. The relatively short urethra of the female opens into a shallow vestibule or urogenital sinus. The long urethra of the male is divisible into a proximal **membranous urethra,** a short, **prostatic urethra** into which open the deferent ducts, and a long **penile urethra.** The last two portions are actually a urogenital sinus (Figure 11, Chapter 11).

SUMMARY

1. All vertebrates have, at least during development, a pronephric type of kidney; only the adult hagfishes, some Chondrostei and teleosts, and lungfishes have a pronephros. Ammocoetes and tadpoles have large functional pronephric kidneys, but they lose them at metamorphosis. The second type of kidney, the mesonephros, is found in adult cyclostomes and in fishes and amphibians; these animals have first a functional pronephros, which later degenerates as the mesonephros differentiates. The metanephros, the functional kidney of amniotes, develops caudal to the mesonephros. All three types of kidneys consist of tubules that filter wastes from arterial blood, and their basic structure and function are similar.

2. The three types of kidneys develop in a cephalocaudal direction in amniote embryos. The pronephros develops first and most anteriorly. The mesonephros is formed next, posterior to it, as the pronephros degenerates, and the metanephros develops last and most posteriorly.

3. When the pronephros is first formed its duct plows its way posteriorly and enters the expanded, posterior part of the digestive tube to establish a cloaca, a receptacle into which open the digestive tube, dorsally, the allantois, ventrally, and the pronephric, or mesonephric ducts, laterally and dorsally. Later the metanephric ducts also open into it. The müllerian ducts, which represent the potential female reproductive ducts, open on the dorsal side of the cloaca between the mesonephric and metanephric ducts. Adult vertebrates, with the exception of the eutherian mammals, have a cloaca.

4. In placental mammals the digestive tube becomes separated from the ventral part of the cloaca, which is then called the urogenital sinus, since both urinary and reproductive ducts open into it. The ventral part of the urogenital sinus at the base of the allantois becomes ballooned into the urinary bladder, which receives the ureters on its dorsal side. The duct of the bladder is the urethra. In the male the mesonephric ducts, now deferent ducts, open into the urethra; in the female these ducts disappear.

SUGGESTED READING

Felix, W., 1912, "Development of Urinogenital Organs." *Manual of Human Embryology.* (F. Keibel, and F. P. Mall, eds.) Vol. II, pp. 752–979.

Flexner, L. B., and I. Girsh, 1937, "The Correlation of Oxygen Consumption, Function and Structure in the Developing Metanephros of the Pig." Contribution to *Embryology,* Vol. XXVI, pp. 121–127. Carnegie Inst. Wash. Publ. 479, Washington, D. C.

Girsh, I., 1937, The Correlation of Structure and Function in the Developing Mesonephros and Metanephros. Contributions to *Embryology,* Vol. XXVI, pp. 33–58. Carnegie Inst. Washington.

Maximow, A. A., and W. Bloom, 1956, *A Textbook of Histology.* W. B. Saunders Co., Philadelphia and London.

Strauss, W. L., Jr., and J. A. Arcadi, 1958, "Urinary System." *Primatologia,* **3,** 507–541. S. Karger, Basel and New York.

Witschi, E., 1956, *Development of Vertebrates.* W. B. Saunders Company, Philadelphia and London.

CHAPTER

11

Figure 1. A pair of tropical fish, *Tomeurus*. The male, below, has the gonopodium extended forward. (Courtesy of the New York Zoological Society.)

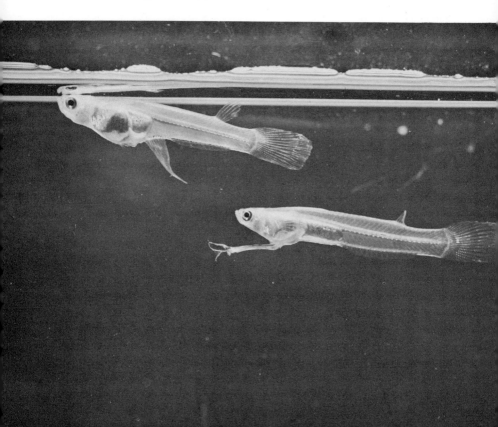

THE REPRODUCTIVE SYSTEM

GENERAL INTRODUCTION

Animals are the carriers of germ cells, and the primary purpose of their existence is to reproduce. The struggle for survival is geared to insure the succession of generations of each species. The offspring maintain the species sturdy and indestructible, and aged individuals are eliminated. Individuals are important only as links in genetic successions.

The success of a species depends on its adaptability to the ecological niche in which it lives. Species that are exposed to hazards have to produce large numbers of young so that a few may survive; species with sheltered lives produce few young. Most teleosts lay such a prodigious number of eggs that if all survived there would soon be no room for them. The size of the litters of mammals corresponds to the number of functional mammary glands of the female. Bats, elephants, horses, man, and others with only two mammary glands or with a single udder rarely have more than one offspring. Pigs, rodents, carnivores, and others with several mammary glands have large litters.

The sexes are physiologically and anatomically distinct. There are interesting cases of ambisexuality, as in the primitive hagfishes and the

271

gilthead, a sardinelike teleost from the Mediterranean, which during the first two years of its life is a male and then becomes a female.

The **primary sex organs** are the **gonads;** those of the male are the **testes,** those of the female, the **ovaries.** The gonads produce germ cells or **gametes;** male gametes are the **spermatozoa** (Figure 2), female gametes, the **ova** (Figure 3). At **fertilization** male and female gametes unite to form a single cell called a **zygote,** from which arises the embryo (Figure 3). The ducts that bring the gametes from the gonads to the outside are the **secondary** or **accessory sex organs.** In those animals in which fertilization takes place internally the accessory sex organs open to the outside through **external genitalia;** males have a **penis,** females, a **vagina.** The act of transferring the spermatozoa to the genital tract of the female is called **copulation** or **coitus.**

Most aquatic vertebrates have simple external genitalia, and their eggs are fertilized externally, there being no contact between the male and female during reproduction. The female releases the eggs in water and the male fertilizes them by spraying spermatozoa near or over them.

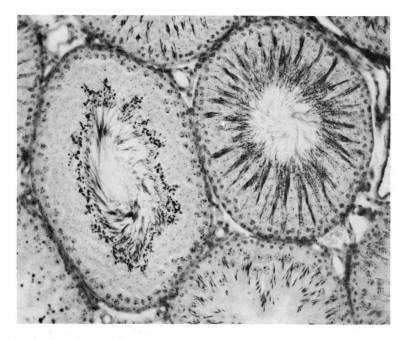

Figure 2. Seminiferous tubules in the human testis showing numerous spermatozoa in the lumen. (Courtesy of Dr. Edward Roosen-Runge, University of Washington, School of Medicine.)

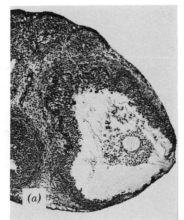

Figure 3. (a) Rat ovary about to discharge an ovum; (b) an ovum from the ovary of a Rhesus monkey, surrounded by the zona pellucida; (c) living ovum of the rat which has just been penetrated by a spermatozoon; (d) living fertilized egg of the rat just before cleavage. (Courtesy of Dr. Richard J. Blandau, University of Washington, School of Medicine.)

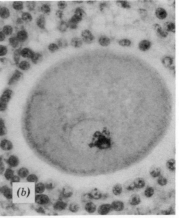

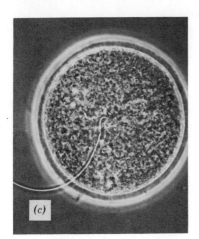

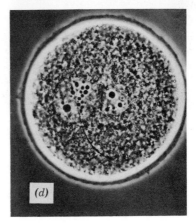

In some salamanders the males deposit spermatozoa over small jelly cones at the bottom of a pond; the females crawl over these mounds, open their cloacas, and pick up the spermatozoa. In all strictly terrestrial vertebrates fertilization takes place internally.

The deferent ducts carry spermatozoa from the testes to the outside. Various glands secrete viscid substances which mixed with spermatozoa form the **semen**. In spite of various degrees of complexity, the standard pattern of the male reproductive system of most vertebrates is similar. The testes of animals with a seasonal breeding cycle are large during the reproductive period and small during the period of sexual quiescence. The countless spermatozoa formed in the testes are very small motile cells with whiplike tails that are either lashed back and forth or rotated for locomotion (Figure 3c). The basic structure of the spermatozoa of most vertebrates is essentially similar. The unessential cytoplasm of each spermatozoon is cast away, leaving only the nucleus and the mechanisms for locomotion and penetration of the egg. Outside the male reproductive tract the vitality and life span of spermatozoa differs in different species. In some turtles spermatozoa may remain viable for several years in the reproductive tract of the female, and the spermatozoa of some bats are viable for several weeks in the reproductive tract of the female. In most mammals, however, spermatozoa are short-lived and perish after a day or two. Kept in cold storage, mammalian spermatozoa remain viable for days.

Eggs are large, nonmotile cells produced in the cortex of the ovary in spherical structures called **graafian follicles** (Figure 4). When the follicles are ripe they break open and the eggs flow into the genital tract. The eggs of **viviparous** animals develop within the genital tract of the female; those of **oviparous** animals develop outside. The eggs of oviparous animals are large and laden with yolk. The large eggs of some fishes and reptiles develop and hatch within the female reproductive tract; these animals are called **ovoviviparous**. Some sharks and the ostriches lay the largest known eggs. The small eggs of mammals have no yolk; they are a little over one tenth of a millimeter in diameter and are barely visible to the naked eye (see Figure 3). The ova of the mouse, the elephant, and man are about the same size. Monotremes are oviparous and lay large yolk-laden eggs. The eggs of marsupials contain some yolk, but even these eggs are very small and not much larger than those of placental mammals. From the monotremes to the placental mammals, a transition takes place from oviparous to viviparous types of reproduction. The **oviducts,** the conduits of the female reproductive system, have an open funnellike **ostium** at their anterior

Figure 4. (a) Detail of the ovary of a Rhesus monkey showing the covering epithelium on the right and a row of three primordial follicles on the left; (b) growing follicle in the ovary of the hedgehog—the ovum in the center is surrounded by a clear zona pellucida; (c) maturing follicle of a hedgehog; (d) mature follicle of a hedgehog showing the fluid-filled space, antrum around the ovum, which is still surrounded by follicular cells. (Courtesy of Professor R. J. Harrison, the London Hospital Medical College, London, England.)

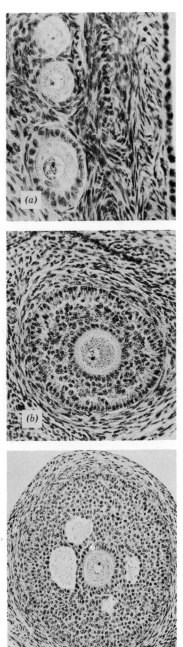

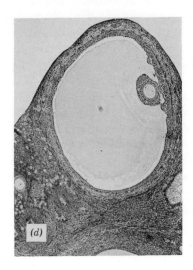

end, near the ovary (Figure 5). The epithelium lining the upper end of the oviduct has cilia that wave back and forth, stirring a mild surface current toward the ostium; this helps to draw the ovum slowly into the oviduct. Once inside the oviduct, contractions of the muscular wall carry the ovum farther down. At the posterior end the oviducts are distended into a uterus, particularly well-developed in viviparous or ovoviviparous vertebrates. In most vertebrates below placental mammals the uterus opens into the cloaca; in mammals the uterus opens into the vagina, a new canal found between the urethra and the anus.

DEVELOPMENT

The development of the indifferent sexual pattern in the embryo (Figure 5) has been described in Chapter 10. In this chapter we are considering briefly only the final differentiation of such indifferent patterns in the male and female reproductive systems.

All young embryos are equipped with the rudiments of both the male and female reproductive organs, and müllerian ducts develop along the wolffian ducts in both sexes. The male reproductive system utilizes the tubules and ducts of the mesonephric kidney; the müllerian ducts disappear or remain vestigial. In female embryos the two müllerian ducts give rise to the oviducts and uterus, and the mesonephric ducts and tubules largely disappear.

A ridge on the ventral border of each mesonephric kidney gives rise to a gonad. The surface layer of the indifferent gonads becomes thickened into a germinal epithelium, which later forms the germ cells. *The cells of the germinal epithelium, however, have arisen from the entoderm of the yolk sac and have migrated into the primitive gonad early in development.* Cellular cords from the germinal epithelium grow into the underlying mesoderm, and sexual differentiation becomes evident. The cords of germinal epithelium are distinct only in the male; in the female the cords break up into small nests of cells.

The Male

Germinal cords form the testis cords, which later differentiate into the convoluted, **seminiferous tubules**. The connective tissue over the gonad forms a thick and fibrous **tunica albuginea**. Connective tissue septa from the tunica albuginea separate the seminiferous tubules. When first recognizable the seminiferous tubules are solid cords of cells; a lumen forms in them late in development. The cells lining the

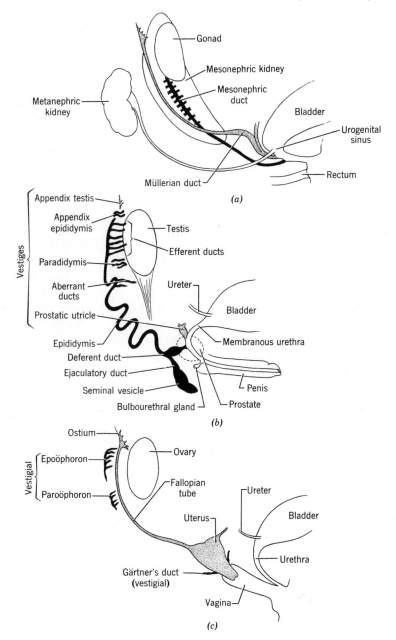

Figure 5. Differentiation of the male and female secondary sex organs from the indifferent model: (a) indifferent; (b) male; (c) female. The mesonephric duct and tubules and their derivatives are solid black; the müllerian duct and its derivatives are stippled.

seminiferous tubules undergo a sequence of complicated changes which culminate in their metamorphosis into spermatozoa. The production of spermatozoa is known as **spermatogenesis,** and the transformation of each germ cell into a spermatozoon is called **spermiogenesis.** Nests of cells in the connective tissue septa accumulate lipid droplets and become known as **interstitial** or **Leydig cells.** These and the cells in the seminiferous tubules manufacture male hormones.

The ducts of the male reproductive system develop from the mesonephric tubules and ducts (Figure 5). The müllerian ducts disappear, except for a small vestige near the testis called **appendix testis.** In the vertebrates below the mammals the adults retain variable amounts of the posterior extension of the müllerian ducts. In the male shark about half of the duct remains attached to the mesonephric kidney, and in the placental mammals the fused portion of the müllerian ducts forms the vestigial **prostatic utricle** or **uterus masculinus.** In the amniotes, except for those parts utilized by the male reproductive system, the mesonephric kidney degenerates. A few anterior mesonephric tubules attach themselves to the testis and become efferent ducts. The anterior portion of the wolffian duct becomes greatly elongated and convoluted and forms the **epididymis;** posteriorly it forms the deferent duct. The **seminal vesicles** and the **ejaculatory duct** also arise from the mesonephric duct. A few vestigial mesonephric tubules stranded in the connective tissue that holds the epididymis together form the **appendix epididymis,** the **paradidymis,** and the **aberrant ducts** (Figure 5).

The Female

After the epithelial cords of the early gonad break up into nests of undifferentiated germ cells, the ovary attains a dense **primary cortex** at the periphery and a looser **primary medulla** in the center. These, however, do not correspond to the cortex and medulla of the adult. The process of differentiation of the primary germ cells into ova, or **oögenesis,** in the embryo begins in the center of the ovary and progresses toward the periphery. The ova develop within graafian follicles.

The female reproductive system does away with the duct system of the mesonephric kidney and uses the müllerian ducts (Figure 5). These do not acquire a direct connection with the ovary, but the anterior end opens by way of the ostium into the peritoneal cavity near the ovary; in some species the lips of the open end extend in fingerlike **fimbriae** around the ovary so that the ova released into the peritoneal cavity flow directly into the ostium. The posterior end of each oviduct forms a uterine enlargement. The right and left halves of the uterus are the uterine horns; these show various degrees of fusion and enter the vagina through an elevation called cervix uteri. The vagina develops secondarily as a new structure.

COMPARATIVE ANATOMY OF THE REPRODUCTIVE SYSTEM

The Male

Amphioxus. The very simple reproductive system has no ducts. Twenty-six pairs of male gonads project into the space called atrium around the pharynx. Spermatozoa shed into this space are carried to the outside by the water in the pharynx.

Cyclostomes. Adult hagfishes and the ammocoetes of lampreys are hermaphroditic, having both male and female reproductive organs. Adult lampreys, however, have separate sexes. The two testes of the males are fused and extend virtually the entire length of the peritoneal cavity. Cyclostomes have no genital ducts; the testes release spermatozoa into the peritoneal cavity from which they escape by way of the abdominal pores through the urogenital sinus.

Fishes. The two testes of elasmobranchs are located just dorsal to the liver. Several mesonephric tubules, or efferent ducts, connect each testis to the coiled mesonephric duct, now called the deferent duct. The tubules of the kidney are drained by accessory urinary ducts (Figure 6). At its posterior end the deferent duct is dilated into a flask-shaped seminal vesicle, from which grows a ventral diverticulum called sperm sac. The deferent ducts open into the cloaca with the urinary ducts at the tip of the urogenital papilla (Figure 6).

The testis of ganoids is less intimately associated with the mesonephric duct (Figure 6), and in some species the developmental history of these two organ systems is different. In some teleosts the ducts of the excretory and reproductive systems open independently into the cloaca (Figure 6). The kidneys and testes of lungfishes and teleosts are completely separate; the deferent ducts have a different origin from that of the mesonephric ducts and are analogous to those of most other vertebrates.

In the males of fishes in which fertilization takes place internally the pelvic or anal fins are modified as copulatory organs. The pelvic fins of male sharks form claspers which are used to hold the female and to deliver sperm into its cloaca. The anal fin of some male teleosts forms a copulatory organ called gonopodium (see Figure 1).

279

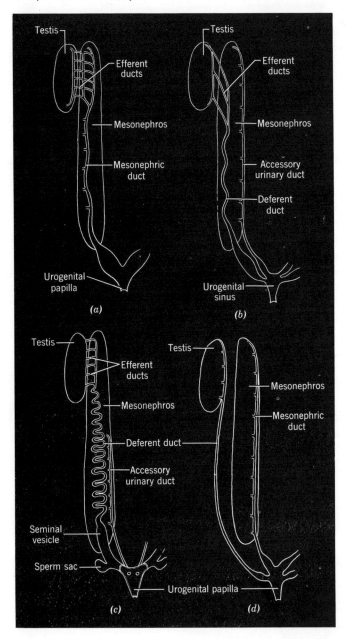

Figure 6. Male urogenital systems of fishes: (a) ganoid; (b) *Polypterus*; (c) elasmobranch; (d) teleost.

Amphibians. The two testes, longer in urodeles than in salientians, are usually located at the rear of the body cavity. The system of reproductive ducts is similar to that of elasmobranchs (Figure 7). The efferent ducts, derived from mesonephric tubules, connect the testis with the anterior extension of the mesonephric duct. This is largely separated from the kidney and is mostly a spermatic duct; only the posterior part of the wolffian duct drains a few mesonephric tubules. In salientians the mesonephric duct serves both as a urinary and a deferent duct (Figure 7). During the breeding season the distal end of the wolffian duct when full of spermatozoa, forms a seminal vesicle. No real copulation takes place in amphibians, and the males have no external genitalia.

Reptiles. The paired testes are attached to the metanephric kidney by the **mesorchium.** One of the testes of lizards and snakes lies considerably ahead of the other. Efferent ducts, formed from mesonephric tubules, connect the testis with the wolffian duct. The mesonephros degenerates and the wolffian duct becomes the principal genital duct; its anterior part becomes so long that it forms a tangled mass called

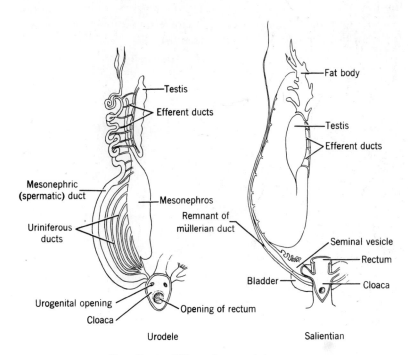

Figure 7. Amphibian male urogenital systems.

epididymis (Figure 8). In most reptiles the deferent duct joins the ureter and opens into the cloaca as a short urogenital sinus. The deferent ducts of turtles and crocodilians open at the base of an open, longitudinal groove on the back of the penis (Figure 9). The entire genital system is very large during the breeding season and small during the quiescent period.

Birds. The two smooth oval testes are suspended by a mesorchium. Birds become sexually mature by the end of the first year, but some forms require two or three years. Spermatogenesis in birds proceeds only at night when the temperature of the sleeping animal falls about 3° C below that of daytime.

Tubules from the mesonephros form the efferent ducts and the epididymis, and the mesonephric duct becomes the convoluted deferent duct. In small birds the distal parts of the deferent ducts are exceedingly long and form skeins called **glomera** (singular, **glomus**) (Figure 10). Near its posterior end the deferent duct is dilated as the **ampullary duct,** which opens into the cloaca as the thick-walled ejaculatory duct. During the breeding season the enlarged duct system stores spermatozoa, and the volume of the gonads is many times greater than during times of sexual quiescence (Figure 10). The male reproductive system of the domestic fowl is functional during the entire year.

Although ducks, geese, swans, and ostriches have a primitive penis,

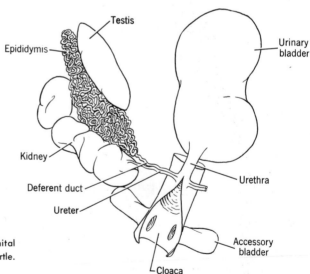

Figure 8. Urogenital system of the male turtle.

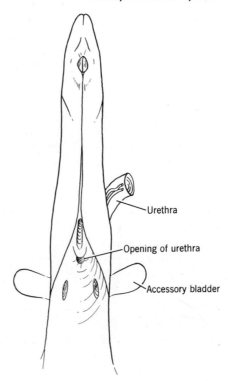

Figure 9. Penis of the turtle viewed from above.

Urethra

Opening of urethra

Accessory bladder

most other birds have none. The large, conical, and turgid cloaca of the male is placed within the flaccid and concave cloaca of the female during copulation.

Mammals. The ovoid testes are compact and their size varies according to the size of the animal. The testes of rodents are disproportionately large. The testes of man weigh around eighteen grams each, and those of the elephant may weigh over ten pounds. The testes of mammals are housed in pockets of body cavity, called **scrotal sacs** or **scrota,** in the posterior end of the trunk. Elephants, whales, and seals are exceptions; their testes remain within the body cavity. The testes of insectivores and rodents descend into the scrotum during the breeding season but are retracted into the body cavity during the periods of sexual quiescence.

The testis is surrounded by the tunica albuginea, a tough sheet of connective tissue. Septa from the tunica albuginea converge toward the slightly concave **hilum,** and the seminiferous tubules rest in the loose con-

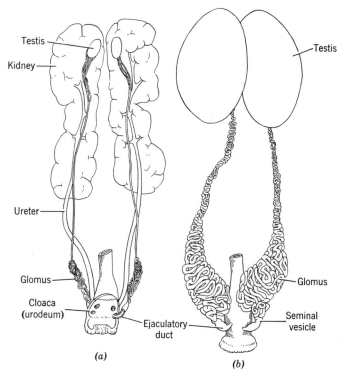

Figure 10. Male urogenital system of a bird: (a) winter; (b) summer.

nective tissue between the septa. The seminiferous tubules are convoluted at the periphery of the testis and straight at the hilum. Efferent ducts, which have arisen from mesonephric tubules, converge toward the single but highly convoluted duct of the epididymis (Figure 11). The epididymis is draped over the testis to form the **head,** a large anterior mass, and a smaller **tail** posteriorly (Figure 11) which emerges as the deferent duct. The wolffian duct gives rise to the epididymis, the deferent duct, and the seminal vesicle (Figure 12). The deferent duct opens into the **prostatic urethra** as the ejaculatory duct. The prostatic urethra is surrounded by the **prostate gland** (Figure 13). The two ejaculatory ducts open at the base of the **prostatic utricle,** a small elevation on the floor of the prostatic urethra derived from the fused müllerian ducts. From this point outward the urethra is really a urogenital sinus and is known as the **penile urethra.** The seminal vesicle, the prostate, and **Cowper's**

284

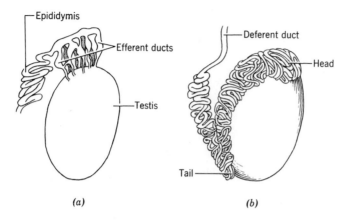

Figure 11. (a) Mammalian testis and efferent ductules; (b) the epididymis.

glands all secrete viscid substances that with the spermatozoa form the seminal fluid.

All mammals have a penis. That of monotremes is withdrawn within the floor of the cloaca, as in some reptiles. In all other mammals the penis is free and ensheathed in a fold of skin called the **prepuce**. The penis is of different size and form in different mammals. It contains the **corpus cavernosum urethrae**, composed of erectile tissue, which when engorged with blood causes the penis to be turgid and erect. In many

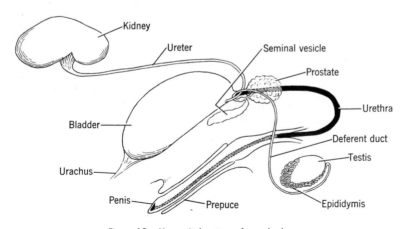

Figure 12. Urogenital system of a male dog.

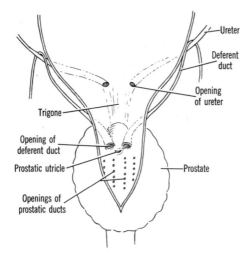

Figure 13. Bladder and membranous urethra of the male dog.

Labels on figure: Ureter; Deferent duct; Opening of ureter; Trigone; Opening of deferent duct; Prostatic utricle; Prostate; Openings of prostatic ducts

mammals the penis has a bone (**os priapi, os penis,** or **baculum**) or a cartilage in the connective tissue septum between the corpus cavernosum.

The Female

Amphioxus. The twenty-six metamerically arranged pairs of gonads release the ripe ova into the atrium. The ova are washed away by the circulating pharyngeal water, and fertilization takes place externally.

Cyclostomes. Ammocoetes have two large ovaries which run the length of the coelom. In the adult the two ovaries fuse into one that grows around the intestine. When ripe the ovary fills most of the body cavity. Thousands of eggs are released into the body cavity, and from there they are squeezed to the outside through the genital pores.

Hagfishes are hermaphroditic, having both male and female gonads. The anterior part is an ovary, the posterior part, a testis. However, only one or the other gonad seems to be functional at any one time. Like the gilthead mentioned earlier, the younger animals are predominantly males; the ovaries mature more slowly than the testes, and older animals are predominantly females.

Fishes. The ovaries are either paired or fused. Elasmobranchs have two ovaries far anterior in the body cavity, which produce few large, yolk-laden eggs. The two oviducts are fused anteriorly and have one ostium surrounded by long fimbriae which extend to the falciform ligament of the liver (Figure 14). The anterior part of the oviducts is narrow, but about midway each becomes enlarged into a **nidamental gland** which secretes the leathery shell of the eggs. The dilated last segment of the oviduct is the uterus, which opens into the cloaca. The uterus is attached to the body wall by a large **mesotubarium** and is movable in the peritoneal cavity. The uteri of ovoviviparous elasmobranchs are larger than those of oviparous species.

The ovaries of teleosts are shaped like sacs with blind ends in front (Figure 14). The two oviducts are attached to the ovaries, and they are generally fused posteriorly, opening to the outside by a single orifice. The oviducts of teleosts are formed directly from peritoneal folds and are not derived from the müllerian ducts.

Teleosts are oviparous and lay thousands of eggs; a few are ovoviviparous. The two **true** oviducts of lungfishes open anteriorly in the peritoneal cavity by a funnel-shaped ostium. The oviducts are fused posteriorly and open into the cloaca by a single orifice.

Amphibians. The paired ovaries of urodeles are longer than those of salientians (Figure 15). Numerous eggs are released from the surface of the ovary into the peritoneal cavity. The male toad has a vestigial structure called **Bidder's organ,** which can form eggs, and the animal is

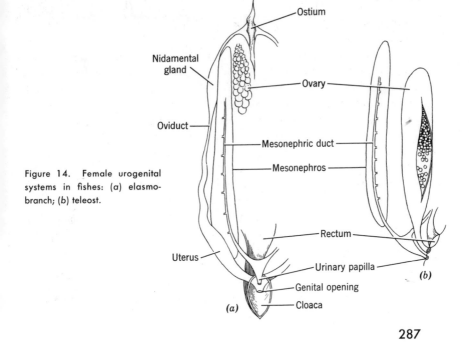

Figure 14. Female urogenital systems in fishes: (a) elasmobranch; (b) teleost.

287

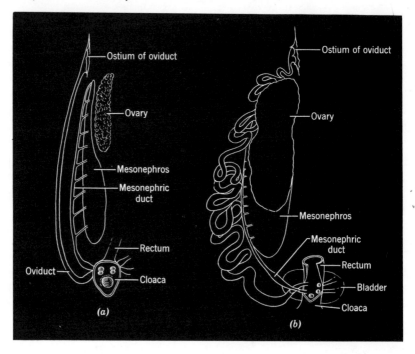

Figure 15. Female urogenital system in amphibia: (a) urodele; (b) salientian.

potentially hermaphroditic. The paired oviducts of all amphibians have ostia far forward in the peritoneal cavity; posteriorly, the oviducts open singly into the cloaca, but in the toads they unite and open into the cloaca through a single orifice. During ovulation the oviducts become very large, and the glands in the posterior part secrete a layer of viscid gelatinous material around each egg as it passes. In urodeles the eggs are fertilized internally, although there is little contact between males and females. In salientians fertilization takes place externally; the male grasps the female above the hind legs and releases spermatozoa over the eggs as they emerge from the cloaca.

Reptiles. The ovaries of reptiles produce a few yolk-laden eggs (Figure 16). The two oviducts open anteriorly in the peritoneal cavity by fairly large ostia. As the eggs of turtles and crocodilians pass down the oviduct, glands in the walls secrete albumen around them. At the posterior end of the oviduct **shell glands** secrete a rubbery substance which forms a soft but resistant shell. Crocodilian eggs have a hard calcareous shell. Since the eggs are protected with a shell and a thick layer of albumen when they are deposited, they have to be fertilized internally at the upper end of the oviduct before these substances are added around them. Most reptiles are oviparous, but some snakes are ovoviviparous; in such cases the wall of the oviduct, in contact with the extraembryonic membranes of the developing young, is specialized into a primitive placenta.

Birds. Most adult birds have only the left ovary; the right one is vestigial and is lost in the surrounding connective tissue (Figure 17). The falcons, accipitrine hawks, and harriers have two ovaries.

The development of the right ovary in the embryo is considerably different from that of the left. A cortex does not develop properly, and the large medulla forms cords which resemble seminiferous tubules. The cortical cells may degenerate, remain undifferentiated, or differentiate into oöcytes. After hatching, the right ovary is a sterile rudiment; occasionally it has both testicular and ovarian characters, or it may resemble an ovary. If the left ovary of the adult bird is destroyed, the right ovary may grow larger, but its fate is unpredictable; it may grow into a sterile or functional testis or into an ovary. The functional ovary of a bird resembles a bunch of grapes, but the eggs visible on its surface differ tremendously in size (Figure 17). Birds with two ovaries have two oviducts, but all others have only the left one. The right one is abortive and can be found with difficulty as a small concrescence on the right side of the cloaca. The long and coiled oviduct is attached to the dorsal body wall by a large mesenteric fold and is freely movable.

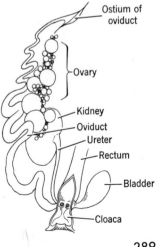

Figure 16. Female urogenital system of a lizard.

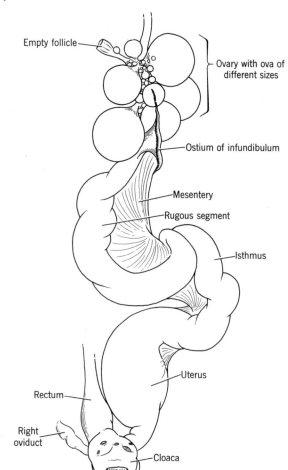

Empty follicle

Ovary with ova of different sizes

Ostium of infundibulum

Mesentery

Rugous segment

Isthmus

Uterus

Rectum

Right oviduct

Cloaca

Figure 17.
The reproductive system
of a hen.

The upper end of the oviduct has a large **infundibulum** lined with ciliated epithelium. Next, the **rugous segment,** with large longitudinal folds, secretes the albumen around the yolk. The next segment, the isthmus, secretes the membranous **shell membrane,** and the dilated shell gland, or uterus, secretes the **calcareous shell.** The ovum proper, formed in the ovary, is only the yolk sphere. This is mostly foodstuff; the viable part, or germinal disc, is a very small part of the egg. Fertilization takes place in the infundibulum before the albumen and the shell are laid down. During sexually quiescent periods the ovaries and the oviducts are small, but during the reproductive periods they are very large.

Next to some sharks, birds lay the largest vertebrate eggs. Remnants of the mesonephric ducts that appear like undeveloped epididymis and efferent ducts are often found in female birds.

Mammals. The eggs and ovaries of monotremes or prototheria resemble those of reptiles and birds. Like birds, these animals have a single ovary, the left one. The oviduct, derived from the müllerian duct, is relatively simple; its dilated distal end, the uterus, secretes the egg-case; it opens into the urethra to form a urogenital sinus, and this, in turn, opens into the cloaca.

The ova of metatherian and eutherian mammals are so small and compact that a large ovary is unnecessary. The ovary is composed of an outer cortex and an inner medulla. Eggs are formed in the cortex within the graafian follicles. When the ovum is ripe the graafian follicle ruptures and the follicular fluid oozes out of it carrying the egg with it; fluid and ovum flow into the oviduct. The broken graafian follicle develops into the **corpus luteum,** an endocrine organ which secretes a hormone called **progesterone.** The cells of the follicles and the interstitial cells of the ovary secrete **estrogen.** These are discussed later in the chapter on the endocrine organs.

The two oviducts of mammals are derived from the müllerian ducts (Figure 18). The oviducts of monotremes secrete a small amount of

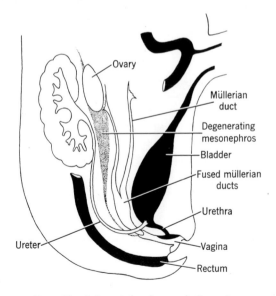

Figure 18. Embryonic female reproductive system.

albumen and a shell around the eggs. Marsupials have long, thin oviducts dilated at the posterior end into uteri which fuse just before they open into the urogenital sinus. The vagina is bifurcated. In true placental mammals the posterior ends of the two müllerian ducts form the uteri. The thin anterior part of the oviducts, or **fallopian tubes,** forms an infundibulum. In some mammals the infundibulum forms a sac around the ovary (Figure 19). When the two uterine swellings are completely separated, as in some rodents and bats, the uterus is **duplex** (Figure 20). When only the lower ends are fused, as in the ox, pig, and carnivores, the uterus is called **bipartite,** and each half is called a **horn** or cornu. When a greater degree of fusion than the bipartite occurs a **bicornuate** uterus is formed; this is found in ungulates and sheep. A complete fusion of the two uterine primordia gives rise to the **simplex uterus** found in primates. In placental mammals the uterus, or

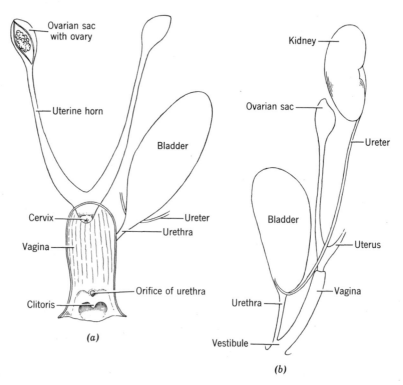

Figure 19. Female reproductive system of the dog: (a) surface view with the vagina opened; (b) lateral view.

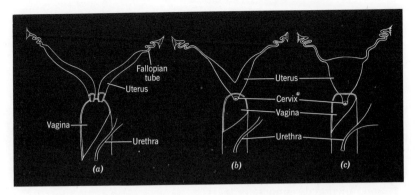

Figure 20. Types of uteri: (a) duplex; (b) bicornuate; (c) simplex.

uteri, empty into the vagina, which is open to the outside just dorsal to the urethra, by a shallow urogenital sinus or **vestibule**. The length of the vestibule varies in different mammals. The orifice of the vestibule is in the vulva. The **clitoris**, homologous with the penis of the male, is on the ventral part of the vulva. In primates the **labia** guard the vulva.

The inner layer of the uterus, the **endometrium**, is rich in blood vessels and uterine glands. The endometrium undergoes cyclic changes parallel to those of the ovary; at the time of ovulation it is very thick. After conception the embryo develops membranes which become attached to the endometrium to form the placenta, through which exchange between the maternal and embryonic membranes takes place. The wastes of the embryo are carried away by the maternal blood, and food, oxygen, and other essential materials are brought to the embryo by the umbilical veins. In spite of this intimacy, there is normally no admixture of fetal and maternal blood.

SUMMARY

1. The reproductive system develops in intimate association with the excretory system. Even though the sex of the individual is determined at fertilization, the embryo prepares itself to develop in either direction. Up to a certain epoch of differentiation the primary sex organs, or gonads, are indifferent, and the embryo is equipped to develop both sexual duct systems.

2. The male accessory organs are formed largely from the tubules and ducts of the mesonephric kidney. In contrast, the accessory organs of the female are formed from the müllerian ducts. The male reproductive system, then, is more intimately associated with the excretory system than the female reproductive system is.

3. In amniotes the efferent ducts of the testes develop from mesonephric tubules, and the epididymis, deferent duct, and seminal vesicle, from the mesonephric duct. The müllerian ducts of the male disappear and leave behind only two small vestiges. The müllerian ducts of the female system differentiate into oviducts and uteri, and the mesonephric tubules and ducts disappear, leaving only a few vestigial structures which have no functional significance.

4. The ducts of the male reproductive system are more primitive than those of the female. Even in amniotes, the male has a urogenital sinus into which both the urinary and reproductive ducts open. In the female these ducts are mostly separated. In mammals the female has a vagina, a new structure which has no counterpart in the male.

5. Most vertebrates, except placental mammals, have a cloaca. Monotremes have a cloaca not appreciably different from that of birds and reptiles.

6. In the amniotes fertilization takes place inside the female reproductive system. These animals, therefore, have external genitalia, differentiated to a greater or lesser degree for copulation. The male genital organ, the penis, is developed in reptiles, in some birds, and particularly in mammals. Internal fertilization also takes place in elasmobranchs and in some teleosts; the pelvic or anal fins of the males are modified as copulatory organs. The salamanders also have internal fertilization, but in most of them the male has no contact with the female.

7. From a phylogenetic as well as a developmental aspect the urogenital system gives evidence of evolutionary trends in two directions: one, toward the separation of the reproductive and excretory system, the other, toward a clear separation of the two sexes. Beginning with the hermaphroditic hagfishes and progressing through the fishes and amphibians, these systems diverge more and more. Complete separation occurs in the female mammals. The occasional congenital aberrations that occur in man and other mammals can be explained from our knowledge of comparative anatomy and embryology.

SUGGESTED READING

Bullough, W. S., 1951, *Vertebrate Sexual Cycles.* Methuen and Company Ltd., London.

Noble, G. K., 1931, *The Biology of the Amphibia.* McGraw-Hill Book Company, Inc., New York.

Witschi, E., 1956, Development of Vertebrates. W. B. Saunders Company, Philadelphia and London.

(See suggested reading in Chapter 10.)

CHAPTER

12

Figure 1.   Portrait of a cat showing the vibrissae, or sensory hairs.

THE SENSE ORGANS

Living organisms are constantly bombarded by disturbances in the environment. Sensory cells "tuned in" to specific disturbances convert them into stimuli, and aggregates of such cells on the surface of the body form receptor organs which translate these excitations into nerve impulses. These are carried by the nerves to the central nervous system, where they are interpreted as sensations. The central nervous system, in turn, coordinates the proper responses of the body to the stimuli. Receptor organs are the receiving sets, or the windows of the brain, which give the animal information about its environment. Each receptor organ is sensitive only to certain kinds and ranges of energies.

All receptor organs are derived from the ectoderm. When the central nervous system withdrew to the center of the body it left feelers on the surface that keep it in touch with the outside. In spite of the gross evolutionary changes that have taken place in the receptor organs, their sensory cells have retained a similar structure and function.

Sensory nerves are afferent fibers that carry impulses from the receptor organs to the central nervous system. Sherrington (1906) classified afferent nerves into **interoceptive, exteroceptive** and **proprioceptive.** Interoceptive nerve fibers carry impulses from the viscera. Exteroceptive and proprioceptive fibers are the somatic afferent elements, concerned with the adjustments of the individual to the external environment. Exteroceptive fibers carry impulses from the surface of the body and are stimulated by external stimuli; proprioceptive fibers convey stimuli that arise from muscles, tendons, joints, and the semicircular canals of the inner ear. Each group of afferent fibers emerges from sense organs which are fashioned to respond to a particular set of stimuli. This chapter describes briefly only the anatomy of the major sense organs that subserve touch, smell, taste, vision, and hearing.

THE CUTANEOUS RECEPTORS

Skin is the most ancient sensitive tissue of the animal body. It records touch, light, deep pressure, contact, several kinds of pain, itch, tickle, vibration, cold, and heat. There are numerous and different nerve endings at different depths from the surface of the skin, and each category of nerve ending has been ascribed specific functions in transmitting certain stimuli, but it is by no means certain precisely what each of these nerve endings really does.

The barbules around the mouth of such bottom-feeding fishes as the carp and catfish are supplied with tactile receptors which enable them to move about in the dark. Elasmobranchs have special cutaneous nerve endings at the bases of their fins. Amphibians have cutaneous receptor organs on the surface of the tongue and free nerve endings throughout the epidermis. Some reptiles are said to have tactile receptors underneath the scaly skin and on the tongue. Birds have cutaneous receptors in the **apteria,** the skin area free of feathers. Nearly all of the skin of mammals has sensory receptors of some sort. Those surfaces that come in contact with external objects are usually free of hair and are rich fields of **tactile** and **pressure receptors.** The foot and digital pads, the ventral side of the prehensile tail of some American monkeys, the bare snout of the pig and other routing animals, all contain tactile receptors.

Mammals have stiff hairs around the face, called **vibrissae** (see Figures 1, 9), whose follicles are surrounded by a blood sinus and extensive plexuses of sensory nerves. These sensory hairs, particularly well-developed in nocturnal animals, help them to guide their movements in the dark. Other hair follicles are also surrounded by sensory nerves and serve as touch receptors. The face, ears, and wings of bats are covered with sensory hairs. These animals depend less on sight for orientation than on auditory acuity and tactile and pressure receptors on the surface of their bodies.

THE LATERAL LINE ORGANS

These cutaneous receptor organs, found around the head and the sides of the body of fishes and larval amphibians, apparently give them orientation in the water, where the accuracy of optic orientation is reduced. These organs supplement vision by helping to locate objects at a distance (see discussion in Brown, 1957). Unlike other cutaneous receptors, most of which are connected to **spinal nerves,** the lateral line organs are connected with branches of cranial nerves VII (facial), IX (glossopharyngeal), and X (vagus). The lateral line organs are rows of pits, depressions, or grooves in which are clustered sensory cells, each with a sensory hair protruding from its free surface. Mucus secreted by surrounding cutaneous glands protects the sensory hairs and keeps debris from accumulating over them. Vibrations caused by water currents passing through the pits or grooves stimulate the sensory hair.

Only aquatic amphibians have a lateral line organ. During the metamorphosis of salientians some of the lateral line organs of the tadpoles become modified into cutaneous tactile receptors.

THE ORGANS OF SMELL

The olfactory sense organs are ancient. They are gigantic in fishes; the olfactory lobes are the largest part of a fish's brain. At their free surface olfactory cells have a "sensory hair"; at their base a process continues back to the olfactory bulbs of the brain to form the olfactory nerve. Nonsensory epithelial cells scattered between the olfactory cells form a protecting palisade for them. Goblet cells secrete mucus over the epithelium, keeping it moist and protected from injury. The stimulus of smell consists of minute chemical particles in the water or air which stimulate the sensory hairs of the olfactory cells.

Cyclostomes have a single median opening on the dorsal side of the head which leads through a short canal to a blind sac, lined with olfactory epithelium. Two olfactory nerves leave this sac, one on each side. Gnathostomes have a pair of blind olfactory sacs. In elasmobranchs a superficial groove extends from each nasal orifice to the corresponding corner of the mouth, which could be considered a primitive oronasal passage. In Choanichthyes the nasal sacs open through the roof of the mouth by **internal nares** or choanae to form the first phylogenetic internal oronasal canals. The epithelial lining of the nasal passages is folded; this increases the surface area of the olfactory epithelium. In amphibians the short nasal passages open at the anterior end of the palate, just posterior to the lateral extensions of the vomer. The olfactory epithelium is located in the upper part of the nasal passage, where in terrestrial forms a lateral fold increases the surface area. Mucous glands secrete a viscid fluid over the epithelium. Since the choanae open into the mouth, olfactory stimuli can be received not only from the outside but through the mouth as well. Salientia have an accessory cavity, **Jacobson's organ,** located ventrolateral to the nasal cavity and derived from it; it is lined with olfactory epithelium which is connected with cranial nerves I (olfactory) and V (trigeminus).

In reptiles, birds, and mammals which have a **secondary palate** the nasal passages are long and the choanae open far back in the pharynx. The anterior part of the nasal passage of reptiles forms a shallow dilated vestibule in which a single bony fold, or **concha,** is covered with sensory epithelium. Jacobson's organ, vestigial in turtles and crocodiles, is best developed in snakes and lizards. It is separated from the nasal passage and opens separately into the mouth. The short and compressed nasal vestibules of birds contain three bony conchae covered with olfactory epithelium. Jacobson's organ, prominent during development, is vestigial in the adult. Birds, whose sense of smell is very poor, have a small olfactory lobe in the brain.

The sense of smell is highly developed in mammals. Their nasal passages are elaborate and varied, and they reach their greatest development in carnivores and ungulates. Three sets of turbinated bones or conchae, the **nasoturbinals, ethmoturbinals,** and **maxilloturbinals,** slow down the passage of air on its way to the pharynx (Figure 2). The olfactory epithelium is usually concentrated over the ethmoturbinals. The basal processes of the olfactory cells travel back to the olfactory lobe through the cribriform plate. Jacobson's organ, well-developed in the embryos of monotremes, marsupials, insectivores, and primates, is not found in adult mammals.

TASTE ORGANS

Taste receptor cells are usually aggregated in taste or gustatory buds. Sensory taste cells have an apical "taste hair" and a basal process that makes contact with fine nerve endings from branches of cranial nerves

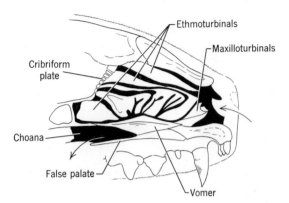

Figure 2.
The nasal passages of a cat.

Ethmoturbinals

Maxilloturbinals

Cribriform plate

Choana

False palate

Vomer

VII (facial), IX (glossopharyngeal), and X (vagus). The majority of the taste buds are in contact with fibers of the glossopharyngeal nerve.

In the cyclostomes taste receptors are found in the pharyngeal lining of the ammocoetes and on the surface of the head in the adult. In fishes taste receptors are generally located on the outer surface of the body, but in elasmobranchs they are located in the mouth and pharynx. Taste receptors of amphibians are confined to the lining of the mouth, tongue, and pharynx; in Salientia they are often concentrated in raised papillae on the tongue. Reptiles and particularly snakes and crocodiles have taste buds located far back in the mouth cavity; the anterior part of the oral cavity of these animals is cornified, and gustatory receptors would serve little purpose there. Birds have few taste buds, usually confined to the floor of the mouth or along the inside of the maxilla; in parrots they are borne on the fleshy tongue.

Mammals have an acute sense of taste. Their taste buds are found primarily at the back of the tongue, on the walls of the circumvallate papillae and folliate papillae, and on the soft palate, the epiglottis, and the pharyngeal and laryngeal walls (see Figure 17, Chapter 7).

THE EYE

Each eye is housed in an **orbit** on the side of the skull. Although the eyes of each class and order of vertebrates have specific recognizable differences, their structural and functional plan is relatively similar. The eyes of fishes are not basically different from those of birds or mammals (Figure 3). A general description of the mammalian eye, therefore, illustrates the general features.

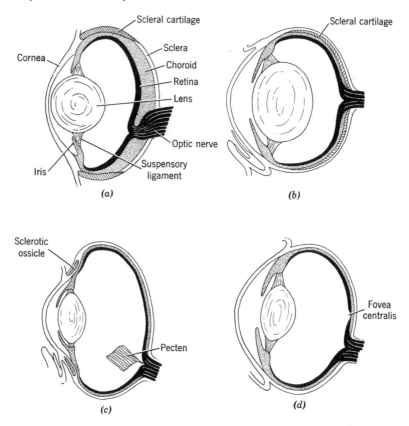

Figure 3.   Types of vertebrate eyes: (a) fish; (b) frog; (c) bird; (d) mammal.

The mammalian eye is a spherical or spheroidal structure composed of three concentric layers (Figure 4).   On the outside is the tough **sclerotic coat** or **sclera,** composed of fibrous connective tissue.   In the front of the eye the sclera bulges out as the cornea, which is transparent. The visible part of the eye in the intact animal consists of the cornea in the center, surrounded by the white sclera; the extrinsic muscles (see p. 144) are attached in characteristic positions to the sclera at the sides and the back of the eye.   The **choroid,** or middle coat of the eye, is attached to the sclera; it is heavily pigmented and richly vascularized.   It continues anteriorly to the base of the cornea, where it forms the **iris,** or shelf, the anterior part of which is the visible colored part of the eye. The center of the iris is perforated by the **pupil,** visible as a black dot.

Smooth muscle fibers in the iris are arranged radially and circularly; their contraction and relaxation constrict and dilate the pupillar opening. The **retina** is the inner coat of the eye; it rests against the choroid and extends anteriorly underneath the iris, with which it is fused. The retina has an inner **photosensory** layer and an outer pigmented layer, against the choroid. Light receptors are found only in the retina at the sides and back of the eye; the retina at the anterior part is nonsensory. Behind the opening of the pupil the transparent, biconvex **crystalline lens** is held in place by a fibrous **suspensory ligament;** this is attached to the **ciliary body** at the base of the iris and is composed of smooth muscle fibers (Figure 5). When these muscles contract they place variable amounts of tension on the inelastic suspensory ligament, and the convexities of the lens decrease or increase anteroposteriorly; the lens is also brought nearer to or farther from the surface of the cornea. The contractions of the ciliary muscles also change the degree of convexity of the cornea. These changes bring about adjustments of the eye in focusing upon objects near or far, adjustments which are controlled by the autonomic nervous system. The space between the cornea and the iris is the **anterior chamber;** the space between the suspensory ligament and the lens and the iris is the **posterior chamber.** The two chambers communicate through the pupil and are filled with a watery **aqueous humor.** The cavity behind the lens and suspensory ligament and in front of the retina is filled with a gelatinous **vitreous humor.**

The sensory layer of the retina is composed of two types of radially oriented sensory cells; **rods,** long and narrow, and **cones,** shorter and

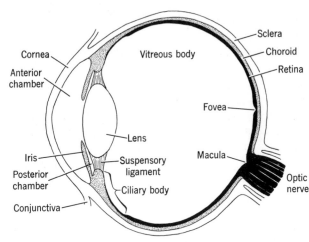

Figure 4.
Diagram of
the mammalian eye.

303

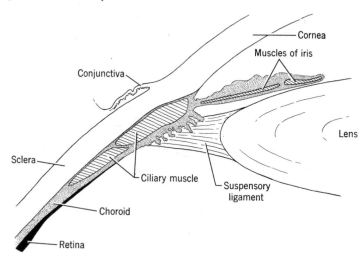

Figure 5. Diagram of a mammalian ciliary body.

stout (Figure 6). *The rods are sensitive to faint light; the cones are sensitive to bright light and are concerned with color discrimination.* The free ends of the rods are oriented toward the pigmented nonsensory outer layer. The centripetal end of the rods and cones is in contact with bipolar nerve cells; these in turn make contact with other **nerve ganglion cells,** the long distal processes of which sweep over the inner surface of the retina and converge toward a place at the back of the eye where they come together and travel through the coats of the eye to form the **optic nerve.** The place on the surface of the retina where these fibers plunge into the optic nerve has no sensory cells and is known as the **blind spot.** The **fovea centralis** is the spot of greatest visual acuity, where cones are so crowded together that they almost exclude the rods. The retina is inverted; that is, the sensory cells face away from the inner surface, and light must pass through several layers of nerve cells before reaching the rods and cones (Figure 6). The eye has several accessory structures. The six extrinsic muscles move the eye within the orbit. Fishes have a fold of skin around the eye, and in some elasmobranchs the fold forms partially movable upper and lower lids or **palpebrae.** Tetrapods have movable muscular lids that generally close over the eye, protecting it from injury and keeping it moist. The inside of the lids is lined with the **conjunctiva,** a smooth epithelium which is continuous over the surface of the exposed eye. In some vertebrates the **nictitating membrane,** a semitransparent third lid, is located under the other two in the median angle of the eye. When it closes it passes laterally over the sclera and cornea. In mammals the membrane is reduced to a small median fold. Various glands pour their serous, mucous, and lipoidal secretions onto the conjunctiva to keep it moist. These glands are different in different species and for convenience all can be called lacrimal glands.

There are no major differences in the eyes of the different vertebrates (see Figure 3). The hagfishes have a very small degenerate eye buried underneath the skin, and the eyes of the lampreys are relatively primitive. They have no ciliary body, and the spherical lens, having no suspensory ligament, is held in place by the vitreous humor. The eyes of fishes are flattened anteroposteriorly. Those of elasmobranchs rest in

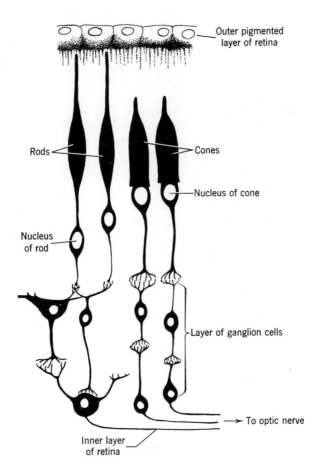

Rods

Cones

Nucleus of cone

Nucleus of rod

Outer pigmented layer of retina

Layer of ganglion cells

Figure 6.
Simplified diagram of
the mammalian retina.

To optic nerve

Inner layer
of retina

the orbit on a cartilaginous **optic pedicle** which has the same relation to the eye that a tee has to a golf ball. The sclera often contains cartilage plates or bone. The lens is nearly spherical, and there are neither ciliary muscles nor a suspensory ligament. Some teleosts have a very small suspensory ligament. The inner surface of the choroid of the eyes of fish characteristically contains guanine crystals which form a light reflector called **tapetum lucidum**. The retina shows many species variations. The elasmobranchs have few or no cones; teleosts may have doubled cones.

The eyes of salientians can be protruded or retracted in the orbit by levator and retractor muscles. The lower lid is transparent and more movable than the upper and in closing it moves up like a nictitating membrane. There are some ciliary muscles, and the suspensory ligament holds the lens, which is slightly flattened anteroposteriorly. Contractions of the ciliary muscle move the lens back and forth. The sensory part of the retina consists of green and red rods and single and double cones. Urodeles have no eyelids, and the entire eye is simpler than that of salientians. The wormlike caecilians have vestigial eyes.

The eyes of reptiles are better developed than those of amphibians. The ciliary muscles are larger and the suspensory ligament is firmly attached to the flattened lens. Contraction of the muscle can change the position and the shape of the lens. Except for snakes, reptiles have movable eyelids, the lower being larger and more movable. A true nictitating membrane is also present. Several orbital glands secrete serous and lipoidal substances that lubricate the lids. In snakes the skin over the eyes is transparent. Some lizards have a curious tuft of capillaries called a **pecten** which projects into the vitreous body at the back of the eye.

Birds have disproportionately large eyes, flattened anteroposteriorly (see Figure 3). A ring of **sclerotic ossicles** surrounds the outward bulging hemispherical cornea. Contractions of the ciliary muscles bring about visual adjustments by changing the shape of the biconvex lens, and the convexity of the cornea. A large pecten protrudes into the vitreous body from the optic nerve. The shape of the pecten is different even in closely related species, and although it is an interesting anatomical feature its function is unknown. Birds have movable upper and lower lids and a true nictitating membrane. In most birds the eyes are set on the side of the head, and each eye has an independent field of vision. Most birds of prey have a **facial disc,** and the eyes are turned anteriorly so that they share, at least in part, fields of vision to give them **binocular** or **stereoscopic** sight.

306

The eyes of birds are miraculous organs. Sparrows or larks must discriminate between small, almost microscopic seeds camouflaged in their environment. Remarkable adaptation must take place in the eyes of a hawk when it swoops on its prey from some distance in the air. The adaptations of the lens and cornea and perhaps of the pecten must be precise and instantaneous.

The mammalian eye has already been described. It, too, is an instrument of infinite precision and efficiency.

THE ORGANS OF EQUILIBRIUM AND HEARING

The ear is the receptor of sound and equilibrium. The second function is older than the first and has remained almost unchanged throughout the phylum. The auditory mechanism consists of an **outer**, a **middle** and an **inner** ear. Only the inner ear is found in every vertebrate; the middle ear makes its appearance in the amphibians, and the outer ear is found only in the amniotes. We will concern ourselves mostly with the inner ear, which has the receptor organs for both equilibration and hearing. The inner ear arises from the ectodermal **otic vesicle** of embryos, alongside the hindbrain. The vesicle becomes sunken in the mesenchyme of the embryo and remains in communication with the surface by a slender tube, which later becomes closed in some classes. A constriction later divides the auditory vesicle into a dorsal **utricle** and a ventral **saccule**. All of the sensory elements of the ear develop from these vesicles. From the utricle develop the three semicircular canals (Figures 7, 8). The basal part of the limbs of the semicircular canals is dilated into an **ampulla**. From the saccule grows the **lagena**, which in mammals shows variable degrees of coiling and is called the **cochlea**. The entire inner ear mechanism, including the utricle and semicircular canals, and the saccule and lagena comprise the **membranous labyrinth**. This is surrounded by a **perilymphatic space**, and the entire structure is enclosed in cartilage or bone which follows every outline of it and is called the **skeletal labyrinth**.

The receptors of equilibrium consist of sensory cells in the ampullae of the semicircular canal, called **cristae acusticae,** and in the utricle and saccule, called **maculae acusticae**. The sensory cells are tall and spindle-shaped and have long sensory hairs on the free border. At their base these cells make contact with cranial nerve VIII (auditory). The long sensory hairs are matted together in a gelatinous mass called **otoconia** (Figure 8), which contains protein and calcium crystals. The

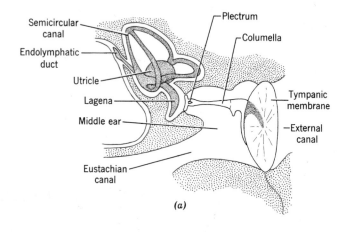

Semicircular canal
Endolymphatic duct
Utricle
Lagena
Middle ear
Eustachian canal
Plectrum
Columella
Tympanic membrane
External canal

(a)

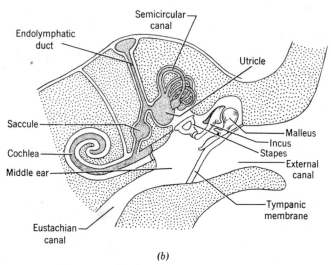

Semicircular canal
Endolymphatic duct
Utricle
Saccule
Cochlea
Middle ear
Malleus
Incus
Stapes
External canal
Tympanic membrane
Eustachian canal

(b)

Figure 7. Diagram of the ear mechanism: (a) reptile; (b) mammal.

entire inner ear apparatus is filled with a fluid called **endolymph.** Disturbances in the endolymph cause pressure by the otoconia on the sensory hairs, which transmit nerve impulses to the auditory centers.

The inner ear of cyclostomes is primitive or degenerated. In fishes it consists of very large semicircular canals, one or two utricles, and one saccule. A canal from the saccule of elasmobranchs, referred to as the **endolymphatic duct,** connects the inner ear with the surface of the head.

The endolymphatic duct of many fishes develops from the saccule. The lagena from the ventral part of the saccule contains a macula.

The inner ear of amphibians is enclosed in a bony labyrinth. The saccule has a lagena and two extra diverticula that are believed to contain the organs of hearing.

The lagena of reptiles is longer than that of amphibians, and that of birds is longer still. In mammals the lagena is very long and in some forms is coiled in a snail-shaped cochlea (Figure 8). The coils of the cochlea may vary from only half in the sloth to five in the guinea pig. The cochlea is hollow and filled with endolymph, as is the rest of the

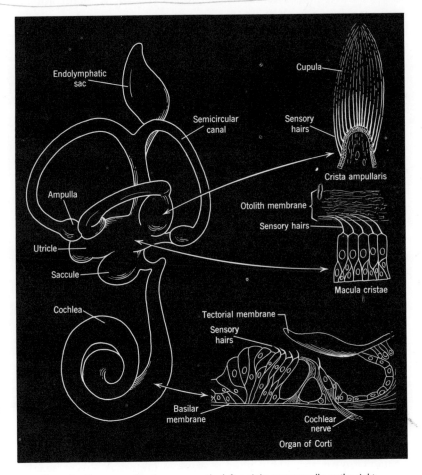

Figure 8. The mammalian inner ear on the left and the sensory cells on the right.

inner ear, and is surrounded by perilymph. Two membranous partitions separate the cochlea into an upper chamber, called **scala vestibulae**, and a lower one called, **scala tympani**. A smaller middle chamber, called **scala media** or **cochlear duct,** contains the acoustic cells. The three chambers are actually three canals which run a parallel course the entire length of the cochlea. The scalae vestibuli and tympani come together at the apex of the cochlea, or the **helicotrema,** but the cochlear duct ends blindly there. The cochlear duct is narrower at the base of the cochlea than it is at its apex. The acoustic sensory cells, referred to collectively as the **organ of Corti,** are located on the floor of the cochlear duct, called the **basilar membrane** (Figure 8). The organ of Corti consists of a band of sensory cells, the free end of which terminates in a tuft of hairs. A gelatinous, noncellular **tectorial membrane** rests over the sensory hairs.

The middle ear or **tympanum,** found first in salientians, is a chamber derived from an extension of the first pharyngeal pouch which communicates with the pharynx by the narrow **Eustachian tube.** The middle ear is separated from the outside by a translucent, avascular membrane, the tympanic membrane or eardrum (see Figure 7). In the middle ear chamber an upper oval opening, the fenestra ovalis, connects with the scala vestibuli and a lower opening connects with the Eustachian tube. In salientians a slender bone, the columella, extends from the center of the tympanic membrane across the middle ear and is fitted into the fenestra ovalis. The vibrations caused by sound waves on the eardrum are transmitted to the fenestra ovalis by the columella.

Reptiles and birds have two small bones in the middle ear: a columella attached to the tympanic membrane is hinged with a **plectrum,** which fits into the fenestra ovalis (see Figure 7). Mammals have three ear ossicles: the malleus, in contact with the tympanic membrane, is hinged with the incus; this in turn is hinged with the stapes, which plugs the fenestra ovalis (see Figure 7). The stapes is homologous with the columella of reptiles and birds. Whether a single columella, as in amphibians, or three ossicles as in mammals, all the bones in the middle ear function in conveying the vibrations of the tympanic membrane to the inner ear. In birds and mammals the tympanic membrane is placed at the end of a deep and often tortuous canal which opens to the outside, the **external auditory meatus.** In most mammals an outer ear, or **pinna,** serves as a parabolic catcher of sound waves. Bats and other mammals with particularly acute hearing have gigantic pinnae (Figure 9). The pinnae of aquatic mammals are reduced or missing.

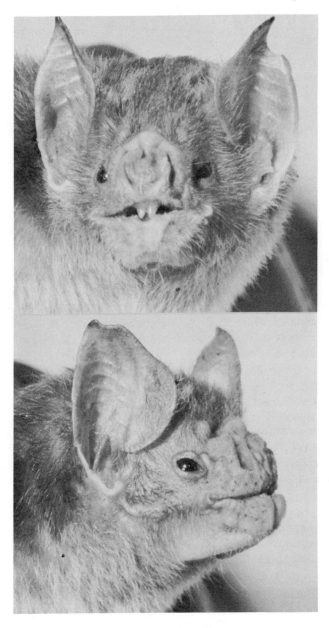

Figure 9. Portraits of a South American vampire, showing the small eyes, enormous ears, and the muzzle studded with sensory hairs, seen here as dark spots in the lower figure. (Courtesy of William A. Wimsatt and David Allen, Cornell University.)

SUMMARY

1. Changes or disturbances outside or within the organism are picked up by sensory cells, aggregates of which form the receptor organs. Disturbances within the body are recorded by interoceptors, those outside the body by exteroceptors. The principal sense organs are five: cutaneous (touch), olfactory (smell), gustatory (taste), visual (light), and auditory (equilibrium and hearing).

2. The sense organs are derived from the surface ectoderm and from the neural ectoderm. With the exception of the tactile organs, the sensory cells of most sense organs have a similar basic structure. The cells are spindle-shaped and terminate in one or several sensory hairs.

3. Cutaneous sensations are many and varied. Numerous different nerve endings in the skin record these stimuli.

The lateral line organs of fishes and aquatic amphibians are systems of cutaneous receptors over the head and the sides of the body.

4. The olfactory organs are best developed in fishes, in which they are blind sacs on the surface of the snout. In Choanichthyes nasal canals open through the palate by the internal nares or choanae, and air may be drawn into the mouth through nasal passages. Amphibians have short nasal passages; in the amniotes the choanae open posteriorly near the pharynx. The olfactory surface is increased by the progressive development of the conchae or convoluted bony supports. These achieve the greatest development in the mammals. Jacobson's organ, found in amphibians and reptiles, is an accessory olfactory organ.

5. Gustatory cells are located in taste buds. In fishes these may be found over the entire surface of the skin; in some they tend to be concentrated on the head, and in a few, in the mouth. Beginning with some amphibians, taste buds are localized in the mouth. In mammals they are found primarily on the back of the tongue.

6. The basic features of the vertebrate eye are little changed in the different classes of vertebrates. The eye consists of three concentric layers, the innermost of which is the light-sensitive retina. The retina is inverted; the light-sensitive rods and cones are on the outer surface, and light must pass through the inner layers of the retina before it reaches them. Numerous progressive changes and additions are found in the eyes of amphibians, reptiles, birds, and mammals.

7. The vertebrate ear records both equilibrium and hearing. The inner ear consists of two connected vesicles, the utricle and the saccule, three semicircular canals attached to the utricle, an endolymphatic duct attached to the saccule, and a lagena, also attached to the saccule. These structures are hollow and connected and filled with a fluid called endolymph. The receptors for equilibrium are found in the ampullae of the semicircular canals and in the utricle and saccule. The sensory cells have long sensory hairs embedded in a gelatinous mass which contains crystalline bodies called otoconia. The lagena, which contains the receptors for hearing, begins to attain some importance in the terrestrial amphibians. It becomes progressively longer in reptiles and birds and is coiled into a snaillike cochlea in mammals. The cochlea is divided into three chambers, of which only the middle one, the cochlear duct, contains sensory receptor cells, called collectively the organ of Corti.

8. An extension of the first pharyngeal pouch gives rise to the middle ear of amphibians and amniotes. This is separated from the outside by a tympanic membrane. A series of otic ossicles connects the tympanic membrane with the inner ear. Amphibians have one ossicle, the columella; reptiles and birds have two, and mammals have three, the malleus, incus, and stapes. Vibrations of the tympanic membrane are transmitted to the inner ear by way of these ossicles. Pressure on the tympanic membrane from the outside is equalized through the Eustachian tube, which connects the middle ear with the pharynx. Only birds and mammals have a prominent outer ear canal. An outer ear, present only in mammals, converges the sound waves toward the outer ear canal.

SUGGESTED READING

Brown, M. E., ed., 1957, *The Physiology of Fishes.* Vol. II. Academic Press Inc., New York.

Geldard, F. A., 1953, *The Human Senses.* John Wiley & Sons, Inc., New York. An excellent book on the structure and function of the sense organs.

Prince, J. H., 1956, *Comparative Anatomy of the Eye.* C. C. Thomas, Springfield, Ill.

Sherrington, C. S., 1906, *The Integrative Action of the Nervous System.* Yale University Press, New Haven, Conn.

Walls, G. L., 1942, *The Vertebrate Eye and Its Adaptive Radiation.* Cranbrook Institute of Science, Bloomfield Hills, Mich.

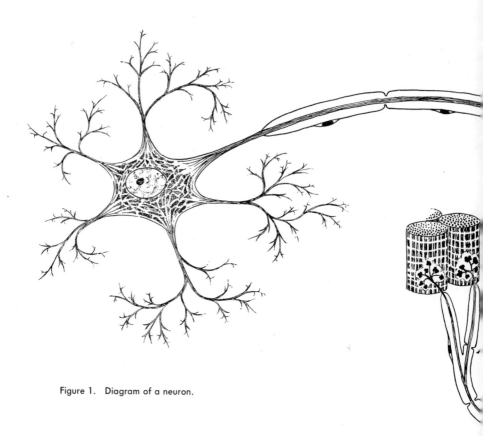

Figure 1.   Diagram of a neuron.

THE NERVOUS SYSTEM

GENERAL INTRODUCTION

The **nervous system** is the principal coordinating center of the body and the relay system for incoming and outgoing messages. It adjusts the activities of the individual to its environment and maintains the integrity of the body. The most characteristic features of nervous tissue are **irritability**, or the ability inherent in all protoplasm to react to stimuli or disturbances, and **conductivity**, the power to transmit energy set off by a stimulus from one locality to another without perceptible change in the conducting tissue. Nerves carry impulses of energy so minute that very sensitive instruments are needed to record them. Yet when these impulses reach muscles they find substances in them so responsive that they discharge sudden bursts of energy. The nervous system is the receiving, conducting, and coordinating mechanism, the specific apparatus of all conscious existence, and it maintains the unity of personality.

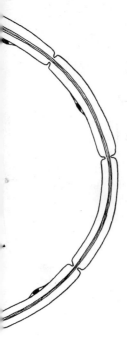

The nervous system has two major components: the **central nervous system**, which consists of the brain and spinal cord, and the **peripheral nervous system**, which includes all the nerves and ganglia. Both systems are composed of contiguous chains of cells called **nerve fibers** or **neurons**, which are the structural and functional units of the nervous system. Neurons have a cell body, with a nucleus and cytoplasm, and two types of cytoplasmic processes, the **dendrites** and the **axons** (Figure 1). According to their shape, neurons may be **unipolar** or **pseudo-unipolar**, having only one process attached to the cell body; **bipolar**, usually

315

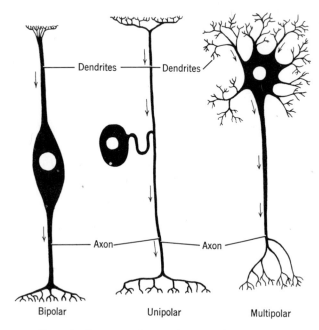

Figure 2.   Three general types of neurons; the arrows indicate the direction of the flow of the nerve impulses.

found in the sense organs, with one dendrite and one axon (pseudo-unipolar cells are embryologically and physiologically bipolar cells [see Figure 10]); and **multipolar neurons,** with several dendrites and one, usually long axon (Figures 1, 2).   Dendrites are cytoplasmic extensions of the cell body that conduct impulses toward the cell body.   Neurons have only one axon, which splits into several branches before it ends in many rootlike **telodendria** (Figures 1, 2).   Axons carry impulses away from the cell body and terminate at various distances from it; those that terminate in the foot, for example, have the cell body in the spinal cord. Many of the axons in the peripheral nervous system are covered with a white, fatty myelin sheath and are known as **myelinated** or **medullated fibers;** those which have no myelin are **nonmyelinated fibers.**   *The axons of all peripheral nerve fibers, myelinated or nonmyelinated, are covered with a tough, hyalin pellicle called the neurilemma sheath; only the telodendria are naked.   The fibers in the central nervous system may or may not be covered with a myelin sheath, but they are never covered with a neurilemma sheath.*   The myelin sheath around the peripheral nerve fibers is interrupted at spaced intervals by circular constrictions, the **nodes of Ranvier,** where the neurilemma sheath dips in and almost comes in contact with the **axis cylinder**

316

or axon (Figure 3). The free ends of the dendrites of the peripheral nervous system are modified into receiving ends, or **receptors,** which translate stimuli into **nerve impulses.** These are carried over chains of neurons, or **transmitters,** which terminate in **effector organs** or **organs of response.** The receptors are the **sensory mechanism;** the fibers to the effector organs carry **motor** impulses. A **nerve** is a bundle of nerve fibers in the peripheral nervous system held together by connective tissue. A bundle of nerve fibers in the central nervous system is a **fasciculus** or **fiber tract.** An aggregate of nerve cell bodies in the peripheral nervous system is a **ganglion;** in the central nervous system, a **nucleus.** Nerve fibers come in contact at a **synapse,** where the telodendria of one fiber transmit impulses to the dendrites of another neuron in the chain.

Nerve impulses travel from the receptors along sensory or afferent nerve fibers toward the brain and the spinal cord, through the **cranial nerves** and **spinal nerves,** respectively. The cell bodies of sensory nerve fibers usually reside outside the central nervous system in the cranial and spinal ganglia.

The spinal cord is a tube which extends posteriorly from the brain. At each intervertebral space the cord receives one pair of **sensory** roots or afferent nerves on the dorsal side, and one pair of **motor roots** or efferent nerves emerges on the ventral side. The cell bodies of the sensory roots are located in the large spinal ganglia; those of the motor roots are located within the spinal cord (Figure 4). When dorsal and ventral roots come together laterally they form mixed spinal nerves, which have both sensory and motor fibers. The spinal cord consists of **white matter** on the outside and **gray matter** in the center. The white color is due to the myelin sheath covering the nerve fibers; the gray color, to nonmyelinated fibers and to cell bodies. A **central canal** occupies the middle of the cord. In a simple reflex the stimulus travels from the receptor organ through the afferent sensory fibers of the dorsal root (Figure 5). These make a synaptic connection with **intraneural neurons** in the dorsal column of the gray matter; the axons of these in turn synapse in the **ventral gray column** with a terminal **motor neuron,** the axon of which emerges through the ventral root.

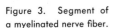

Figure 3. Segment of a myelinated nerve fiber.

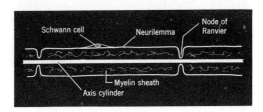

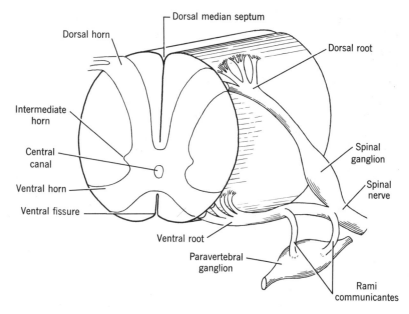

Figure 4.   Spinal cord and spinal nerves.

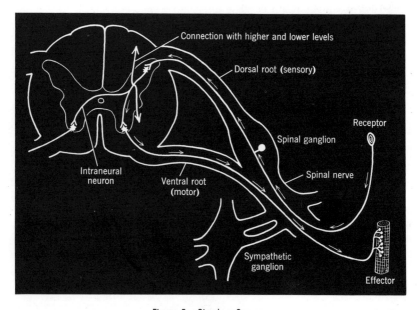

Figure 5.   Simple reflex arc.

A nerve impulse consists of volleys of disturbances traveling over many of the fibers of a nerve. It is actively propagated and normally conducted without dissipation, following the **all-or-none law.** This means that over the same fiber under most conditions the impulse travels at the same rate or not at all. The frequency of these disturbances is between 200 and 400 per second in nerves which are experimentally stimulated directly and between 25 and 60 when the receptors are stimulated. This is the frequency over sensory fibers. Motor fibers conduct from 10 to 90 impulses per second. *The velocity of a nerve impulse over a given nerve is constant, and only the frequency is increased with the intensity of the stimulus.* The velocity of nerve impulses is greater over the larger nerve fibers, and in mammalian nerves it ranges from 0.5 to 100 meters per second.

DEVELOPMENT

When the vertebrate body plan has just been established in the embryo all of the materials of the future nervous system are embodied in the neural plate, an epithelial thickening, broader anteriorly than posteriorly, located on the surface over the middorsal line (Figure 6). The edges of the neural plate become raised to form a neural groove; when the edges of the groove come together on the middorsal line they fuse

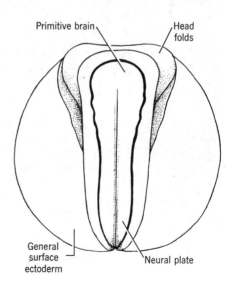

Figure 6. Early development of the neural plate in an amphibian egg.

Primitive brain

Head folds

General surface ectoderm

Neural plate

in the form of a neural tube. At the same time that the neural tube is being fashioned the edges of the epidermis lateral to the neural plate come together and fuse over the neural tube (Figure 7*a,b*). A mass of cells on each side of the line of the junction of the neural ectoderm with the general surface ectoderm, the **neural crest**, remains outside the neural tube (Figure 7*c,d*). Even before the neural tube is completely closed, it becomes enlarged at the anterior end and begins to show the three **primary brain vesicles**. The rest of the tube remains slender and gives rise to the spinal cord. The neural tube and neural crest are the raw materials from which the entire nervous system develops. In the early developmental stages the nervous system forms a very large part of the total mass of the embryo.

The neural tube shows no special structural organization at first, but subsequent proliferation of cells, their movements and differentiation, convert its wall into the characteristic structure seen in the central nervous system. The tube consists of a dorsal **alar sensory plate** and a ventral basal **motor plate,** the two being divided by the **sulcus limitans.** In spite of general differences, the spinal cord and the brain have the same basic structural plan.

Two constrictions separate the enlarged anterior end of the neural tube into the three primary divisions of the brain or **encephalon:**

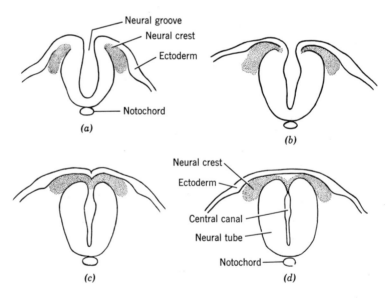

Figure 7. (a) to (d) Progressive closure of the neural plate showing the neural crest, stippled.

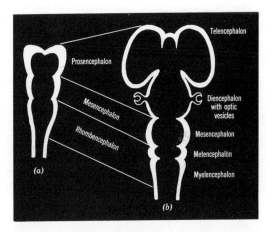

Figure 8. The early segmentation of the brain in a mammalian embryo: (a) primitive division; (b) further segmentation.

the forebrain, or prosencephalon, the midbrain, or mesencephalon, and the pear-shaped hindbrain, or rhombencephalon (Figure 8a). These early divisions are particularly distinct in the embryos of birds (see Figures 12a to f). The forebrain becomes divided linearly into the telencephalon and diencephalon; the midbrain remains undivided (Figure 8b). The telencephalon forms the two lateral vesicles which give rise to the cerebral hemispheres, and the diencephalon develops the optic vesicles. The rhombencephalon gives rise to the metencephalon, which later differentiates into the cerebellum and the pons, and the myelencephalon, which forms the medulla oblongata. These five segments are the essential parts from which the brain of higher vertebrates evolves (see Figure 11).

The undifferentiated nerve cells or neuroblasts develop processes and are gradually transformed into neurons. The number of neurons in an individual species is relatively constant and does not increase after late embryonic life. In spite of their size, adult animals have no more neurons than older embryos. The neuroblasts are bipolar at first, but later one of the processes, the axon, grows much longer than the others; the axon may remain entirely within the central nervous system, as in intraneural neurons, or it may emerge at the ventrolateral border of the neural tube as the efferent motor nerves (Figure 9). In the spinal cord these form the ventral root; in the brain, the motor roots of the cranial nerves. In the meantime the neural crest, which rests between the neural tube and the myotomes and extends the full length of the spinal cord to the level of the brain, becomes enlarged at the level of each mesodermal segment and assumes a beaded appearance. The attenuated segments between the successive swellings disappear, and the

321

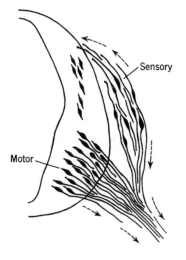

Figure 9. Migration of the neuroblasts from the neural tube and neural crest to form the motor and sensory nerves, respectively.

stranded aggregates of neural crest cells form the future spinal ganglia. The ganglia formed in the region of the hindbrain are not arranged segmentally. The neuroblasts become bipolar, and the two processes extend linearly at right angles to the axis of the cord, one toward it, the other away from it (Figure 9). The processes grow in parallel bundles which form the dorsal roots. The axons penetrate the neural tube, and the dendrites form the peripheral portion of the dorsal root nerve. Dorsal and ventral roots come together to form the spinal nerve; in the region of the brain the cranial nerves emerge as either ventral or dorsal roots. The spinal ganglia contain the cell bodies of the sensory neurons. The sensory neuroblasts are bipolar at first, but the two poles grow toward each other until they come into actual contact and form a single stalk, which gives rise to pseudo-unipolar neurons (Figure 10).

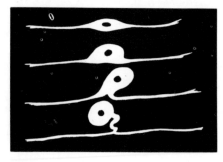

Figure 10. Development of a pseudo-unipolar neuron from a bipolar neuroblast.

Some neuroblasts from the neural crest migrate down the dorsal roots and come to rest in paired clusters, dorsolateral to the aorta. The segmentally paired masses of neuroblasts form bilateral chains of sympathetic ganglia along the dorsal aorta. Other ganglia, known as **collateral** or **prevertebral ganglia,** also arise from the neural crest. With the exception of the spinal and cranial ones, all ganglia belong to the autonomic nervous system. The neuroblasts in the autonomic ganglia differentiate into multipolar neurons. In fishes the neurons in the ganglia are unipolar and multipolar; in amphibians they are largely unipolar. Each cell in a ganglion makes a synaptic connection with the axon of a cell which resides in the central nervous system.

COMPARATIVE ANATOMY OF THE CENTRAL NERVOUS SYSTEM

The Brain

In spite of its complexity, the basic principles of the structure of the brain can be grasped easily. The brain is the principal correlating center of the sense organs and of locomotion. Birds, for instance, with their large, keen eyes, have a brain which is largely devoted to coordinating and relaying visual impulses. Animals with good ability for movement in more than one plane of space have a large cerebellum; sluggish ones usually have a small one. Only such points as these are emphasized in this chapter.

The brain and the spinal cord are covered with **meninges,** which support and protect them and bring the blood supply to them. Cyclostomes and fishes have a single-layered continuous **primitive meninx,** with a **perimeningeal** space between the meninx and the perichondrium or periosteum of the skull and neural canal. Strands of connective tissue cross the perimeningeal space, joining the meninx with the periosteum or perichondrium, and a lymphlike **cerebrospinal fluid** circulates in the space. Beginning with the amphibians, the meninx splits into a vascular **pia mater** in contact with the nerve tissue and a fibrous **dura mater** on the outside. The cerebrospinal fluid circulates in the **subdural space** between the two layers. Mammals have a spongy **arachnoid membrane** between the pia and dura mater; the **subarachnoid space** is filled with cerebrospinal fluid. In the cranium of mammals the dura mater is fused with the inner periosteum of the skull.

The central nervous system has remained a hollow structure; the individual cavities can be understood best by referring to the early embryonic stages shown in Figure 8. The original plan is modified in development, but it is not drastically altered. The neural canal is a continuous space in the brain and spinal cord. During the formation of the brain various sacculations develop and the original single canal attains chambers or ventricles. The cerebral hemispheres of the forebrain contain **ventricles I and II** or lateral ventricles, whereas the original unchanged space in the diencephalon remains as **ventricle III** (Figure 11). The lateral ventricles communicate with ventricle III through the **foramen of Munro.** A large capillary tuft, the **anterior choroid plexus,** secretes cerebrospinal fluid in all three of these ventricles. Ventricle III extends posteriorly through the midbrain as the **aqueduct of Sylvius** and posterior to that into the broad **ventricle IV** in the medulla oblongata. The large **posterior choroid plexus,** which hangs from the thin roof of ventricle IV (Figure 11), secretes the largest amount of the cerebrospinal fluid. The cavity of ventricle IV extends posteriorly as the central canal of the spinal cord. The cerebrospinal fluid escapes through small openings in the roof of ventricle IV to the subarachnoid space, where it is absorbed by the numerous arachnoid capillaries.

The central nervous system is composed of white matter, consisting

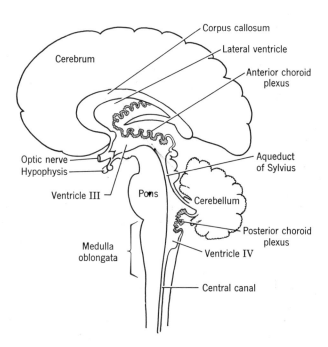

Figure 11. Median sagittal section of the brain of man.

of myelinated fibers without a neurilemma, and gray matter, consisting of aggregates of nerve cell bodies, or nuclei, nonmyelinated fibers, blood vessels, and supporting tissue.   In the spinal cord the white matter is on the outside and the gray matter, inside; in the brain the two are intermingled; and in the cerebrum and cerebellum the white matter is inside and the gray matter outside, indicating that myelinated fibers are on the inside and the cell bodies and nonmyelinated fibers on the outside.   There is no visible boundary between the medulla oblongata and the spinal cord, but the division occurs just anterior to the first spinal nerve.

The brain of early embryos, and of lower vertebrates, is all in one plane and almost in a straight line, but that of adult higher vertebrates becomes progressively folded so that it may be housed in the relatively small space of the cranium.   During development the forebrain bends forward to form a right-angle **cephalic flexure** at the level of the midbrain (see Figure 12).   A **pontine flexure** forms at the metencephalon, and a **cervical flexure** occurs at the junction of the spinal cord with the medulla.

The olfactory lobes, resting just behind the olfactory apparatus, are the most anterior and probably most ancient part of the brain.   These are very large in lower vertebrates, but their relative size decreases steadily as other parts of the brain become progressively larger (Figures 13, 14).   The telencephalic vesicles, or cerebral hemispheres, begin to develop in the reptile, in which the median dorsal portion broadens out to form the socalled **neopallium**, the **archipallium** being the olfactory lobe and associated older parts of the brain (Figures 13, 14).

Nerve cells migrate into the outer surface of the telencephalon, which differentiates into the **cortex of the cerebrum**.   The surface of the cortex of vertebrates below mammals is smooth; that of many mammals has ridges and grooves known as **gyri** and **sulci**, respectively.   The cerebral hemispheres of mammals are connected by three commissures: the **anterior** and **hippocampal commissures** connect the older, olfactory portions of the two hemispheres, and the large **corpus collossum** connects the new or neopallial, nonolfactory parts of the two hemispheres (see Figure 19).

The diencephalon, or the posterior part of the forebrain, contains the third ventricle and the large anterior choroid plexus.   Behind the diencephalon is the **epiphyseal apparatus,** composed of an anterior **parietal body**, well-developed in amphibians and reptiles, and a posterior **pineal body,** found in the brain of all vertebrates (see Figure 19), both thought to be vestiges of an ancient visual apparatus.   The pineal body

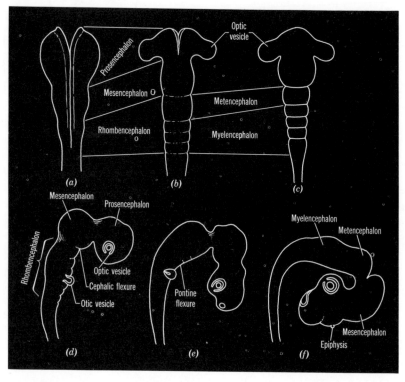

Figure 12. The development of the brain of the bird: (a) (b) (c) dorsal view of early embryos; (d) (e) (f) lateral view of progressively older embryos.

is glandular and is suspected of having an endocrine function. The **thalamus,** which corresponds to the thick lateral walls of the diencephalon, consists of fiber tracts to and from the telencephalon. These massive tracts form the large middle commissure across the middle of ventricle III. On the ventral part of the diencephalon is the **optic chiasma,** a structure composed of the optic nerves as they partially cross from one side to the other on the way to the brain. Next comes the **hypothalamus,** which controls the autonomic nervous system and most of the involuntary activities of the body. It consists of the **tuber cinereum** just behind the chiasma, which controls parasympathetic action, and the **mammillary bodies** behind it, which integrate olfactory sense. Behind the mammillary bodies is the infundibulum, a funnel-shaped outgrowth, from which extends the stalk of the posterior lobe of the pituitary. The anterior lobe of the pituitary is not of neural origin and develops from **Rathke's pouch,** a diverticulum of the stomodeum.

326

The midbrain is marked off from the hindbrain by a constriction called the isthmus. Two large peduncles on the floor of the mesencephalon connect the forebrain with the hindbrain (see Figure 18). The two dorsolateral optic lobes are divided in mammals by a transverse groove which forms four rounded elevations called, collectively, **corpora quadrigemina.** Of these, the **superior colliculi,** in front, are the visual receptive centers; the **inferior colliculi,** behind, integrate auditory sense. A posterior commissure contains fibers connecting the two sides of the brain. The floor of the mesencephalon also has the centers of cranial nerves III and IV (oculomotor and trochlear).

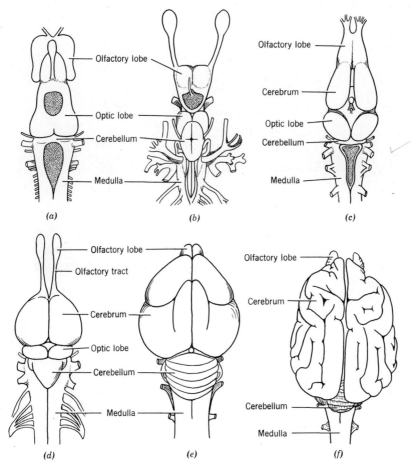

Figure 13. Comparative anatomy of brains, dorsal view: (a) cyclostome; (b) shark; (c) frog; (d) alligator; (e) bird; (f) mammal.

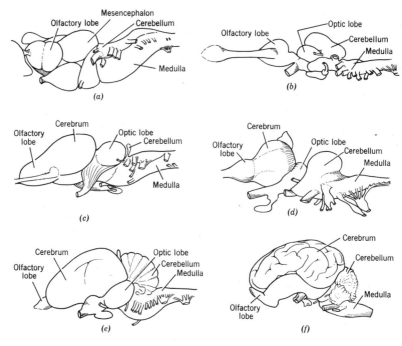

Figure 14. Comparative anatomy of brains, lateral view: (a) cyclostome; (b) shark; (c) frog; (d) turtle; (e) bird; (f) mammal.

The cerebellum is the expanded roof of the metencephalon; it controls coordinated muscle action and equilibrium and is more highly developed in active than in sluggish animals. Birds and mammals have a large and convoluted cerebellum with a gray cortex on the outside and a white medulla, or **arbor vitae**, in the center (see Figure 19). The cerebellum of mammals is roughly divided into a median lobe, **vermis**, and two lateral hemispheres. The entire surface is folded so as to form sulci and gyri.

The medulla oblongata has thick walls and a thin membranous roof from which the large posterior choroid plexus hangs into the broad ventricle IV. All of the fibers that connect the spinal cord and the brain pass through the medulla oblongata, and its walls contain the centers of cranial nerves V to X in cyclostomes, fishes, and amphibians and V to XII in amniotes. The medulla contains the centers of nearly all vital, involuntary reflexes.

Impulses that enter the spinal cord and travel upward to the brain cross over from one side to the other by means of **commissural neurons.** In this way the activities of the two sides of the body are integrated; in the medulla oblongata the fibers **decussate,** or cross over to the other side. Injury to one side of the brain results in damage to the other side of the body.

Amphioxus. The brain is a small vesicle at the front end of the neural tube, with no enlargements into separate parts. In transverse sections the brain is triangular; it has a broad base and a narrow roof and is similar to the neural tube of early vertebrate embryos.

Cyclostomes. The small brain resembles that of the more primitive fishes and amphibians; the medulla oblongata, however, forms a larger part of the brain than does that of the fishes (Figures 13, 14). The anterior parts of the brain are foreshortened, probably to accommodate the large, round oral sucker. The forebrain has two lateral vesicles, each divided into an olfactory bulb in front and an olfactory lobe in back. The midbrain, the chief optic center, is smaller than that of fishes and has two small eyelike pineal structures. The cerebellum is rudimentary and amounts to a continuation of the lobe of the lateral line, which is just behind it.

Fishes. The aquatic environment has imposed upon fishes conditions which have changed little in time. In such a medium the nervous system is tailored on a reflex plane, each reflex system dealing with some reaction to its environment. Fishes have highly developed olfactory and taste mechanisms and special acoustic and lateral line organs (Figures 13b, 14b). The forms that inhabit shallow, muddy waters have greatly developed gustatory and olfactory centers and a small cerebellum; active forms that swim swiftly have smaller gustatory and olfactory centers and a cerebellum as highly developed as that of birds. Fishes that depend more on vision than olfactory sense have well-developed optic lobes as have amphibians, reptiles, and birds.

The brain is a hollow, elongated, narrow structure easily divisible into its component parts and its form is molded by the particular connections it makes with the sense organs (Figure 15). The walls of the brain contain the nerve centers and tracts in connection with the cranial nerves and sense organs. The medulla oblongata owes its great size to the central connections of cranial nerves V to X (Figure 16). Nerves V, VII, and X are very large.

The olfactory bulbs are connected with the forebrain by the olfactory tracts; the olfactory lobes form most of the forebrain (Figures 15, 16). The thalamus, a narrow segment which connects the forebrain with the midbrain, has a well-developed ventral dilatation, the hypothalamus.

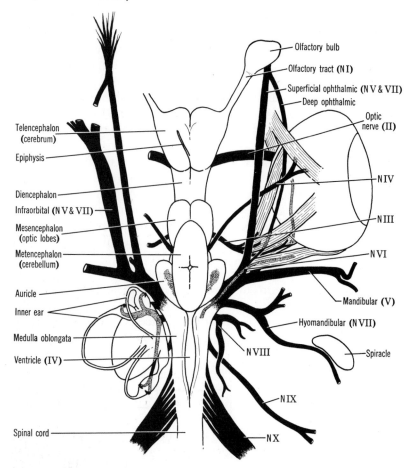

Figure 15. Dorsal view of the brain of dogfish: the cranial nerves are shown solid black; the stippled nerves are actually on the ventral side.

The optic tracts terminate in the two optic lobes of the midbrain. The size of the optic lobes, which varies with the degree of visual acuity in the particular groups, is larger in bony fishes than in elasmobranchs. The optic lobes are probably comparable to the superior colliculi in the midbrain of mammals. The oculomotor and trochlear nerves originate from the floor of the midbrain or tegmentum. The cerebellum is very highly developed; this is understandable since its main function is to control the equilibrium and to discharge motor impulses for the coordination of the movements of skeletal muscles. The large medulla oblongata has a pair of anterior **vagal lobes;** these centers for taste are not found in the brains of more advanced vertebrates.

Gustatory sensations, after reaching the hypothalamus, are relayed forward to the olfactory lobes; these are largely the correlating centers of smell, but they are also concerned with taste and the initiation of ocular, opercular (for breathing), and feeding movements. The optic lobes coordinate spatial orientation; the cerebellum and the vestibular apparatus coordinate equilibrium and kinesthetic functions.

Amphibians. The brain of amphibians seems to bridge presumptive gaps between the lungfishes and the reptiles and birds. The urodeles and the salientians have evolved along different lines, and, although similar, their brains have some differences.

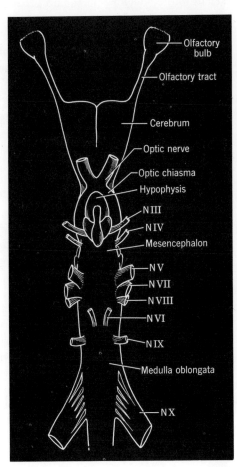

Figure 16. Ventral view of the brain of dogfish.

The two hemispheres of the forebrain are connected anteriorly with the olfactory bulbs (see Figures 13, 14). In urodeles the olfactory bulbs are continuous with the forebrain, but in salientians they are partially separated by a constriction. The forebrain of amphibians, like that of fishes, is mainly an organ for receiving and intensifying the olfactory impulses and for transmitting them to the motor systems. The forebrain is considerably advanced from that of the fishes; in the frog it has vesicles that resemble vestiges of a cerebrum, but they do not contain nervous tissue. The two small cerebellar vesicles are connected by a cerebellar commissure.

Reptiles. The brain of reptiles is small, narrow, and elongated (see Figures 13, 14). The forebrain, larger than that of amphibians, is attached to the olfactory bulbs and surrounds a small thalamus. A large **corpus striatum** or **basal ganglia** is a characteristic feature of reptilian brains. This appears to be a sensory-motor correlation center in which afferent connections are with the optic lobes and the thalamus. Rudimentary cerebral vesicles, encountered here for the first time, evaginate from the forebrain. The optic vesicles of the midbrain are the most conspicuous part of the brain. The degree of development of the cerebellum is different among different groups. The medulla oblongata has a ventral flexure like that of mammals.

Birds. The brains are larger, broader, and shorter than those of reptiles. The most noteworthy advance is the great development of the forebrain and the reduction of the olfactory lobes, bulbs, and nerves (see Figure 13). The two hemispheres of the forebrain are broader than they are long. The forebrain consists of the rudimentary olfactory lobe and the corpus striatum. The midbrain has large optic lobes. The cerebellum has a convoluted middle part divided into an anterior, a middle, and a posterior lobe, with a small lateral lobe on each side. Birds perform great feats of locomotion, and a large convoluted cerebellum controls these movements. The broad medulla oblongata has a pronounced **pontine flexure** (see Figure 14). Since the eyes are the best developed sense organs, the largest structures of the brain are the corpus striatum and the optic lobes, both participating in visual integration.

Mammals. Continuous impulses of vision, hearing, cutaneous and deep sensibility, and volitional motor impulses pour into the cerebrum of mammals where they undergo modulation, refinement and analysis. The most characteristic feature of the brain is the great size of the forebrain. This is divided into the ancient olfactory brain and the new cerebrum, or cerebral cortex (Figures 17, 18). The cerebrum is separated from the olfactory brain by the deep **rhinal fissure**. Although rela-

332

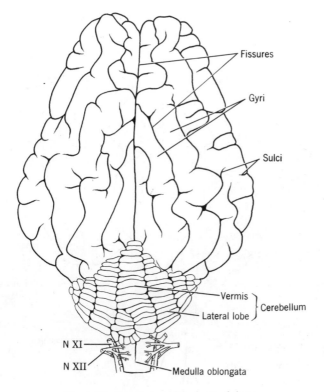

Figure 17. Dorsal view of the brain of sheep.

tively small in some mammals, the olfactory bulbs and **pyriform lobes** are large in monotremes and marsupials, both of which have a highly developed sense of smell. The surface of the cerebral hemispheres of the monotremes is smooth or has shallow grooves; in the higher mammals, and particularly in the primates and cetaceans, it is furrowed by grooves, or sulci, with ridges, or gyri, between them (Figure 17). Deep infoldings which involve the entire wall of the cortex are called **incisures**. Although neuroanatomists have found it convenient to name each of the many inscriptions on the surface of the brain, only two landmarks, the **Sylvian fissure** and the **central sulcus** are mentioned here. All of the cortex in front of the central sulcus constitutes the frontal lobe. This is small in carnivores, very large in primates, and comprises about half of the cortex of man. The Sylvian fissure occurs between the temporal and frontal lobes. With the increase in the size of the cortex, man has developed new gyri and sulci, probably correlated with the great pre-

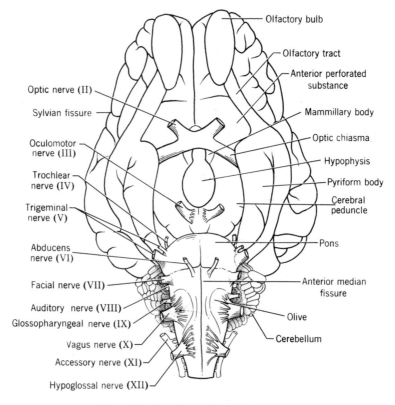

Optic nerve (II)

Sylvian fissure

Oculomotor
nerve (III)

Trochlear
nerve (IV)

Trigeminal
nerve (V)

Abducens
nerve (VI)

Facial nerve (VII)

Auditory nerve (VIII)
Glossopharyngeal nerve (IX)

Vagus nerve (X)

Accessory nerve (XI)

Hypoglossal nerve (XII)

Olfactory bulb

Olfactory tract

Anterior perforated
substance

Mammillary body

Optic chiasma

Hypophysis

Pyriform body

Cerebral
peduncle

Pons

Anterior median
fissure

Olive

Cerebellum

Figure 18.   Ventral view of the brain of sheep.

hensile function of the limbs, with walking, and with the articulation of
speech.   Although a great deal is known about the function of the frontal lobe, vast areas of it still remain unknown.   Another distinctive feature of the brain of the primates is the development of the temporal,
parietal, and occipital lobes which contain the centers that integrate the
rest of the sensory and motor impulses.

The diencephalon is differentiated into hypothalamus, thalamus, and
epithalamus.   The hypothalamus, to which the posterior lobe of the
pituitary is attached, is primarily concerned with the integration of the
functions of the autonomic nervous system (Figure 19).   The thalamus
contains a center through which the entire autonomic system may be
activated, and, with the cerebral cortex, regulates the centers of the
hypothalamus.   The primates, therefore, having the largest cerebral
cortex, also possess the largest thalamus.   The cerebrum receives, by

way of the thalamus, all sensations that require discrimination. The epithalamus contains the pineal body and an important olfactory correlation center called **habenula** (Figure 19).

The roof of the midbrain is differentiated into the corpora quadrigemina. The superior colliculi contain the centers for the coordination of sight and oculomotor activity; the inferior colliculi are associated with auditory reflexes.

The cerebellum is divided into anterior, middle, posterior, and floccular lobes (see Figure 17); these are composed of compact, transversely arranged leaflike gyri. The anterior lobe is subdivided into a median lobe called vermis and two lateral lobes; these three lobes are not very clearly separated in the primates. The cerebellum is concerned with motor functions, including posture and movements, and helps in the control of equilibrium. It discharges impulses which maintain, alter, and synergize the rate of flow of impulses to the muscles. It reinforces reflex tonus, maintains postural tonus, and regulates the duration, strength, and speed of muscular movement. One part of the cerebellum is concerned with the release of impulses which tend to inhibit postural reflexes. The cerebrum can acquire a progressive control over the functions of the cerebellum.

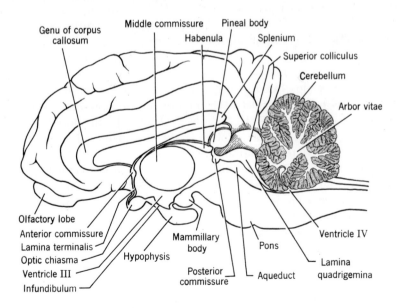

Figure 19. Sagittal section of the brain of sheep.

335

When the cerebellum is removed from an animal there are no disturbances to consciousness and sensation but severe disturbances in equilibrium result. When decerebellated animals first attempt to walk they are seized by convulsions. Their condition, however, improves and some ability to walk and take food returns. This compensation is probably brought about by the assumption of increased control over the muscles by the cerebrum.

The Spinal Cord

The cord of mammals is described first to help the student understand the discussion on comparative anatomy which follows. The spinal cord is continuous with the medulla oblongata and extends from behind the last cranial nerve to the tail. In the posterior lumbar region the cord is attenuated abruptly in a **filum terminale** (see Figure 24). In the cervical and lumbar regions, the cord has enlargements from which spring the **brachial plexus** and **lumbosacral plexus,** respectively. The degree of enlargement is related to the degree of development of the anterior and posterior limbs. Numerous nerves from the lumbar enlargement give it a fancied resemblance to a horse tail, and it is called **cauda equina.** A deep ventral median fissure and a dorsal septum which extends from the dorsal median sulcus separate the cord into symmetrical halves (see Figures 4, 5). A central canal, continuous with the fourth ventricle of the medulla, traverses the length of the cord to the filum terminale. Segmentally arranged sensory spinal nerves enter the cord on the dorsal side, and corresponding motor nerves emerge from the ventral side. In a transverse section (see Figure 4) the spinal cord is seen to consist of a central gray matter completely surrounded by white matter. The gray matter has the general shape of an H or a butterfly; the dorsal limbs of the H are the dorsal horns or columns, the ventral ones, the ventral columns. Smaller lateral columns project between the dorsal and ventral ones (Figure 20). A crossbar of gray matter above the central canal is the dorsal commissure and below it, the ventral commissure. The dorsal columns contain the sensory nerves; the lateral and ventral columns contain motor cells. The spinal cord is the seat of many reflex centers controlling the muscles of the trunk and limbs and is the conductive pathway to and from the brain.

Amphioxus. The spinal cord is a bilateral tube with a laterally flattened canal (Figure 21a). Sensory and motor nerves, which correspond in position to the connective tissue septa between the myotomes, connect the walls of the cord to the myotomes and, therefore, alternate on

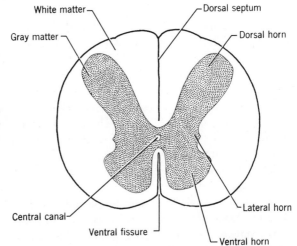

White matter

Gray matter

Dorsal septum

Dorsal horn

Figure 20. Diagram of a transverse section of the mammalian spinal cord.

Central canal

Ventral fissure

Lateral horn

Ventral horn

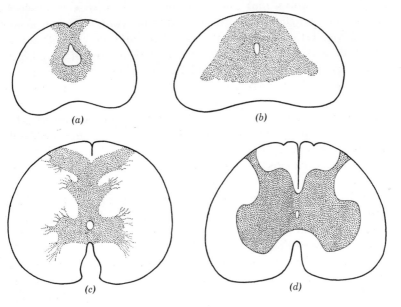

(a)

(b)

(c)

(d)

Figure 21. Transverse sections of the spinal cord of: (a) *Amphioxus*; (b) cyclostome; (c) teleost fish; (d) amphibian.

the two sides. The dorsal roots have no true spinal ganglia, since the cell bodies of sensory fibers lie within the dorsal part of the cord. Occasional bipolar cells within the dorsal root may be the beginning of true spinal ganglia. The sensory cells synapse with **giant cells** in the dorsal midline of the cord. The axons of the giant cells constitute the main reflex mechanism. Commissural fibers from them pass up and down, making connections at other levels. The motor fibers, which supply the myotomes, diverge as collateral branches of the longitudinally running fibers. Thus, the chains of reflexes are arranged longitudinally rather than transversely and are concerned only with somatic motor reactions.

Cyclostomes. The spinal cord is flattened dorsoventrally. The gray matter is a solid mass with no dorsal and ventral horns (Figure 21*b*). The cells of the spinal ganglia lie partially within the dorsal wall of the cord but mostly outside it within the dorsal nerves. The motor cells are in the ventral part of the gray matter. The dorsal roots contain visceral and somatic sensory fibers.

Fishes. The gray matter has dorsal and ventral columns, but the dorsal column is one solid mass from left to right (Figure 21*c*). In elasmobranchs the dorsal root ganglia are outside the cord, but in teleosts a few sensory ganglion cells are still within the cord. The dorsal root has both visceral and somatic afferent fibers, and the ventral root has visceral and somatic motor fibers. At the forward end of the cord the dorsal roots of the spinal nerves, which appear to be the forerunners of cranial nerve XII (hypoglossal nerve) of tetrapods, are large; the ventral ones are small or absent.

Amphibians. The spinal cord of urodeles resembles that of fishes, but that of salientians shows cervical and lumbar enlargements for the first time. The gray matter has dorsal and ventral columns (Figure 21*d*), and the sensory ganglia are completely extracordal. Motor neurons lie in the ventral horn.

Reptiles. The cord of reptiles resembles that of mammals. Reptiles with well-developed appendages have cervical and lumbar enlargements, but snakes have none. Sensory and motor roots have both somatic and visceral fibers.

Birds. The spinal cord has large cervical and lumbar enlargements from which emerge the brachial and lumbar plexuses to the wings and legs. The relative size of these enlargements is directly related to the degree of development of one or the other pair of appendages. A **lumbosacral sinus,** a dilatation in the sacral region found only in birds, is associated with the sensory roots. The gray matter is differentiated like that of mammals.

THE PERIPHERAL NERVOUS SYSTEM

All the nerve fibers in the peripheral nervous system are connected to the central nervous system by way of the spinal and cranial nerves. Whereas the central nervous system is the integration center of the body, the peripheral nervous system is the mechanism for receiving and relaying impulses and for setting off the responses. The principal generalities of the peripheral nervous system have been described, and we now discuss some specific details of the peripheral nervous system of mammals only, although the autonomic system in other classes is different.

The two divisions of the peripheral nervous system are the somatic and the autonomic. *The somatic system consists of motor fibers which terminate in skeletal muscle; the autonomic system is a purely efferent system consisting of fibers which terminate in glands, viscera, blood vessels, and smooth muscle.* The last synapse of a fiber of the somatic nervous system is always within the central nervous system but that of the autonomic system occurs in ganglia outside the cerebrospinal axis. The motor nerves to skeletal muscles are myelinated, but the terminal fibers of the autonomic system are chiefly nonmyelinated.

The general plan of the somatic nervous system can be elucidated by a reflex arc, as shown in Figure 22. Afferent neurons make synaptic connection in the dorsal gray horn with an interneuron, or a chain of such neurons, which are interposed between the afferent and efferent neurons of a reflex chain. The interneurons bring afferent neurons in contact with many efferent ones located at different levels on one or both sides of the spinal cord (Figure 23). Interneurons make synaptic connection with motor neurons in the ventral horn; the latter terminate in the muscle by special endings called motor end plates (see Figure 3, Chapter 6).

THE AUTONOMIC NERVOUS SYSTEM

The autonomic system, also known as visceral or vegetative, is composed of the **thoracicolumbar** or **sympathetic** division and the **craniosacral** or **parasympathetic** division. There are certain consistent anatomical differences between the sympathetic and parasympathetic divisions. It will be seen, however, that anatomical criteria alone are not sufficient to enable one to separate the two systems.

Two columns of ganglia, comprising the vertebral (lateral or chain) ganglia, also known as **sympathetic trunks,** are aligned in a beaded fash-

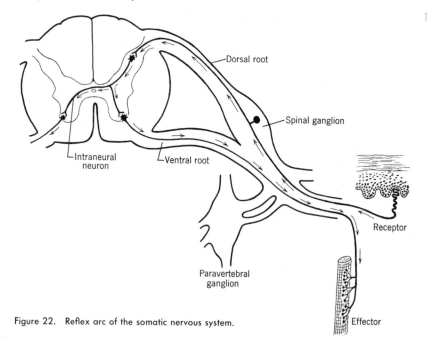

Figure 22.   Reflex arc of the somatic nervous system.

ion along the sides of the spinal cord, outside the vertebrae (Figure 24). Each ganglion of the chain is located underneath an efferent root of a spinal nerve in the thoracic and lumbar region. Only two or three ganglia are found in the cervical and sacral regions.   Nerve fibers to the ganglia issue only from the thoracic and the lumbar nerves, even though the sympathetic trunks extend anteriorly and posteriorly beyond these levels.   The ganglia are connected with the spinal nerves by the white ranni communicantes, which contain the myelinated fibers of the penultimate neurons of the autonomic chains.   Since all of these fibers will make one final synaptic connection outside the central nervous system, they are all preganglionic fibers.   These fibers run up and down the sympathetic trunk and either make a synaptic connection there with terminal neurons in several of the chain ganglia or leave the chain without making synapse as preganglionic fibers. Such preganglionic fibers pass to one or more prevertebral ganglia outside the chains, where a final synapse takes place (Figure 25).   The axons of the nerve cells leaving a terminal sympathetic ganglion are postganglionic fibers. The postganglionic fibers that originate in the vertebral ganglia rejoin the spinal nerve in a separate bundle. Since these fibers are nonmyeli-

340

nated, the bundle they form is gray and is called the gray ramus communicans. Each vertebral ganglion, then, is connected to a spinal nerve by an incoming white and an outgoing gray ramus communicans (Figure 25). Many of the postganglionic fibers that emerge from the vertebral ganglia travel to the skin where they are vasoconstrictors, secretory fibers to sweat glands, and motor fibers to the muscles of the hairs (Figure 26). The sympathetic trunk has three cervical ganglia; the cervical nerves, however, have no sympathetic outflow, and the preganglionic fibers to these ganglia sweep upward along the trunk from the thoracic nerves. Many of the postganglionic fibers from the cervical sympathetic ganglia

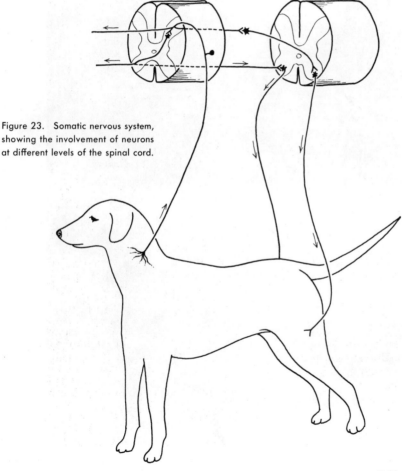

Figure 23. Somatic nervous system, showing the involvement of neurons at different levels of the spinal cord.

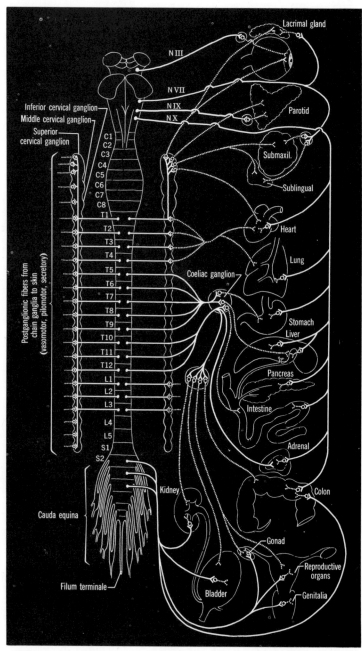

Figure 24. Plan of the autonomic nervous system: the preganglionic fibers are indicated as solid lines, the postganglionic fibers, as broken lines.

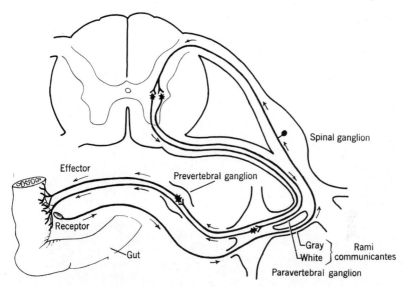

Figure 25. Sympathetic nervous system showing one motor fiber making synaptic connection in the paravertebral ganglion and one in a prevertebral ganglion.

innervate the structures of the head and chest, such as the pupil, the salivary glands, and the blood vessels of the head, the heart, and the bronchi. The postganglionic fibers from the various prevertebral ganglia are very widely distributed to the abdominal and pelvic organs. The number of postganglionic fibers is always greater than that of the preganglionic, indicating that each preganglionic fiber enters into synaptic connection with several ganglionic cells. This mechanism permits a divergence of nerve impulses to many effector organs.

The parasympathetic or **craniosacral outflow** consists of motor fibers from cranial nerves III, VII, IX, X, and XI and nerves from the sacral region. These nerves have several anatomical peculiarities: the preganglionic fibers are very long, and the postganglionic fibers are relatively short; the terminal ganglion is within, or very near, the organ innervated. The entire intestinal tract, which receives preganglionic fibers from cranial nerve X, has two layers of ganglia in its wall, which comprise the **plexus of Auerbach** and that of **Meissner**. These plexuses are composed of the terminal ganglion cells and their processes. In the sacral division the first three sacral nerves come together to form the **pelvic nerve**. These long preganglionic fibers make synaptic connections with ganglion cells near the pelvic organs they innervate; short

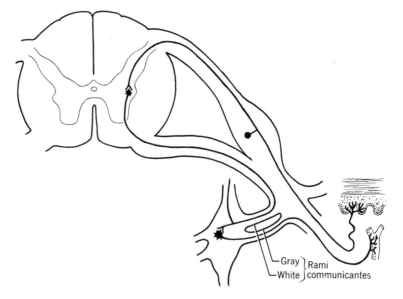

Gray ⎱ Rami
White ⎰ communicantes

Figure 26. Sympathetic nervous system showing a postganglionic fiber emerging through the gray ramus communicans.

postganglionic fibers go to the arterioles and muscles of the colon, rectum, anus, bladder, and external genitalia.

The autonomic nervous system regulates the activities of involuntary organs which control circulation, respiration, digestion, metabolism, and body temperature. Most viscera are innervated by both the sympathetic and parasympathetic systems. The two systems are considered to be antagonistic in action; if one inhibits a function the other enhances it. *Under stress, the sympathetic system discharges all at once as a unit,* and all structures innervated by it are affected simultaneously. During such conditions the heart rate is accelerated, gut motility stopped, blood pressure and the concentration of blood sugar are raised, and red blood corpuscles are mobilized from such depots as the spleen; blood is shifted from the skin and viscera to skeletal muscle, the pupils dilate, and the entire animal body is converted into a machine ready for "flight or fight." *The parasympathetic system functions to conserve and restore energy rather than to expend it.* It slows the heart rate, lowers blood pressure, enhances gastrointestinal movements and absorption of food, increases the secretion of saliva, constricts the pupil, and relaxes the sphincters of the urinary bladder and rectum.

All impulses traveling over preganglionic fibers, whether sympathetic or parasympathetic, *cause the release of acetylcholine* when they reach the synapse, and *ganglion cells are stimulated through the intervention of acetylcholine.* Injection of very small amounts of this substance in the blood supply of ganglia stimulates the ganglion cells. Acetylcholine is also abundant at the terminations of the postganglionic fibers of the parasympathetic system but not in those of the sympathetic system; acetylcholine, then, is the principal nerve transmitter substance of that system. Most of the postganglionic fibers of the sympathetic system, on the other hand, release a substance very much like adrenalin, which must be the transmitter substance of these fibers. These differences transcend the anatomical differentiations. Whereas the general anatomical classification of the two systems is largely parallel to the physiological, there are some striking exceptions, and for this reason it has been suggested that the name **adrenergic fibers** be used to designate sympathetic fibers and **cholinergic fibers** for parasympathetic ones. Those postganglionic fibers in anatomically sympathetic pathways which release acetylcholine are physiologically cholinergic and thus parasympathetic. The long postganglionic fibers which emerge from the vertebral chain ganglia and go to the blood vessels of the skin and to eccrine sweat glands (Figures 24–26) are anatomically a part of the sympathetic system, but they are cholinergic and must be considered parasympathetic.

One final important consideration here is the role of the medulla of the adrenal gland in the autonomic nervous system. This endocrine organ secretes **norepinephrine,** which for convenience we shall call adrenalin, directly into the blood stream; its action is similar to the total effect of sympathetic stimulation. The anatomical and physiological relations of the sympathetic system to the medulla of the adrenal gland are interesting. Long preganglionic fibers from the thoracic segments go through the vertebral ganglia, emerge from it still as preganglionic fibers, and come together to form the greater splanchnic nerves, one branch of which goes to the adrenal medulla (see Figure 24). There is no synapse in the usual way, but the terminal ends of these preganglionic fibers make contact with the cells of the adrenal, mediating the transmission of the impulses through acetylcholine; upon stimulation the adrenal cells secrete adrenalin. This is an anatomical oddity, for the adrenal cells are the homologs of ganglion cells. The sympathetic system, then, includes not only nerves but also the adrenal medulla, and together they are referred to as the **sympathicoadrenal system.**

In summary, although certain anatomical differences divide the autonomic nervous system into the sympathetic and the parasympathetic outflows, the real differences are physiologic. The presence of adrenergic and cholinergic systems indicates that the effector impulses are mediated through adrenalin and acetylcholine.

COMPARATIVE ANATOMY OF THE AUTONOMIC NERVOUS SYSTEM

The autonomic nervous system of the lower classes of vertebrates is not understood so well as that of mammals, and much investigation still remains to be done before its anatomy and physiology are clarified. The brief account that follows here emphasizes only a few details; for more information the student should consult the review by Nicol (1952).

In *Amphioxus* the simple autonomic nervous system consists of fibers that emerge from every dorsal segmental nerve and which continue to the viscera. Although primitive, the autonomic system of cyclostomes has both sympathetic and parasympathetic components. In the sympathetic division segmental fibers from dorsal and ventral spinal nerves enter diffuse ganglia located in the dorsal body wall. The postganglionic fibers from these ganglia innervate the blood vessels and viscera. There are no known autonomic fibers to the skin. The parasympathetic division is cranial and largely from the vagus, the fibers of which go to the heart and gut where they synapse with terminal fibers. Physiological data suggest that the visceral branch of the vagus has a motor function.

Elasmobranchs have anatomically distinct sympathetic and parasympathetic components. The sympathetic system is abdominal and has no cranial components; preganglionic fibers emerge from the ventral root nerves through rami communicantes. They enter dorsally located sympathetic ganglia, of which there may be one or two for each spinal nerve. Successive ganglia are often connected longitudinally by fibers, but there is no sympathetic trunk. These ganglia have more postganglionic than preganglionic fibers. Fibers from these ganglia innervate the blood vessels; the heart, however, receives no sympathetic fibers. The gut and the abdominal viscera are innervated by postganglionic fibers; the rectum, which is surrounded by an enteric plexus, receives preganglionic fibers. The adrenal tissue of elasmobranchs is innervated by postganglionic sympathetic fibers, in contrast to mammals in which preganglionic fibers innervate the medullary cells directly. The parasympathetic system stems entirely from cranial nerves III, VII, IX, and X. A visceral branch of the vagus supplies the heart and the alimen-

346

tary canal, the walls of which contain ganglionic plexuses. The gut, then, has a double innervation, whereas the heart has only vagal innervation. The function of the parasympathetic nerves to the heart seems to be inhibitory. In the gut vagal and sympathetic action is motor and additive; no apparent antagonistic action exists between the two.

Teleosts have an autonomic nervous system which shows some similarities to that of land vertebrates. A sympathetic chain extends from the first spinal nerve to the tail. The two sympathetic cords in the anterior trunk fuse into a single one between the kidneys; but on entering the hemal canal the sympathetic trunk again becomes paired. In some forms the sympathetic chain may extend forward as far as the third cranial nerve. There are usually two ganglia to each segment, joined to the spinal nerves by rami communicantes. Sympathetic fibers from these ganglia innervate the blood vessels and the skin; fibers from the anterior part of the trunk provide the entire innervation of the gut and its appendages. Some preganglionic fibers from the posterior trunk terminate in a plexus in the wall of the urinary bladder. This seems to be a forerunner of the sacral outflow of mammals. The principal parasympathetic division of teleosts is from outflows in the oculomotor and vagus nerves. Visceral branches from the vagus go to the esophagus, stomach, and intestine, where they terminate in the myenteric and submucosal plexuses. Cardiac branches go to the sinus venosus of the heart, which has no sympathetic innervation. The vagus has an inhibitory action upon the sinus venosus and auricle, but it is without effect on the ventricle; it has motor action in the stomach but not in the intestine. In lungfishes the sympathetic cords are regularly arranged, but the sympathetic system appears to be at a lower level of organization than that of teleosts.

Urodele amphibians have paired sympathetic trunks along the dorsal aorta, extending from the first spinal segment to the tail. The parasympathetic system has a cranial component only (cranial nerves III, VII, IX and X). The sympathetic system of salientians consists of two sympathetic trunks along the vertebral column, extending from the head to the coccygeal region. The part of the sympathetic trunks extending to the head consists of postganglionic fibers arising lower in the trunks. Fibers from these ganglia innervate the skin and blood vessels. Some preganglionic fibers pass through the sympathetic chain ganglia without making synapses and terminate in the **coeliac ganglia**. The fibers from these ganglia innervate the viscera. The parasympathetic system has both cranial and sacral divisions, the sacral nerves going to the pelvic organs. All of the viscera are innervated by both sympathe-

347

tic and parasympathetic fibers which seem to act antagonistically. The general organization of the autonomic system of amphibians, then, is like that of mammals.

The Cranial Nerves

The brain communicates with the organs of the body through the spinal cord and its nerves and through the cranial nerves. Amniotes have thirteen pairs of cranial nerves (see Figure 18); all other vertebrates have eleven pairs (see Figure 16). The cranial nerves are distributed mostly to the head; the vagus and the accessory are exceptions. Most cranial nerves are mixed nerves, although some are purely sensory. The motor nerves contain fibers of both the somatic and the autonomic systems. The sensory nerves have ganglia at the base of the brain.

The fundamental pattern of all vertebrate brains and cranial nerves is similar. One brief general description, therefore, suffices.

Cranial Nerve 0. The terminal nerve is sensory. This is actually the first cranial nerve, but it was discovered after the others had already been numbered and has remained without a number of its own. Its fibers run to the forebrain from the nasal epithelium and septum, together with the olfactory nerve.

Cranial Nerve I. The olfactory is purely sensory. Its fibers go from the nasal epithelium to the telencephalon.

Cranial Nerve II. The optic is a purely sensory nerve with fibers joining the retina of the eye and the mesencephalon. Beneath the floor of the diencephalon, the two optic nerves join to form the optic chiasma where the nerve fibers partially cross from one side to the other. This is known as decussation (Figure 27).

Cranial Nerve III. The oculomotor is a mixed nerve, mostly motor, which contains both somatic and autonomic efferent motor fibers. The somatic efferent fibers innervate four of the six extrinsic muscles of the eye (superior and inferior rectus, internal rectus and inferior oblique), and the superior levator palpebrae of the eyelid. In the visceral efferent portion the preganglionic fibers terminate in the ciliary ganglion, whence the postganglionic fibers run to the ciliary muscles of the eye. This belongs to the parasympathetic system. The afferent sensory fibers are proprioceptive for the extrinsic muscles of the eye. Proprioception is the awareness of the muscular system of changes in position and balance during muscular action.

348

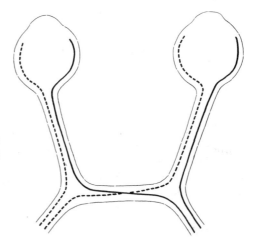

Figure 27. Diagram showing the fibers of the optic nerves decussating in the optic chiasma.

Cranial Nerve IV. The trochlear is a mixed nerve, mostly motor, originating from the mesencephalon. Its somatic efferent fibers innervate the superior oblique muscle, and its somatic afferent fibers are proprioceptive for the superior oblique.

Cranial Nerve V. The trigeminal is a very large mixed nerve (see Figures 16, 18). The ophthalmic, maxillary, and mandibular trunks are sensory branches; their pseudo-unipolar cell bodies are located in the large semilunar ganglion. Other afferent fibers are proprioceptive. Motor fibers, limited to the mandibular division, supply the muscles of mastication.

Cranial Nerve VI. The abducens is a mixed nerve, largely motor. The largest part is the motor branch to the lateral rectus muscle of the eye; the afferent fibers are proprioceptive for this muscle.

Cranial Nerve VII. The facial is a mixed nerve. Its motor fibers supply the muscles of the head and face which are of visceral origin; efferent visceral fibers supply the sublingual, submaxillary, and lacrimal glands by way of the submaxillary ganglion. The chorda tympani, a bundle of special visceral afferent fibers, is composed mostly of fibers from the taste buds on the anterior part of the tongue.

Cranial Nerve VIII. The acoustic is a purely sensory nerve. It is composed of a vestibular branch from the semicircular canals, utricle and saccule and a cochlear branch from the cochlea.

Cranial Nerve IX. The glossopharyngeal is a mixed nerve whose visceral afferent fibers come from the taste buds on the back of the tongue and from the pharynx. The visceral efferent fibers go to pharyngeal muscles and to the parotid gland.

Cranial Nerve X. The vagus is a mixed nerve with many ramifications. It is the largest nerve of the parasympathetic nervous system (see Figures 15, 16). A small afferent branch from the skin of the external ear has its cells in the jugular ganglion: a large afferent visceral branch from the pharynx, larynx, trachea, and viscera has its cell bodies in the nodosal ganglion. The visceral efferent nerve consists mostly of long preganglionic fibers which synapse with the so-called vagal plexus in the thoracic and abdominal viscera.

Cranial Nerve XI. The accessory is a purely motor nerve. Its fibers innervate the trapezius and the sternocleidomastoid muscles.

Cranial Nerve XII. The hypoglossal is a purely motor nerve. Its somatic fibers innervate the muscles of the tongue. The nerve may also contain proprioceptive fibers for the tongue, in which case it would have to be considered a mixed nerve.

SUMMARY

1. The nervous system is the coordinating center of the body and the relay system for incoming and outgoing messages. It consists of neurons composed of a cell body, one or more dendrites, and a single axon which carries the impulses away from the cell body. Nerve fibers are medullated when the axon is covered with a myelin sheath and nonmedullated if it is not. Peripheral nerves are always covered with a neurilemma sheath.

2. The central nervous system consists of the brain and spinal cord, and the peripheral nervous system, of all the nerves and ganglia. Afferent nerves bring impulses toward the central nervous system; efferent nerves contain motor fibers which carry impulses away from it.

3. The nervous system develops from the neural plate and neural crest. The neural plate forms the neural tube, which becomes enlarged anteriorly into the primary brain vesicles: the prosencephalon (forebrain), the mesencephalon (midbrain), and the rhombencephalon, (hindbrain). The forebrain becomes divided into an anterior telencephalon and a posterior diencephalon; the midbrain remains undivided, and the hindbrain is divided into an anterior metencephalon and a posterior myelencephalon.

350

4. The sensory nerves of the peripheral nervous system are formed from the neural crest. There are two systems of motor nerves: (*a*) those that travel from the central nervous system to skeletal muscles comprise the somatic nervous system; and (*b*) those that go from the central nervous system to the glands, blood vessels, viscera, and smooth muscle belong to the autonomic nervous system. The fibers of the somatic nervous system develop from the neural tube; those of the autonomic system develop both from the neural tube and the neural crest.

5. The ventricles of the brain and the central canal of the spinal cord are the remnants of the original cavity of the neural tube. Lateral ventricles I and II, each in one of the lobes of the cerebrum, open into ventricle III, located in the diencephalon; this is connected posteriorly with ventricle IV in the medulla oblongata, by way of the aqueduct of Sylvius, in the midbrain.

6. The brain and spinal cord are covered with connective tissue coats called meninges.

7. The brain and spinal cord consist of white matter composed of myelinated nerve fibers without a neurilemma, and gray matter composed of nerve cell bodies, nuclei, nonmyelinated fibers, blood vessels, and supporting tissue. In the spinal cord the white matter is on the outside, the gray matter, on the inside; in the brain the two are intermingled. In the cerebrum and cerebellum the white matter is on the inside, the gray matter, outside.

8. The brains of lower vertebrates and those of the early embryos of amniotes occur almost in a straight line. The forebrain later bends forward to form a right-angle cephalic flexure at the level of the midbrain. A pontine flexure forms in the opposite direction at the metencephalon, and in birds and mammals a cervical flexure occurs at the junction of the spinal cord with the medulla oblongata.

9. The olfactory lobes are very large in the lower vertebrates; their relative size decreases steadily as other parts of the brain become progressively larger. The telencephalic vesicles become large at the same pace at which the olfactory lobes become less conspicuous. The telencephalic vesicles form the cerebral cortex. The cortex of vertebrates below mammals is smooth; that of many mammals has grooves and ridges called sulci and gyri, respectively. The cerebral hemispheres of mammals are connected by the corpus callosum, which is composed of nerve fibers that connect nearly all the parts of the two hemispheres.

10. The diencephalon, or posterior part of the forebrain, develops on its dorsal side the epiphyseal apparatus, well-developed in amphibians

351

and reptiles, and, posterior to it, the pineal body, found in all vertebrates. The lateral walls of the diencephalon form the thalamus, which consists of fiber tracts to and from the telencephalon. On its ventral side the diencephalon has anteriorly the optic chiasma, which consists of fibers from the eyes to the brain, and behind it the hypothalamus, which controls the entire autonomic nervous system and most of the involuntary activities of the body. Behind the hypothalamus is the infundibulum which forms part of the posterior lobe of the pituitary.

11. The ventral portion of the midbrain is composed of two large peduncles which connect the forebrain with the hindbrain; the dorsolateral sides form the optic lobes. In mammals these are divided into two to form a set of four eminences called the corpora quadrigemina.

12. The expanded roof of the hindbrain is the cerebellum, which controls coordinated muscle action and equilibrium; it is more highly developed in swiftly moving animals than in sluggish ones. Behind the cerebellum is the large medulla oblongata with its very thick walls and thin membranous roof. All of the fibers between the spinal cord and brain pass through the medulla oblongata.

13. The brain of *Amphioxus* has no separate parts and is a simple enlargement at the anterior end of the neural tube. The brain of cyclostomes resembles that of more primitive fishes and amphibians. It has large optic lobes, a small midbrain, a rudimentary cerebellum, and a large medulla oblongata.

14. The brains of fishes have large olfactory and taste centers and special acoustic and lateral line organs. The fishes that inhabit shallow, muddy waters have large gustatory and olfactory centers and a small cerebellum; active forms have smaller gustatory and olfactory centers and a highly developed cerebellum. Fish that depend more on vision than on olfactory sense have large optic lobes.

15. The brains of amphibians are not advanced a great deal beyond that of fishes.

16. The brains of reptiles are small, narrow, and elongated. The forebrain is larger than that of amphibians. Small lateral vesicles evaginate from the forebrain and are the forerunners of the cerebral vesicles. The most conspicuous parts of the brain are the large optic vesicles of the midbrain.

17. The brains of birds resemble those of reptiles but are larger and broader. The most characteristic features are the great development of the forebrain and the reduction of the olfactory lobes. The greater part of the forebrain consists of the corpus striatum, a sensory-motor correlation center whose fibers connect with the optic lobes and the thalamus.

The optic lobes are very large. The large convoluted cerebellum is divided into several lobes.

18. The most noteworthy feature of the brains of mammals is the great size of the forebrain, particularly the cerebral cortex. The cerebral cortex of higher mammals, especially that of the primates, is furrowed by deep grooves and ridges between them. The diencephalon is differentiated into hypothalamus, thalamus, and epithalamus. The roof of the midbrain is differentiated into the corpora quadrigemina; the superior colliculi contain centers for the coordination of sight and oculomotor activity, and the inferior colliculi are associated with auditory function. The very large cerebellum is divided into several lobes.

19. In *Amphioxus* motor and sensory nerves to and from the simple spinal cord correspond in position to the connective tissue septa between the myotomes. The dorsal roots have no true spinal ganglia and their cell bodies lie within the dorsal part of the cord; these sensory cells synapse with giant cells whose axons pass up and down making connections with other levels and sending motor fibers to the myotomes through the ventral roots.

20. The spinal cord of cyclostomes is primitive. Some sensory cells are found in the ill-defined spinal ganglia, but many of them lie still within the spinal cord. The spinal cord is composed of gray matter in the center and white matter at the periphery. The ventral part of the gray matter contains the cells of the motor root fibers. The gray matter is a solid mass without differentiation into dorsal and ventral columns.

21. In the spinal cords of fishes the gray matter has dorsal and ventral columns. A few sensory ganglion cells are still within the cord.

22. The spinal cords of amphibians are similar to those of fishes; in salientians there are cervical and lumbar enlargements. The gray matter has dorsal and ventral columns, and sensory ganglion cells are located entirely within the spinal ganglia.

23. The cords of reptiles resemble those of mammals. Except in the snakes, which have none, there are thoracic and lumbar enlargements.

24. The spinal cords of birds have large cervical and lumbar enlargements. The relative size of these enlargements is directly related to the degree of development of the appendages.

25. The mammalian cord is similar to that of reptiles and birds. The cervical and lumbar enlargements are conspicuous, and the gray matter is differentiated into dorsal, lateral, and ventral columns. The cord extends from the brain to the tail; in the lumbar region it becomes attenuated into a filum terminale. Numerous nerves enter and leave the posterior part of the cord, giving it the appearance of a horsetail, or cauda equina.

26. The peripheral nervous system is divided into the somatic and autonomic. The somatic nervous system is that division whose fibers terminate in the skeletal muscle. The fibers of the autonomic system terminate in glands, viscera, blood vessels, and smooth muscle.

27. The autonomic nervous system is composed of sympathetic and parasympathetic divisions. The sympathetic division consists of fibers which come from the thoracic and lumbar regions. The parasympathetic nervous system consists largely of fibers stemming from cranial nerves III, VII, IX, X, and XI and nerves from the sacral region. The two divisions of the autonomic nervous system work antagonistically.

28. The vertebrates below the amniotes have eleven cranial nerves, amniotes have thirteen. The olfactory, optic, and auditory nerves are purely sensory. The oculomotor, trochlear, abducens, spinal accessory, and hypoglossal are largely motor. The others, which comprise the trigeminal, the facial, the glossopharyngeal, and the vagus, are mixed nerves. A small nerve anterior to the olfactory is designated Nerve 0 because it was discovered after all the others had been named and numbered.

SUGGESTED READING

Dukes, H. H., 1942, *The Physiology of Domestic Animals*. Comstock Publishing Company, Inc., Ithaca, N. Y. This book contains a clear account of anatomical and functional details.

Goodman, L. S., and A. Gilman, 1956, *The Pharmacological Basis of Therapeutics*. The MacMillan Company, New York. This book contains an excellent account of the autonomic nervous system.

Healey, E. G., 1957, "The Nervous System," in *The Physiology of Fishes* (M. E. Brown, ed.). Vol. II, pp. 1–119. Academic Press Inc., New York.

Nicol, J. A. C., 1952, "Autonomic Nervous Systems in Lower Chordates." *Biol. Rev.* Cambridge, **27**, pp. 1–49.

Papez, J. W., 1929, *Comparative Neurology*. Thomas Y. Crowell Company, New York.

Rasmussen, A. W., 1945, *The Principal Nervous Pathways*. The MacMillan Company, New York.

CHAPTER

14

THE
ENDOCRINE
ORGANS

INTRODUCTION

Survival of the animal depends on the regulation and coordination of the activities of its organs and tissues. Quick adjustments, such as the secretion of glands or the contraction of muscles, in response to changes in the environment are mediated mostly by the nervous system. Metabolism, growth, and reproduction, which require prolonged coordination, are regulated by specific blood-borne chemical regulators called hormones. The name hormone, used first by Starling in 1905, means **exciting,** from the Greek *hormon.* In common usage, however, *a hormone is any agent liberated by cells and diffused or transported to all parts of the organism and bringing about adjustments that integrate its component parts.* Hormones are remarkably species-nonspecific and are effective indiscriminately for nearly all vertebrates. A number of different tissues and organs secrete hormones directly into the body's fluid media, which carry them to all parts of the body. Thus all of the cells of the body come in contact with all hormones. Some organs are not affected by a specific hormone; others, being delicately attuned to it, are stimulated, and still others are depressed. Hormones are produced and secreted by endocrine organs or organs of internal secretion. In contrast with endocrine organs, exocrine organs secrete their product onto a surface or to the outside. Although the endocrine organs have been called ductless glands, this name is not appropriate, since many of the assortments of localized groups of cells which release hormones are not in the form of glands. Endocrine organs are like broadcasting stations that transmit specific disturbances; only the receiving sets, or target organs, which are properly tuned in are affected by them.

Hormones unify the metabolic activities of the organism by feed-back mechanisms or control systems. Hormones from some endocrine organs influence directly or indirectly the secretion of hormones of other organs. The thyroid-stimulating hormone from the anterior lobe of the pituitary, for example, stimulates the thyroid gland to secrete the hormone thyroxin, which in turn inhibits the secretion of too much thyroid-stimulating hormone, and the two glands keep each other in a state of reciprocal interaction. If, by some disturbance, the balance of this circuit is unsettled, the thyroid may secrete either too much or too little thyroxin. Although each hormone affects specific responsive cells in target organs, all cells must be affected in some subtle way by all hormones. For example, the gonad-stimulating hormones from the anterior lobe of the pituitary gland specifically stimulate the gonads, but they also affect other tissues, such as the plumage of certain birds or the pelage of some mammals. Hormones have a number of functions, some of them redundant. Some organs have a dual role, having both an endocrine function and performing some other role. The pancreas is an exocrine digestive gland and contains the endocrine islets of Langerhans which secrete insulin. The stomach and the intestine secrete a variety of hormones in which the action is directly or indirectly related to digestion. A large number of tissues and organs comprise the endocrine system. It is not feasible to enumerate all of them or to discuss in detail any of them. Only the principal ones receive brief attention here.

Endocrine organs can be divided into two groups: those which have only an endocrine function and those which have other functions as well. To the first group belong the pituitary, the thyroids, parathyroids, and the adrenals; to the second group belong the pancreas, gonads, intestinal mucosa, and the placenta.

THE PITUITARY GLAND

Suspended by a stalk from the diencephalon of the brain and housed in the sella turcica of the sphenoid bone is the pituitary gland, or hypophysis cerebri, a compound gland. It consists of an anterior lobe, derived from Rathke's pouch, from the ectoderm of the stomodeum, and a posterior lobe, derived from the infundibulum of the diencephalon. The anterior lobe is divided into a large anterior lobe and a smaller intermediate lobe. The origin, structure, and function of the hypophysis are similar in all vertebrates.

The first recognizable hypophysis is found in the cyclostomes at the anterior end of the notochord, between the floor of the diencephalon and a blind-sac extension of the olfactory sac. Even in these primitive animals the hypophysis has the same origin as that of other vertebrates, and its organization and function are relatively similar.

Each lobe of the hypophysis secretes characteristic hormones. The hormones secreted have a profound effect on nearly all other endocrine glands by regulating the rate of most metabolic activities. The anterior lobe of the hypophysis secretes growth hormones, which stimulate and regulate growth; gonadotropic, thyrotropic, and corticotropic hormones, which stimulate the gonads, the thyroids, and adrenal glands, respectively; and lactogenic hormones, which stimulate the secretion of mammary glands. In addition, a parathyrotropic hormone probably stimulates the parathyroids, and a diabetogenic hormone influences carbohydrate metabolism. The intermediate lobe secretes intermedin, a hormone which controls pigment formation in melanocytes. The posterior lobe secretes pitocin, which influences the contractibility of the uterus, and pitressin, which induces the contraction of blood vessels and prevents excessive formation of urine.

Since this gland secretes so many hormones, its removal is followed by varied physiological disturbances. When the hypophysis is removed during infancy, or when it is deficient in infancy, the animal fails to mature and to grow and remains dwarfed. Overactivity of the gland causes gigantism and a variety of other disturbances.

THE THYROID

Found in all vertebrates, the thyroid is phylogenetically uniform in origin, anatomy, and function. It develops from the entoderm of the pharynx as a median ventral diverticulum of the floor of the pharynx. In mammals the ultimobranchial bodies become attached to the thyroid diverticulum secondarily and they differentiate with it into thyroid tissue. The gland consists of epithelial spheres or follicles, filled with a colloidal secretion that presumably contains thyroxin. The hormone seeps through the wall of the follicles and is picked up by the rich capillary

357

bed that surrounds each follicle. The vascular supply is exceptionally rich.

A recognizable thyroid is first encountered in adult cyclostomes. In the ammocoetes a blind sac, or endostyle, is found on the floor of the pharynx, between the third and fourth gill clefts. At metamorphosis the endostyle is detached from the pharynx and becomes involuted. The fragment that remains then develops into typical thyroid tissue.

The thyroid of fishes has a variety of forms and lies at different levels in different forms. It may be single-lobed, as in the elasmobranchs, double-lobed, as in some teleosts, or diffusely scattered in clusters of cells. The thyroid consists of two completely separated lobes in amphibians. In the urodeles the two lobes lie just ahead of the aortic arches; in salientians each lobe is lateral to the hyoid apparatus. The thyroid of frogs begins to be hormonally active at the time the tadpoles begin to feed. Thyroxin initiates and guides metamorphosis of tadpoles; thyroidectomized or hypophysectomized tadpoles do not metamorphose. Conversely, the feeding of small amounts of thyroxin to tadpoles initiates metamorphosis precociously.

The thyroid of reptiles is single-lobed, except in lizards, in which it is paired. The gland is usually far back in the neck, often just anterior to the pericardial cavity. The two lobes of the thyroid of birds are placed far posteriorly, near the bifurcation of the trachea.

The thyroid of mammals has two lobes, one on each side of the larynx. A band of thyroid tissue, the isthmus, connects the two lobes ventrally. The foramen caecum at the base of the tongue represents the original site of invagination of the thyroid diverticulum.

A deficiency of thyroxin leads to sluggishness and to a general lowering of the metabolic rate. Thyroxin contains iodine, a deficiency of which leads to the formation of an ineffective thyroxin which cannot keep in check the secretion of thyrotropic hormones. Stimulated by great amounts of thyrotropic hormone, the thyroid tissue grows disproportionately to form a **goiter**.

THE PARATHYROIDS

So-called because they lie alongside, above, or dorsal to the thyroids, the parathyroids are understood only in mammals. In amphibians, reptiles, and birds parathyroid bodies develop from the ventral extensions of pharyngeal pouches V and VI, but in mammals they develop from the dorsal extension of pharyngeal pouches III and IV. They usually come to rest on the lateral sides of the thyroid, two on each side. In man and in some other mammals the posterior pair represents the parathyroid bodies derived from pouch III and the anterior pair, from pouch IV. In the mouse and the rat only an anterior pair from pouch III is present; the fourth pharyngeal pouch of the embryos of these animals is poorly defined. In the rat and the mouse the parathyroids are completely embedded in the thyroid, and it is not possible to remove the thyroid surgically without also removing the parathyroids.

Parathohormone secreted by these glands regulates calcium-phosphorus metabolism; when removed surgically a deficiency of serum calcium results, and the animal goes into tetanic rigidity. This condition can be relieved by the intravenous administration of parathohormone or calcium. The removal of the parathyroids is fatal in most animals, but some survive it. Rats and mice nearly always survive; these animals have only one recognizable pair of parathyroids and may have accessory ones.

THE ADRENALS

These glands, also called **suprarenals,** are located in all vertebrates above or near the kidneys. The mammalian adrenals are a combination of two glands that are embryologically, anatomically, and physiologically distinct. The core of the gland, the medulla, originates from the neural crest; it stains readily with chromium salts and is called the **chromaffin body.** The thick outer part of the gland, the cortex, is derived from the mesoderm near the differentiating gonads. In cyclostomes and fishes cortical and chromaffin elements are completely separated; in the former numerous small cortical bodies lie along the renal arteries and postcardinal veins, and the chromaffin bodies lie along the dorsal aorta. In fishes the cortical bodies rest along the caudal ends of the kidneys, and the chromaffin bodies are diffusely scattered along the aorta and postcardinal veins. In amphibians the two elements come close together, and in salientians the chromaffin and cortical tissue are compressed together and lie over the kidneys. In reptiles and birds the mixture of the two component glands is complete, and the large, often amorphous-shaped adrenals lie ahead of the kidneys, wrapped around the posterior vena cava.

In prototherian mammals the medulla of the adrenal is intermingled with the cortex in a way similar to that of birds. In the Eutheria the cortex encapsulates the medulla.

The adrenal medulla secretes adrenalin, which has an immediate and fleeting action on the animal, causing an acceleration of the heartbeat, constriction of blood vessels, rise in blood pressure, and elevation of blood sugar levels. It dilates or relaxes the air passageways and constricts the pupil. These adjustments prepare the animal body to meet stress. The adrenal cortex secretes a number of substances called **corticosteroids**, among them **compounds E and F** (**cortisone** and **hydrocortisone**) and **desoxycorticosterone**. These hormones control electrolyte balance and carbohydrate metabolism; without them animals die.

THE PANCREAS

The entire parenchyma of the pancreas is derived from the entoderm of the primitive gut. Distributed throughout the pancreas are clusters of cells, the islets of Langerhans, which secrete the hormone insulin. Cyclostomes have clusters of isletlike cells in the liver and the intestinal wall. In fishes with a diffuse pancreas islets are difficult to find, but those with a compact pancreas have fairly distinct islets. In all other vertebrates the islets are relatively similar. Insulin regulates the storage and utilization of carbohydrates. A deficiency of it or the surgical removal of the pancreas results in *diabetes mellitus*. This is characterized by an elevation of blood sugar levels beyond the renal threshold so that sugar is excreted in the urine.

THE GONADS

The gonads, whose proper maintenance is regulated by the gonadotropic hormone from the anterior lobe of the pituitary, have a dual function; they manufacture gametes, or germ cells, and secrete **sex hormones** into the blood stream. Male and female gonads secrete several hormones called **androgens** and **estrogens**, respectively. Sex hormones maintain the gonads in a functioning state and guide and maintain the development of the secondary sex characters. These include temperament, size, shape, strength, external features, color, and sex drive. **Castration**, or the removal of the gonads from young males or females, leads toward the development of an indifferent type which tends to resemble the female. In some birds, however, the gaudy plumage of the male is closer to the indifferent type than is that of mousy-colored females. Capons, or castrated roosters, are usually even more brilliantly colored than the cocks.

The action of androgens and estrogens is more or less antagonistic; yet, normally, both sexes produce various amounts of both types of sex hormones. The stallion, for example, manufactures large amounts of estrogens in its testes and the mare, high quantities of androgens. In spite of this, the fundamental point is that the cells of the body of each sex are keenly sensitive to the characteristic hormone of its sex.

THE TESTES

It is not known for certain what part or parts of the testes constitute the endocrine organ. Specialized clusters of connective tissue cells couched between the seminiferous tubules, called Leydig or interstitial cells, are probably the main site of male sex hormone. In birds and mammals the primary germ cells at the periphery of the seminiferous tubules also produce androgens. The sertoli cells in the seminiferous tubules are thought to produce estrogenic hormones; these cells do not participate in spermatogenic activity. This is an interesting situation because the maturing spermatozoa remain attached to the sertoli cells for a time before they break free into the lumen of the tubule. The spermatozoa, then, seem to be weaned on the cytoplasm of cells that manufacture some estrogen.

THE OVARIES

Ovaries also have a dual function; they manufacture gametes and they secrete sex hormones. The main hormone of the ovary is estrogen. In the classes below mammals this is the only hormone that is known to exist. Estrogen is secreted by the cells of the theca interna which surround the gräafian follicle. When follicles degenerate or become atretic the theca interna cells remain as nests of interstitial cells, which also secrete estrogen. Some estrogen is also secreted by the cells of the stratum granulosum of the follicle.

After the follicles of mammals have ruptured and released the ova their cells become enlarged and laden with lipid substances and acquire a yellow color. This new organ, the corpus luteum, secretes progesterone. This hormone, with estrogen, stimulates the female accessory sex organs, prepares the female for pregnancy, maintains pregnancy, and regulates lactation.

A typical reproductive cycle in mammals consists of a series of ovarian changes characterized first by the growth of the follicles, then by the rupture of the follicles and the release of the ova, and finally by the formation of the corpus luteum. These changes are accompanied by the following sequences: a period of estrogen production by the follicle, or **follicular phase,** is followed by a period of progesterone production, or **luteal phase.** The rhythmic ovarian changes are under the control of gonadotropins from the anterior lobe of the hypophysis. Coincident with the ovarian changes, the reproductive tract changes in such a way that at the time of ovulation the uterus is ready for the ovum to begin developing, should it become fertilized. In man and some other primates the cyclic ovarian and uterine changes take approximately one month to complete. **Menstruation,** or the sloughing off of the surface of the uterine mucosa, takes place at the end of the luteal phase; the follicular phase begins at the end of menstruation. In other mammals the sex hormones create a physiological condition in the female known as **heat** or **estrus,** during which time the female is receptive to the male. This period corresponds closely to ovarian and uterine cycles.

THE PLACENTA

In many mammals the gestation period, or the time required for the embryo to develop within the uterus, is longer than the limits of the estrus cycle. This is made possible by the placenta, which secretes large amounts of chorionic gonadotropins whose primary function is to maintain the corpus luteum. The continued secretion of progesterone in turn keeps the uterus in fit condition for pregnancy. The placenta of some mammals also secretes large amounts of estrogens and progesterone, thus duplicating the combined functions of the hypophysis and the ovary.

THE DUODENAL MUCOSA

The duodenal mucosa secretes several important hormones, although the exact place in which these substances are formed is not known. A hormone called **secretin** regulates the flow of pancreatic juice, one called **cholecystokinin** controls the contractions of the gall bladder, and thus the flow of bile, and another, **enterogastrone,** inhibits the motility of the stomach and the secretion of gastric juices.

SUMMARY

Organ	Origin	Hormones	Action
Hypophysis Anterior lobe	Rathke's pouch Stomodeal ectoderm	Growth hormone	Controls growth
		Gonadotropic	Stimulates gonads
		Follicle-stimulating hormone (FSH)	Stimulates growth of ovarian follicles
		Lutein stimulating hormone (LSH)	Stimulates growth of corpus luteum
		Thyrotropic	Stimulates thyroid
		Parathyrotropic	Stimulates parathyroids
		Corticotropic	Stimulates adrenal cortex
		Lactogenic	Stimulates secretion of mammary glands
Intermediate lobe	Rathke's pouch	Intermedin (melanocyte stimulating hormone)	Controls the formation and dispersion of pigment
Posterior lobe	Infundibulum	Pitocin	Controls uterine contraction
		Pitressin	Controls the contraction of blood vessels and prevents diuresis
Thyroid	Thyroid diverticulum from the entoderm of the pharynx	Thyroxin (iodothyroglobulin)	Controls metabolic processes
Parathyroid	Entoderm of pharyngeal pouches II and III or III and IV	Parathohormone	Controls metabolism of calcium and phosphorus
Adrenal Cortex	Mesoderm of dorsal body wall	Desoxycorticosteroids Cortisone (compound E). Hydrocortisone (compound F)	Carbohydrate metabolism and electrolyte balance
Adrenal Medulla	Neural crest	Adrenalin (Epinephrine)	Accelerates heartbeat, contracts blood vessels, raises blood pressure, elevates blood sugar, dilates lungs, constricts pupils, etc.
Pancreas Islets of Langerhans	Entoderm of gut (pancreatic diverticula)	Insulin	Regulates storage and utilization of carbohydrates

Organ	Origin	Hormones	Action
Gonads	Mesoderm of dorsal body wall		
Testes		Androgens	Maintain maleness
Ovaries		Estrogens	Stimulate female accessory organs, regulate secondary sex characters, influence sexual behavior
		Progesterone	With estrogens regulates secondary sex organs, prepares female for pregnancy and lactation
Placenta	Uterine mucosa and extra embryonic membranes	Chorionic gonadotropins Estrogen Progesterone	Maintain ovary and particularly corpus luteum. Adjuncts to the ovarian secretions
Duodenal mucosa	Entoderm of the gut	Secretins Cholecystokinin Enterogastrone	Regulate flow of pancreatic juice Regulates contraction of gall bladder Inhibits gastric motility and secretion

SUGGESTED READING

Allen, E., C. H. Danforth, and E. A. Doisy, 1939, *Sex and Internal Secretion.* The Williams and Wilkins Company, Baltimore, Md.

Bullough, W. S., 1951, *Vertebrate Sexual Cycles.* Methuen and Company, Ltd., London.

Symposium. "Glandular Physiology and Therapy," 1942. *Amer. Med. Assoc.*

Turner, C. D., 1948, *General Endocrinology.* W. B. Saunders Company, Philadelphia and London.

GLOSSARY

When using scientific terms the student should know exactly what they mean. For his convenience, key words and phrases used in this book are listed here and defined tersely. The student is urged to make use of this glossary and to make it a practice to consult any of the standard medical dictionaries. For that matter, most scientific terms are also defined in any comprehensive general dictionary.

A-. Prefix (Gr. without).
Ab-. Prefix (Lat. away from).
Abdomen. Belly.
Abducens. Sixth cranial nerve.
Abduct. To move a structure away from the median plane.
Aberrant. Deviation from the usual form, structure, or course.
Abomasum. The true stomach of a ruminant.
Accessory. Supplementary, assisting.
Acelous. Without concavities, as in vertebrae with centra flat anteriorly and posteriorly.
Acentrous. Without a centrum.
Acetabulum. The socket in the pelvic bone for the articulation of the head of the femur.
Acoustic. Pertaining to hearing.

Acrodont. Tooth attached to its side, as in lizards.

Acromion. The lateral extension of the spine of the scapula.

Ad-. Prefix (Lat. to, toward, upon).

Adduction. Drawing a structure toward the median plane.

Adipose. Fatty connective tissue.

Adrenal gland. An endocrine organ located near the kidney.

Adrenalin. Hormone secreted by the medulla of the adrenal.

Afferent. Going toward the center.

After-birth. Placenta and extraembryonic membranes discharged after a mammal is born.

Alar. Winglike.

Albumen. White of an egg; nutritive proteinous material.

Alecithal. Egg without yolk.

Alisphenoid. Wings of the sphenoid, derived from the chondrocranium.

Allantois. Outgrowth of the embryonic hindgut.

Alveolus. Tooth socket, rounded body of a gland, or a respiratory unit of a lung.

Ammocoetes. Larva of lamprey.

Amnion. Liquid-filled sac within which the embryos of reptiles, birds, and mammals develop. Composed of ectoderm and somatic mesoderm.

Amniotes. Animals whose embryos develop within the amnion.

Amphi-. (Gr.). Combining form meaning on both sides.

Amphicelous. Biconcave centrum of a vertebra like that of a fish.

Ampulla. Flask-shaped dilatation.

Amylase. Enzyme which hydrolyzes starch to sugar.

Analogy. Resemblance based on similar function but different origin.

Anastomosis. Connection of two blood vessels or nerves.

Ankylosis. Fusion or fixation of a joint.

Anterior. Toward the head (relative).

Antlers. Hornlike outgrowths of the frontal bones of deer.

Anura. Amphibians without a tail (Salientians).

Anus. The egestive opening of the intestine.

Aorta. The chief distributing artery of the body.

Apocrine. Type of cutaneous gland whose secretion is formed from a fragmentation of the apical part of the cytoplasm.

Aponeurosis. Connective tissue membrane surrounding muscles.

Apophysis. A projection or protuberance.

Appendage. Limb or anything that hangs from another structure.

Appendicular. Pertaining to the limbs.

Appendix. An appendage.

Apposition. Fitting together.

Apteria. Bare areas on the skin of birds.

Aqueduct. Canal for the passage of fluid.

Aqueous humor. Fluid in the anterior chamber of the eye.

Arachnoid. Spongy meninx between the dura mater and pia mater.

Arbor vitae. Treelike white matter in center of the cerebellum.

Arch. Curved or bent structure.
Archenteron. Primitive gut in the gastrula.
Archetype. Original.
Archipallium. The olfactory cerebral cortex.
Arcualia. Embryonic elements which make up the arches of vertebrae.
Arrectores pilorum. Muscles of hair follicles.
Arteriole. Terminal segment of an arterial system.
Artery. Blood vessel carrying oxygenated blood away from the heart.
Articular. The bony articular element of the mandible of lower vertebrates.
Arytenoid. Funnellike cartilage of the larynx.
Astragalus. The tarsal bone which articulates with the tibia.
Atlas. The first cervical vertebra which supports the skull.
Atrioventricular bundle. Conducting mechanism of the heart which connects atria and ventricles.
Atrium. Chamber of the heart which receives systemic venous blood; chamber surrounding the gills of lower chordates.
Auditory. Pertaining to hearing.
Auditory meatus. The external ear canal from the eardrum to the outside.
Auditory (Eustachian) tube. Passage from the middle ear to the pharynx.
Auerbach's plexus. Autonomic nerve plexus in the wall of the intestine.
Auricle. Appendage of the atrium of the heart; the outer ear.
Auto-. (Gr. *autos,* self). Combining form meaning independent.
Autonomic. Independent, self-governing.
Autonomic nervous system. Sympathetic and parasympathetic nervous systems.
Aves. Birds.
Axilla. Armpit.
Axis. The second cervical vertebra.
Axon. Process of a neuron which carries impulses away from the cell body.
Azygos. Unpaired anatomical structure.

Basalia. Basal elements of the skeleton of appendages.
Basidorsals. Dorsal, anterior arcualia.
Basihyal. The ventral element of the hyoid arch.
Basilar membrane. In the cochlea, the membrane upon which rests the organ of Corti.
Basiventrals. Ventral, anterior arcualia.
Bidder's organ. Aberrant ovary in some amphibians.
Bilateral. Symmetry whereby one plane divides a body into equal halves.
Bile. Secretion manufactured by the liver which helps to emulsify fats in the intestine.
Blastocele. Cavity of the blastula.
Blastula. One-layered ball of cells during early development.
Body stalk. Mesodermal connection between the embryo and the extraembryonic membrane.
Bowman's capsule. Dilatation of the nephron around the glomerulus.

Brachial. Pertaining to anterior appendages.
Branchial. Pertaining to gills.
Bronchiole. Subdivision of a bronchus.
Bronchus. One of two or more branches of the trachea.
Buccal cavity. Space between cheek and gums and teeth.
Bulbus. Enlarged origin of the aorta.
Bursa. Pouch or pouchlike cavity.

Caecum or cecum. Blind sac.
Calcaneum. Heel bone.
Canaliculus. Very fine canal.
Cancellous bone. Spongy bone.
Canine tooth. Single cusped tooth between lateral incisor and first premolar.
Capillary. Smallest division of blood vessels connecting arteries with veins.
Capitulum. Head.
Capsule. Envelope or membranous investment.
Carapace. Shell of a turtle.
Cardia. Aglandular part of the stomach of some mammals, lined with stratified epithelium.
Cardinal veins. Paired veins which drain head and trunk in lower vertebrates. Systemic embryonic veins found in all vertebrate embryos.
Carina. Keel.
Carnivorous. Flesh-eating.
Carotid. Principal artery to the head.
Carpus. Wrist.
Cartilage. Firm, resilient, translucent connective tissue; gristle.
Caudal. Toward the tail (relative).
Celiac plexus. Large sympathetic ganglion and nerve net at the base of the celiac artery.
Cementum. Special bony tissue that covers the roots of teeth in man, and parts of the crown in ungulates.
Centrum. Body of a vertebra.
Cephalic. Pertaining to the head.
Cerebellum. Expansion of the hindbrain; coordinating center of voluntary movements, posture, and equilibrium.
Cerebrum. Anterior, upper part of the brain; the principal coordinating center of the entire nervous system.
Cervical. Pertaining to the neck.
Cheiropterygium. The skeleton of the fingered appendage.
Chevron bones. Hemal arch, particularly in crocodilians.
Chiasma. Crossing of nerve fibers from one side to the other (see decussation).
Choana. Internal naris.
Chondrocranium. Primitive cartilaginous skull.
Chordae tendineae. The tendons of the heart-valve muscles.
Chorioallantois. Fused allantois and chorion.

Chorion. Outer extraembryonic membrane of amniotes, composed of ectoderm and somatic mesoderm.

Choroid. Pigmented middle coat of the vertebrate eye between the retina and sclera.

Chyle. Milky emulsion of fat in lymph.

Ciliary body. Part of the choroid of the eye containing smooth muscles, to which the lens is attached.

Cisterna chyli. Common pool into which drain most of the lymph channels of the mammalian body.

Clavicle. Ventral, anterior, dermal bone of the pectoral girdle of tetrapods.

Cleavage. Division of a fertilized egg, characterized by an increase in cells but no appreciable increase in total mass.

Cleithrum. Membrane bone in the pectoral girdle of fishes and amphibia.

Clitoris. Female homolog of the penis.

Cloaca. Common receptacle for the digestive and urogenital systems.

Cochlea. Spiral organ containing the sensory auditory cells.

Coelom or **celom.** Body cavity.

Colic. Pertaining to the colon.

Collagen. Principal organic constitutent of connective tissues.

Colliculus. Hillock. One of the divisions of the corpora quadrigemina.

Colloid. Gluelike.

Colon. The large intestine, exclusive of the rectum.

Columella. The ear bone of amphibians, reptiles, and birds.

Columnar. Shaped like a column.

Commissure. Bundles of nerve fibers which connect right and left halves of the central nervous system.

Concha. Shell; as the external ear or the three ethmoid bones.

Condyle. Rounded articular surface of a bone.

Cones. Light-sensitive cells of the retina.

Congenital. Born with.

Conjunctiva. Epithelium covering the front of the eyeball and the inside of the eyelid.

Conus arteriosus. The part of the right ventricle which joins the pulmonary artery or the basal region of the ventral aorta.

Copulation. The act of transferring the sperm from the male to the female genital tract.

Coracoid. The posterior ventral bone of the pectoral girdle.

Corium. The connective tissue layer of the skin; the dermis.

Cornea. Anterior portion of the sclera of the eye, usually white.

Cornified. Horny.

Corona. Crown.

Coronary. Surrounding, like a crown.

Corpora quadrigemina. The four hillocks in the midbrain of mammals.

Corpora cavernosa. Spongy erectile tissue of the penis.

Corpus. Body.

369

Corpus callosum. Mass of commissural fibers connecting the two cerebral hemispheres.

Corpuscle. Small body.

Corpus luteum. Endocrine, yellow organ formed from the grÃ¤afian follicle of mammals after the ovum is discharged; secretes progesterone.

Corpus striatum. The basal ganglion of the cerebral hemisphere, particularly well-developed in reptiles and birds.

Cortex. Rind or outer part.

Costa. Rib.

Cotyledon. Original meaning, any cup-shaped hollow. Tufts of villi on the chorion of ruminants.

Cranium. Skeleton of the head.

Cribriform plate. Sievelike plate of the ethmoid bone through which passes the olfactory nerve.

Cricoid. Ringlike laryngeal cartilage.

Crista. A crest or ridge.

Crop. Enlarged lower part of the esophagus of birds.

Crypt. A pit or hollow.

Cuboid. The most lateral distal tarsal bone.

Cuneiform. Wedge-shaped.

Cusp. Cuplike element in the atrioventricular and semilunar valves. Also conical projection of the crown of a tooth.

Cutaneous. Pertaining to the skin.

Cycloid. Type of scale.

Cystic duct. Duct from the gall bladder to the common bile duct.

Cytoplasm. Living substance of a cell exclusive of the nucleus.

De-. Prefix (Lat. down, without).

Decussation. X-shaped crossings of symmetrical parts or nerve fibers from the eyes that cross to connect centers on the two sides of the central nervous system.

Deferent. Carrying away from.

Deltoid. Shaped like a delta (Δ).

Demi-. Prefix (Lat. *dimidius,* half).

Dendrites. Processes of a neuron carrying impulses toward the cell body.

Dentary. Teeth-bearing membrane bone of the lower jaw.

Dentine. Bonelike substance of a tooth; ivory.

Dentition. Kind, number, and arrangement of teeth.

Depressor. A muscle that lowers an organ; nerves or chemical substances which inhibit action.

Dermatocranium. That part of the skull derived from dermal bones.

Dermatome. Portion of the somite which forms some of the dermis.

Di-. Prefix (Gr. *dis,* twice).

Dia-. Prefix (Gr. between, apart, through).

Diaphragm. The muscular wall in mammals which separates thorax and abdomen.

Diapophysis. In a vertebra the process of the neural arch which articulates with the tubercle of a rib.

Diarthrosis. Movable joint.

Diastema. Gap between the teeth.

Diencephalon. The second of the five primary divisions of the brain.

Digestion. The process of making foods absorbable.

Digitigrade. Animal that walks on its toes.

Diphyodont. Having two sets of teeth.

Diploë. Spongy bone in the bones of the skull.

Diplospondyly. Two centra in one vertebra.

Distal. Away, far (relative).

Distalia. Distal row of carpals or tarsals.

Dorsal. Pertaining to the back.

Duct. Tube or passage.

Duodenum. First segment of the small intestine.

Dura mater. Outer layer of the meninges.

E-, ex-. Prefix (Lat. out, from).

Ectoderm. The outer germ layer.

Effector. Any end-organ which responds to nervous stimulation.

Efferent. Away from.

Egg. Female gamete or germ cell.

Ejaculatory duct. Terminal part of the deferent duct as it enters the urethra.

Enamel. Hard, glassy, calcareous outer structure of the crown of teeth, formed from the ectoderm.

Encephalon. The brain.

End-, endo-. Prefix (Gr. inside).

Endochondral bone. Bone which develops within cartilage and replaces it.

Endocrine organ. Any tissue that secretes hormones.

Endolymph. Fluid in the inner ear.

Endometrium. Lining of the uterus.

Endosteum. Cellular connective tissue layer inside of a bone.

Endothelium. Epithelium which lines blood and lymph vessels.

End-plates. Specialized terminations of motor nerves in skeletal muscle fibers.

Ensiform. Long and pointed or sword-shaped.

Enzyme. A catalytic organic compound which speeds up or represses chemical changes in other organic substances.

Eosinophile. Granular leucocyte whose granules stain with eosin.

Ep-, epi-. Prefix (Gr. upon).

Epaxial. Dorsal to the vertebrate axis.

Epidermis. The outer layer of the skin.

Epididymis. Convoluted tubule attached to the testis, and conveying spermatozoa to the deferent duct.

Epiglottis. Lidlike structure in front of the entrance to the larynx of mammals.

Epinephrine (adrenalin). Hormone secreted by the medulla of the adrenal.

Epiphysis. The ends of a long bone or the pineal body.

Epithelium. A tissue which covers a surface.

Epoöphoron. Rudiment of mesonephric tubules near the ovary.

Erythrocyte. Red blood corpuscle.

Esophagus. The alimentary canal between the pharynx and the stomach.

Estrogens. Female sex hormones.

Estrus cycle. Heat or the period of receptivity in the female.

Ethmoid. Bone at the front of the skull, which forms part of the bony nose.

Ethmoturbinals. Parts of the ethmoid which form the superior and middle turbinated bones.

Eustachian tube. Passage connecting the middle ear with the pharynx.

Eutherian. Placental mammal.

Excretion. The elimination of wastes.

Exocrine. Gland secreting to the outside.

Extensor. Muscles that stretch out a limb.

Exteroceptive. Receptor of external stimuli.

Extremity. Limb.

Extrinsic. Originating outside an organ or structure.

Falciform. In the shape of a sickle.

Fallopian tubes. Oviducts of a mammal.

Fasciculus. Bundle of nerves within the central nervous system.

Femur. Thigh bone.

Fenestra. Window.

Fertilization. The union of sperm and egg.

Fiber. Synonomous with "cell" in the case of muscle and nerve. Complex proteinous substances in which the molecules are aligned to form threads or bands.

Fibril. Small thread.

Fibroblast. Connective tissue cell which forms fibers.

Fibula. Outer bone of the leg.

Filoplume. Pin feather.

Filum terminale. The attenuated end of the spinal cord.

Fimbria. Threads or fringe around an opening.

Fissures. Deep grooves in the cerebral cortex.

Flexion. Bending.

Flexor. A muscle that bends a limb or a part of it.

Flexure. A bend or a fold.

Foliate. Leaflike.

Follicle. A small sac; spherical or tubular organ.

Foramen. A small opening.

Fossa. Pit or depression.

Fossil. Any remains, impression, or trace of an animal or plant of a former geologic era.

Fovea centralis. A depression in the macula of the retina.

Frenulum. A median fold that attaches the lips or tongue.

Frontal. Bones of the forehead or a plane that divides a body dorsoventrally.

Function. The normal activity of an organ.

Fundus. The body of a hollow organ.

Fungiform. Mushroom-shaped.

Gall bladder. Receptacle that stores bile.

Gamete. Germ cell; ovum or spermatozoon.

Ganglion. An aggregate of nerve cells outside the central nervous system.

Gärtner's duct. Rudiment of the wolffian duct in the female mammal.

Gastralia. Riblike dermal bones in the abdominal wall of Crocodilia.

Gastrula. In early development a two-layered structure during the establishment of the body plan.

Genitalia. Organs of reproduction.

Gestation. Duration of pregnancy.

Gingiva. The gum.

Gizzard. The grinding part of the digestive system of reptiles and birds.

Glans penis. The terminal part of the penis.

Glenoid fossa. Depression in the scapula for the articulation of the head of the humerus.

Glomerulus. Knot of arterial capillaries associated with the nephron.

Glossopharyngeal. Pertaining to the tongue and pharynx.

Glottis. The pharyngeal opening to the larynx.

Gluteal. Pertaining to the buttocks.

Gnathostomes. Fishes with jaws.

Goblet cells. Mucus-secreting cells.

Gonad. Primary sex organ; produces gametes.

Gonopodium. Pelvic fin of some male fishes specialized as an intromittent organ.

Graafian follicle. Roughly spherical structure in the mammalian ovary which contains the ovum.

Granulosus. Pebbled or granular.

Gray matter. Part of the central nervous system containing nonmyelinated fibers.

Gular. Pertaining to the throat.

Gustatory. Pertaining to the sense of taste.

Gut. Digestive tube.

Gynandromorph. An organism having both male and female characteristics.

Gyrus. Convolution of the brain cortex.

Haustra. Sacculations of the colon.

Haversian System. In lamellar bone, units of concentric lamellae in the center of which is the Haversian canal, containing blood vessels and nerves.

Hemibranch. Half gill.

Hemoglobin. Pigment in red blood corpuscles or in muscle.

Hemopoietic. Blood-forming.

Henle's loop. Loop of the nephron.

Hepatic. Pertaining to the liver.

Hermaphrodite. Animal with both male and female sex organs.

Heterodont. Having several types of teeth.

Hilus; hilum. The concave side of an organ.

Hindbrain. The posterior of the three primary embryonic brain vesicles.

Holobranch. An entire gill.

Homodont. Having teeth all alike.

Homologous. Having the same structure and origin.

Hormone. Substance secreted by an endocrine organ which affects the metabolic activity of the organism.

Hyalin. Translucent.

Hyoid. Skeleton of the tongue and larynx; the second visceral arch.

Hypaxial. Below the axis.

Hypomere. Lateral mesoderm.

Hypophysis. The anterior lobe of the pituitary gland.

Hypothalamus. Ventral portion of the diencephalon.

Ichthyopterygium. The skeleton of the appendages of fishes.

Ileum. Last segment of the small intestine.

Ilium. The dorsal bone of the pelvic girdle.

Imbricate. Alternating shinglelike arrangement.

Impulse. Changes transmitted along a nerve fiber.

Incisor. Front teeth borne on the premaxilla.

Incus. The anvil; one of the three ossicles of the middle ear of mammals.

Insertion. Attachment of a muscle to a bone which it moves.

Intercalated. Placed between.

Intercostal. Between the ribs.

Interoceptor. End-organ situated in the viscera.

Intrinsic. Situated within a structure or organ.

Iris. Contractile circular diaphragm which forms the visible colored portion of the eye.

Ischium. The posterior of the two ventral bones of the pelvic girdle.

Islets of Langerhans. Groups of cells in the pancreas which secrete the hormone insulin.

Jacobson's organ. Accessory olfactory organ, particularly well-developed in snakes.

Jejunum. The middle segment of the small intestine.

Keratin. Complex fibrous protein produced by several cutaneous structures.

Kidney. Principal organ of excretion.

Labium. Lip.

Labyrinth. A maze. The inner ear of vertebrates.

Lacrimal. Pertaining to tears.

Lacteal. Small lymphatic bladder in the center of intestinal villi.

Lacuna. A cavity, hollow, or pit.

Lagena. Outgrowth of the saccule of the inner ear which contains the auditory sensory cells.

Lamella. A thin sheet or plate.

Larva. Immature free-swimming stage of fish and amphibians.

Larynx. Vocal apparatus.

Lateral line. Sense organs which extend linearly along the sides of the body of fishes.

Leucocyte. White blood corpuscle.

Lieberkühn, crypts of. Intestinal glands.

Linea alba. Tendinous longitudinal white line in the middle of the abdominal wall.

Lingual. Pertaining to the tongue.

Lipase. Fat-splitting enzyme secreted by the pancreas, stomach, and intestine.

Lobe. A roundish division of an organ.

Lobule. Division of a lobe.

Lumen. Canal or cavity of a hollow organ.

Lymph. Clear yellowish fluid from the tissues of the body returned to the blood stream by way of lymph vessels.

Maculae acusticae. Patches of sensory cells in the saccule and utricle.

Macula lutea. Point of clearest vision in the center of the retina.

Malleus. Ossicle in the middle ear of mammals, attached to the tympanic membrane.

Maltase. The enzyme which splits maltose into dextrose.

Mamma. Breast.

Mandible. Lower jaw.

Mastoid. A process of the temporal bone.

Maxilla. Upper jaw.

Maxilloturbinals. Inferior turbinated bones.

Meatus. A passage or opening.

Meckel's cartilage. The lower division of the first pharyngeal arch.

Mediastinum. Partition of the two pleural cavities.

Medulla. The marrow or core of an organ.

Medulla oblongata. The posterior division of the brain.

Melanophore. Melanin-bearing cell.

Membrane bones. Bones formed directly from embryonic connective tissue believed to have arisen from the dermal bony plates of fishes.

Meninges. The membranes which surround the central nervous system.

Mentum. The chin.

Mesencephalon. Midbrain.

Mesenchyme. Embryonic mesodermal tissue.

Mesentery. Peritoneal sling which suspends the viscera from the body wall.

375

Mesethmoid. Cartilage bone anterior to the presphenoid.

Mesocardium. Mesentary of the heart.

Mesoderm. The middle germ layer.

Mesonephros. The functional kidney of most fishes and amphibians.

Mesothelium. The cells which line the coelom.

Metabolism. Sum of chemical changes in an organism by which food is converted to living protoplasm (anabolism) and by which protoplasm is broken down (catabolism) into simpler compounds with the exchange of energy.

Metacarpals. Bones between the wrist and the fingers.

Metamerism. Segmentation.

Metamorphosis. In development, transformation from the larva to the adult form.

Metanephros. The functional kidney of amniotes.

Metatarsus. The bones of the ankle.

Metencephalon. The fourth division of the brain which forms the cerebellum and pons.

Midbrain. The third division of the brain.

Mitral valve. Left atrioventricular valve of the heart.

Monocyte. Large leucocyte with a kidney-shaped nucleus.

Monophyodont. Having a single permanent dentition.

Morphology. Study of the form and structure of organisms.

Motor neuron. Nerve cell which carries impulses away from the central nervous system.

Mucus. Viscid complex polysaccharide containing esters of sulfuric acid.

Müllerian duct. Embryonic structure which gives rise to oviducts and uterus.

Muscularis mucosae. Layers of smooth muscle fibers below the mucosa of the intestine.

Myelencephalon. The fifth division of the brain; the medulla oblongata.

Myelin. The complex fatty covering of myelinated nerve fibers.

Myenteric plexus. Network of parasympathetic fibers between the muscle layers of the intestine.

Myocardium. The muscular layer of the heart.

Myocommata. The connective tissue between two myotomes.

Myotome. The portion of a somite which gives rise to skeletal muscle.

Naris. Nostril.

Nephrostome. Opening of a pronephonic tubule into the body cavity.

Nerve. A bundle of nerve fibers outside the central nervous system.

Nerve fiber. A neuron or its axon.

Nerve tract. A bundle of nerve fibers of similar origin and function within the central nervous system.

Nervus terminalis. Cranial nerve 0, a sensory nerve associated with the olfactory nerve.

Neurilemma. A sheath covering the axons of all peripheral nerve fibers.

Neuroblast. Embryonic nerve cell.

Neuroglia. Supporting tissue of the central nervous system.

Neuron. Functional unit of the nervous system.

Neutrophile. White blood corpuscle whose granules stain with "neutral stains."

Nonmedullated (nonmyelinated). Without a myelin sheath.

Notochord. Axial rod in the middorsal line, between the neural tube and the dorsal aorta.

Nuchal. Pertaining to the nape.

Obturator foramen. Opening between the pubis and the ischium.

Occipital. Pertaining to or relating to the occiput or back of the head.

Odontoid process. The toothlike process of the axis.

Olecranon process. The proximal tip of the ulna; the elbow.

Omasum. The third division of the ruminant's stomach.

Omentum. A sac formed by the doubling of the mesentery.

Ontogenesis. Development of the individual.

Operculum. Lid or cover of the gills of fishes.

Optic vesicle. The lateral outpocketing of the forebrain of embryos which forms the retina of the eye.

Orbit. The bony socket which houses the eye.

Ossification. The formation of bone.

Osteoblast. Bone-forming cell.

Os uteri. Opening of the uterus into the vagina.

Otic. Pertaining to the ear.

Otoconia. Calcium crystals in the otolith, in the maculae of the inner ear.

Oviduct. The egg duct; uterine tube.

Oviparous. Egg-laying.

Ovulation. The discharge of an egg from the ovary.

Oxytocin. Hormone from the posterior lobe of the pituitary which affects the uterine muscle.

Palate. The roof of the mouth.

Palatine. The membrane bone of the posterior hard palate.

Paleocortex. The primitive or olfactory cortex.

Paleontology. The study of fossils.

Pallium. The cerebral cortex.

Pancreas. Large digestive gland which empties into the duodenum. The gland also contains the islets of Langerhans.

Panniculus carnosus. A thin layer of skeletal muscle beneath the hypodermis of the skin.

Papilla. Small soft elevation.

Parachordals. Cartilages along the anterior end of the notochord which form the posterior part of the chondrocranium.

Paradidymis. Rudiment of the mesonephric tubules near the testis.

Parapophysis. Bony process from the centrum of a vertebra.

Parasympathetic. The craniosacral outflow or cholinergic part of the autonomic nervous system.

Parathyroid glands. Endocrine organs near the thyroids, whose secretion controls calcium metabolism.

Parenchyma. The essential specialized substance of an organ, as distinguished from the stroma.

Paroöphoron. In the mammalian female, a rudiment of the mesonephric tubules near the ovary.

Parotid. Serous salivary gland below the ear.

Patella. Kneecap.

Pecten. Tuft of capillaries in the vitreous body of the eyes of reptiles and birds.

Pectoral. Pertaining to the chest.

Pedal. Pertaining to the foot.

Pedicle. Slender foot or stem.

Peduncle. Fiber tract which connects the cerebellum with the brain stem.

Pelvis. The bony ring bounded by the ilia and pubes and sacrum.

Penis. Male external genital organ.

Perennibranch. Persistent gill.

Pericardium. The membranous sac which encloses the heart.

Perichondrium. The connective tissue membrane which surrounds cartilage.

Perilymph. Fluid in the space between the membranous and the skeletal labyrinth of the internal ear.

Perimysium. Connective tissue capsule which surrounds bundles of skeletal muscle fibers.

Periosteum. The connective tissue membrane which surrounds a bone.

Peristalsis. Waves of contraction of the intestine.

Peritoneum. Serous lining of the body cavity and viscera.

Petrosal. Petrous portion of the temporal bone.

Phagocyte. A cell which ingests foreign substances or debris.

Phalanges. Bones of the fingers and toes.

Pharynx. Posterior part of the oral cavity connecting mouth and esophagus.

Phylogeny. History of the race or group.

Pia mater. Innermost layer of the meninges.

Pineal body. The epiphysis of the diencephalon.

Pinna. External ear.

Pisiform. Pea-shaped, sesamoid carpal bone on the ulnar side.

Pituitary gland. Endocrine organ that controls directly or indirectly nearly all of metabolic activity of the organism.

Pituitrin. Extract of the posterior lobe of the pituitary gland.

Placenta. Principal organ of exchange between the embryo and the maternal blood.

Placoid scale. Toothlike scale of elasmobranchs composed of dentine and containing a pulp cavity.

Plantigrade. Animal that walks flat-footed.

Plasma. The liquid part of blood.

Plastron. The ventral bony shield of the turtle.

Platysma. Integumentary muscle in the neck.

Pleura. Serous membrane lining the plural cavities and lungs.

Plexus. A network of nerves or blood vessels.

Plica. A fold.

Polyphyodont. Having more than two sets of teeth.

Pons. Bridge of fibers below the cerebellum which connects cerebrum, cerebellum, and medulla oblongata.

Precoracoid. The anterior ventral bone of the pectoral girdle; it is usually replaced by the clavicle.

Premolar. A bicuspid tooth.

Prepuce. Fold of skin around the glans penis or clitoris.

Primitive streak. Thickening of the blastodisc of amniotes, homologous to the lip of the blastopore.

Proctodeum. That portion of the hindgut derived from ectoderm.

Progesterone. Hormone secreted by the corpus luteum, which affects the endometrium of the uterus.

Pronation. The act of turning the palm downward.

Pronephros. Most primitive vertebrate kidney.

Proprioceptors. Receptors of stimuli originating within the body.

Prosencephalon. The anterior division of the embryonic brain which forms the cerebral hemispheres.

Prostate gland. Gland around the base of the urethra of male mammals.

Prototype. The original form or type from which others may have evolved.

Proximal. Near or toward the body (relative).

Pterygoids. Bones of the mandibular arch of reptiles and birds. In mammals, processes of the sphenoid.

Puberty. Physiological age at which the reproductive organs become functional.

Pubis. Inferior ventral bone of the pelvic girdle.

Pylorus. Opening of the stomach into the duodenum.

Pyramid, renal. Conical medullary part of the kidney.

Rathke's pouch. Primordium of the hypophysis of amniote embryos.

Receptor. Sensory organ.

Rectum. The last segment of the large intestine.

Red gland. Plexus of capillaries in the swim bladder of fishes.

Reflex arc. Chain of a sensory and a motor neuron.

Renal corpuscle. The glomerulus and Bowman's capsule of a nephron.

Respiration. Burning of carbon compounds in living cells.

Rete testis. Network of ducts between the seminiferous tubules and the efferent ducts.

Retina. Photosensitive layer of the eye.

Rhombencephalon. Hindbrain.

Rods. Photoreceptor cells of the retina.

Rumen. The anterior and largest sac of the stomach of ruminants.

Saccule. Sac connected with the lagena or cochlea of the ear.

Sacrum. Fused sacral vertebrae which support the pelvic girdle.

Sagittal plane. Median longitudinal dorsoventral section.

Santorini, duct of. Accessory dorsal pancreatic duct.

Scala media. Cochlear duct.

Scala tympani. The ventral descending duct of the cochlea.

Scala vestibuli. The dorsal ascending duct of the cochlea.

Scapula. Dorsal bone of the pectoral girdle.

Schwann cells. Cells of the neurilemma sheath.

Sclera. Fibrous outer layer of the eye.

Sclerotome. Part of the somite which forms the vertebra.

Scrotum. Sac which contains the testes of mammals.

Sebaceous gland. Cutaneous gland which produces a fatty secretion.

Secretin. Intestinal hormone which activates the pancreas.

Secretion. Product of cell metabolism which is thrown out as waste or is used by the organism.

Sella turcica. Saddle-shaped notch in the sphenoid bone in which the pituitary rests.

Semen. Viscous liquid containing spermatozoa.

Semicircular canals. Ducts of the inner ear in which are found the receptors for equilibrium.

Semilunar valves. Valves at the root of the aorta and pulmonary artery which prevent a backflow of blood.

Seminal vesicle. Gland that secretes a viscid fluid into the deferent duct.

Seminiferous tubules. Tubules of the testis in which spermatozoa are formed.

Serous gland. Gland which secretes a watery fluid.

Serum. Clear yellowish fluid which separates from the clot in the coagulation of blood.

Sex. The differentiation of males and females.

Shell membrane. Fibrous inner membrane attached to the shell of an egg.

Sino-auricular node. The "pacemaker" of the heart beat.

Sinus. Hollow recess or pocket.

Sinusoid. Irregularly dilated venous channel lined with endothelium.

Somatopleure. The fused embryonic layers of ectoderm and somatic mesoderm.

Somites. Segmental blocks of dorsal mesoderm.

Splanchnopleure. The fused embryonic layers of splanchnic mesoderm and ectoderm.

Stapes. Ear ossicle shaped like a stirrup in the middle ear of mammals.

Stensen's duct. Duct of the parotid gland.

Sternebra. One of the segmental bones of the sternum.

Stomodeum. Anterior ectodermal invagination in the embryo which forms the mouth.

Stroma. The connective tissue framework of an organ.

Stylo-, styl-. (Gr. *stylos*). Combining form meaning pillar.

Sub-. Prefix (Lat. under).

380

Sublingual gland. Salivary gland below the tongue, usually mucous.

Submaxillary gland (submandibular gland). A mixed salivary gland below the angle of the mandible.

Submucosa. Connective tissue layer below the mucous membrane of the digestive tube.

Succus. Juice.

Sucrase. Enzyme in plants and microorganisms which hydrolyzes disaccharides to monosaccharides.

Sulcus. A groove or fissure.

Superficial. On the surface or above (relative).

Superior. Above (relative).

Supination. Turning the palm upward.

Supra-. Prefix (Lat. under).

Sympathetic nervous system. Thoracicolumbar outflow of the autonomic nervous system; cholinergic system.

Symphysis. Fusion of adjacent bones.

Syn-. Prefix (Gr. together).

Synapse. Contact between the axon of one neuron and the dendrites of another in a chain.

Synarthrosis. Fusion of two adjacent bones.

Syncytium. A cell or mass of cytoplasm with many nuclei.

Synsacrum. Fused thoracic, lumbar, sacral, and caudal vertebrae of birds.

Syrinx. Vocal apparatus of birds found at the junction of the bronchi with the trachea.

Systemic. Pertaining to the body.

Systole. Contraction of the heart.

Taenia, tenia. Band or bandlike structure.

Talus (astragalus). Ankle bone which articulates with the tibia.

Tarsometatarsus. Fused tarsal and metatarsal bones, particularly of birds.

Tarsus. The ankle and its bones.

Taste bud. Aggregate of gustatory cells.

Taxonomy. Study of classification.

Tectorial membrane. Gelatinous membrane in the cochlear duct in contact with the sensory cells in the organ of Corti.

Tectum. Roof of the midbrain.

Tel-, tele-. Prefix (Gr. *tele,* far).

Tela. (Lat. *tela,* web.)

Telencephalon. The most anterior of the five embryonic brain vesicles.

Telodendria. The branching terminations of an axon.

Telolecithal. Eggs with massive amounts of yolk.

Tendon. Fibrous attachment of a muscle.

Testis. Male gonad.

Tetany. Muscular spasm, usually caused by calcium deficiency.

Tetrapod. Vertebrate with four appendages.

Thalamus. Gray matter in the lateral walls of the diencephalon.

Thebesian veins. Small veins in the myocardium which open directly into the atria and ventricles.

Theca. Sheath.

Thecodont. Animals bearing teeth set in sockets or alveoli.

Thoracic duct. Main lymph channel which conveys lymph from the lower half and the upper left half of the body to the left jugular vein.

Thymus. Lymphoid tissue of uncertain function.

Thyroid gland. Endocrine organ located on the sides of the trachea which secretes thyroxin.

Thyroxin. Hormone of the thyroid gland which controls metabolism.

Tonsil. Lymphoid tissue associated with an epithelial surface.

Tonus. The normal state of tension of a muscle.

Trabecula (Lat. little beam). Any fibrous or skeletal band properly described by the term.

Trachea. Air canal from the larynx to the bronchi.

Transverse. Plane at right angle to the axis.

Transverse septum. Partition between the pericardial cavity and the abdominal cavity.

Tri- (Lat. *tres,* three). Combining form denoting three.

Tributary. Any vein opening into another vein.

Trigeminus. Fifth cranial nerve.

Trochanters. Processes below the head of the femur.

Trochlea. A pulleylike structure.

Trophoblast. The outer fetal membrane of amniote embryos.

Trypsin. Protein-splitting enzyme secreted by the pancreas.

Tuberculum (Lat.). Tubercle.

Tuberosity. Protuberance of a bone.

Tunica (Lat.). Coat or membrane.

Tympanic membrane. Eardrum.

Tympanum. Middle ear.

Typhlosole. Longitudinal fold in the intestine of primitive forms.

Ureter. Excretory duct of metanephric kidneys conveying urine to the bladder.

Urethra. The outlet of the bladder; in the male, the urinogenital passage.

Urogenital. Pertaining to the urinary and genital organs.

Uropygeal gland. Gland over the tail of a bird which secretes oily substances.

Urostyle. Terminal bone of the vertebral column of salientians.

Uterine. Pertaining to the uterus.

Uterus. The "womb" in which the fetus develops.

Utriculus; utricle. Part of the inner ear with which the semicircular canals connect.

Uvula. The median posterior pendulous process of the soft palate.

Vagina. In mammals, the passage from the uterus to the outside.

Vagus. Tenth cranial nerve.

Vas. Vessel.

Vein. Vessel that carries blood toward the heart.

Ventral. Pertaining to the belly; below (relative).

Ventricle. A small cavity.

Venule. Segment of a vein receiving blood from capillaries.

Vermiform. Like a worm.

Vermis. Worm. The median lobe of the cerebellum.

Vesicle. A liquid-filled sac or cavity.

Vibrissa. Sensory hair.

Villus. Thin, elongated projection from a surface.

Vitelline. Pertaining to the yolk.

Vitreous humor. Gelatinous substance between the retina and the lens.

Viviparous. Giving birth to living young.

Vulva. Female external genital organs.

Wharton's jelly. Embryonic, semiliquid connective tissue.

Wirsung, duct of. Ducts of the submaxillary gland.

Wolffian duct. Duct of the mesonephros. In the male, the ductus deferens.

Xiph-, xiphi (Gr. *xiphos*, sword). Combining form, meaning sharp or sword-shaped.

Xyg-, xygo-. (Gr. *Zygon*, yoke). Combining form, meaning yoke-shaped.

Zygapophysis. Articular process of a vertebra.

Zygomatic bone. The malar bone.

Zygote. Fertilized egg.

INDEX

Acelous centrum, 74
Acetylcholine, in nerves, 345
Adrenalin (epinephrine), 345, 360
Adrenal medulla, 345
Adrenals (suprarenals), 359–360
Adrenergic fibers, 345
Afterbirth, 23
Agnatha, 33–34
Air sacs, birds, 244
  reptiles, 243
Alecithal ova, 11
Alisphenoid, 90
Allantois, 19, 21, 262–264
Alveoli of lungs, 238, 242, 246–247
Ambisexuality, 271–272, 286
Amnion, 16, 19, 21
Amniotes, 19, 33
Amphibia, 34–35
Amphicelous centrum, 74, 77
Amphioxus, 11, 13, 33
Amphiplatyan centrum, 74, 84
Analogy, 2
Androgens, 360, 361
Animal pole of eggs, 11
Anterior cardinal veins, 216–217
Anterior vena cava, 216–217
Antlers, 56, 99

Aorta and its branches, 214
Aortic arches, 209–213
  amphibians, 212
  birds, 212
  fishes, 210–211
  mammals, 213–214
  reptiles, 212
Appendages, amphibians, 119–120
  birds, 121–124
  fishes, 118–119
  mammals, 124–127
  reptiles, 120–121
Appendages of skin, external, 44, 50, 57
  internal, 44, 50
Appendicular skeleton, 107–127
  phylogenetic development, 107–111
Apteria, 49, 50, 298
Archenteron, 13, 14
Archipallium, 325
Arcualia, 70, 76
Arteries, 192–194
  conducting, 193
  development, 198–201
  distributing, 193
  elastic, 194
  muscular, 194
  structure, 193–194

Arterioles, 192
Arteriovenous anastomoses, 194
Articular, 95, 97
Artiodactyla, 37
Atlas, 79, 82
Atrioventricular node, 209
Atrioventricular valve, 203
Auditory nerve, 307
Aves, 35
Axis, 79, 82
Axon, 315–316

Baleen, 57
Barbs of feathers, 50
Barbules of feathers, 50
Basal ganglia, 232
Basal layer of epidermis, 51
Basapophyses, 78
Basicranial fenestra, 90
Basidorsals, 70, 75, 77
Basilar plate, 90
Basioccipital, 90
Basisphenoid, 90
Basiventrals, 70, 77
Beak, 48
Biscuspid valve, 206
Bidder's organ, 287
Bilateral symmetry, 1
Biogenetic law, 4
Blastocele, 13
Blastocyst, 16
Blastodisc, 14, 15, 20
Blastomeres, 13, 14, 16
Blastopore, 13, 14, 15
Blastula, 9
Blood, 24, 26, 196–197
Blood islands, 197
Blubber, 52, 57
Body plan, 2, 15
Bone, cartilage, 61
   cells, 63–64, 65
   compact, 63
   composition, 63–64
   decalcified, 63, 64
   dense, 63
   dermal, 61, 90, 97
   diaphysis, 62
   endochondral, 61
   epiphysis, 62

Bone, general features, 61–62
   growth, 66–67
   incinerated, 63
   investing, 61
   marble, 67
   membrane, 61
   otic, 90
   parts, 64
   replacement, 61
   sesamoid, 62
   spongy (cancellous), 63, 67
Bowman's capsule, 255
Brachial plexus, 336
Brain, 323
   development, 323–329
   flexures, 325
   ventricles, 324
Brain, amphibians, 331–332
   Amphioxus, 329
   birds, 332
   cyclostomes, 329
   fishes, 329–331
   mammals, 332–336
   reptiles, 332
Branchiomeric musculature, 141, 143
Bronchi, 238, 239, 242, 243, 244, 245, 246

Calyces (major and minor), 259, 261
Cannon bone, 125
Capillaries, 192
Capitulum, 78
Carapace, 80, 81
Carapidae, 19
Carina, 86
Carnivora, 37
Carpals, 110
   amphibians, 119
   birds, 121
   mammals, 125
   reptiles, 121
Cartilage, cells, 62
   elastic, 62
   fibrous, 62
   growth, 62
   hyalin, 62
Cauda equina, 336
Cavernous tissue, 194
Cavities of body (coelomic), 24

Central lacteal, 224, 225
Central nervous system, 1, 315
Central sulcus, 333
Centrum, 2, 70, 71, 84
Cephalization, 1
Cephalocaudal development, 1
Cephalochordata, 33
Ceratohyal cartilage, 94
Cerebellum, 323, 325, 328, 329, 330, 332, 335–336
Cerebrospinal fluid, 323, 324
Cerebrum, 325, 332–335
Cetacea, 36
Chambers of eye (anterior, posterior), 303
Chelonia, 35
Chevron bones, 80
Chiroptera, 36
Choanae, 236–237
Cholinergic fibers, 345
Chondrichthyes, 34
Chondrocranium, 89–90, 93, 94, 95
Chordae tendineae, 203, 206
Chordata, 30–40
Chorion, 19, 21
Choroid plexus, 324, 328
Chromaffin body (medulla of adrenals), 356–357
Chyle, 195
Ciliary body, 303
Ciliary ganglion, 348
Ciliary muscles, 348
Circulatory system, 190–230
  development, 197–201
  general, 190–197
Cisterna chyli, 226, 227
Cistern of breast, 54
Classification (*see* taxonomy), 32–40
Claw, 48, 49, 54, 55
Cleavage, 9, 14, 16
Clitoris, 293
Cloaca, 1, 261, 262–263, 264, 265, 276, 279, 281, 282, 283, 285, 287, 288, 289, 291
Cochlea of the ear, 307–310
Coelom, 1, 2, 20, 21, 24
Coitus (copulation), 272
Columella of middle ear, 93, 310
Commissures of brain, 325, 327
Conchae, 300

Cones of retina, 303–304
Conjunctiva, 304
Connective tissues, 24, 26
Convergence, 2, 30
Convoluted tubules (proximal and distal), 259–260
Corium, 43
Corneal layer of skin, 42, 44
Coronary circulation, 195, 205, 208
Corpora quadrigemina, 327, 335
Corpus luteum, 291, 361–362
Corticosteroids, 360
Corticotropic hormone, 357
Costal processes, 74, 84
Cranial nerves, 348–350
Cribriform plate, 102, 300
Crocodilia, 35
Crossopterygii, 34
Crystalline lens, 303
Cuvier, duct of, 199
Cyclostomata, 33–34

Decussation, 329, 348
Deferent duct, 267, 274, 279, 282, 284
Demifacets, 83
Dendrite, 315, 316
Dentary, 94, 95, 97
Dentition, 104–107
Dermamyotome, 69
Dermatocranium, 89
Dermatome, 24, 141
Dermis, 42, 43, 52
Dermoptera, 36
Diapophysis, 78
Diencephalon, 321, 325, 326, 330
Digestive system, 154–189
  development, 157–162
Digitigrade, 124
Digits, amphibians, 119, 120
  birds, 121, 124
  mammals, 125–126, 127
Diplospondyly, 71
Dipnoi (lungfishes), 34
Divergence, 3

Ear (inner, middle, outer), 307–310
Ear ossicles, 310
Ecdysis, 47
Ectoderm, 9, 23

Index

Ectopterygoid, 95
Edentata, 36
Efferent ducts, 264, 265, 278, 279, 281, 282, 284
Eggs, 10, 14, 15, 19
Electric organs, 136
Encephalon, 320–321
Endocrine organs, 355–364
  adrenals, 359–360
  duodenal mucosa, 362
  general, 355–356
  gonads, 360–361
  ovaries, 361–362
  parathyroid, 358–359
  pituitary, 356–357
  placenta, 362
  testes, 361
  thyroid, 357–358
Endolymphatic duct, 308
Endometrium, 293
Endosteum, 64
Endostyle, 358
Entoderm, 9, 21, 23, 24
Epicoracoid cartilage, 86
Epidermis, 42, 43, 51–52
Epididymis, 278, 282, 284
Epiglottis, 238, 243, 244
Epiphyseal apparatus, 325
Epiphyseal eye, 95
Epiphyseal plate (synchondrosis), 66
Epithalamus, 334–335
Epithelia, 24, 25, 26
Eras, geologic, Cenozoic, 31, 32
  Mesozoic, 31, 32
  Paleozoic, 31
  Pre-Cambrian, 31
Esophagus, 172
  amphibians, 173
  birds, 173
  fishes, 172–173
  mammals, 173–175
  reptiles, 173
Estrogen, 29, 360, 361, 362
Estrus, 362
Ethmoid region, 90
Ethmoturbinals, 90
Eustachian tube, 310
Eutheria, 35, 36–37
Evolution, 5

Excretory system, 253–268
  development, 260–264
Excretory system, amphibians, 265
  Amphioxus, 264
  birds, 265–267
  cyclostomes, 264
  fishes, 264
  mammals, 267
  reptiles, 265
Exoccipital, 90
Exocrine organs, 356
Exteroceptive nerves, 298
Extraembryonic (fetal) membranes, 18, 20, 21
Eye, 301–307
Eye muscles, 141–142, 302–303, 304

Fatty layer of skin, 52
Feathers, 48–50, 51
Fertilization, 272–274, 288, 289, 290
Fertilized ovum, 9
Fetal (extraembryonic) membranes, 18, 20, 21
Fibers, connective tissue, 26
Filoplume, 49
Filum terminale, 336
Fingerprints, 52, 53
Foramen magnum, 90
Foramen ovale, 206
Fossils, 31
Fovea centralis, 304
Frog of hoof, 56
Frontal bone, 92
Frontal lobe of cerebrum, 333, 334
Funnel, buccal, 45

Ganglia, 317, 339
  cranial, 317, 322
  prevertebral, 323, 340
  spinal, 317, 321–322, 338
  vertebral, 323, 340
Ganoidea, 34
Ganoin, 45
Gastralia, 48, 80
Gastrocele, 13
Gastrula, 13
Genitalia (external), 272, 279
Germ cells, 276
Germinal disc, 11, 13

Germinal epithelium, 276
Germ layers, 9, 10, 13
Gestation, 21, 22, 362
Gill arch, 92
Gills (external, internal), 234
Girdles, 107–109
  pectoral, 109
    amphibians, 111
    birds, 111–112
    fishes, 111
    mammals, 113
    reptiles, 111
  pelvic, 109
    amphibians, 114
    birds, 116–117
    fishes, 113
    mammals, 117–118
    reptiles, 114–116
Glands, poison, 45, 47
  salivary, 169
  scent, 47, 48
  unicellular, 45
  uropygial, 48
Glomera, in birds, 282
Glomerulus, 255, 256, 257, 260
Glottis, 238, 242, 243, 244
Gnathostomes, 33, 34
Goblet cell, 44
Goiter, 358
Gonadotropic hormone, 357, 362
Gonads, 272, 276, 360–362
Gonopodium, 279
Gräaffian follicle, 274, 291, 361, 373
Granular layer of epidermis, 51
Gray matter, 317, 325, 336, 338
Growth hormone, 357
Gustatory (taste) buds, 300–301

Hair, 50, 56–57
Hair club, 56
Hair follicle, 56–57
Haversian system, 64
Head cavities, 141–142
Heart, 195
  contraction, 209
  development, 199–202
  skeleton, 208
  valves, 206

Heart, *Amphioxus*, 203
  birds, 206
  cyclostomes, 203
  fishes, 203–205
  mammals, 206–208
  reptiles, 205–206
Hemal arch, 70, 77, 80
Hemichordata, 33
Hemoglobin of muscle, 134
Hemopoietic organs, 226–227
Hepatic portal vein, 217
Hermaphrodite, 279, 286, 288
Heterocelous centrum, 74, 81
Hierarchy in taxonomy, 32
Hindgut, 21
Holoblastic ova, 12
Homology, 2
Hoof, 49, 54, 55, 56
Hormones, 355–364
Horns, 56
Humor of eye (aqueous, vitreous), 303
Hyalin layer of epidermis, 51
Hyoid apparatus, 93, 98, 243, 245
Hyoid arch, 92, 93
Hyomandibular cartilage, 94
Hypapophysis, 80, 81
Hypocentrum, 70, 80, 84
Hypophyseal fenestra, 90
Hypothalamus, 326, 329, 331, 334
Hyracoidea, 37

Incus, 93
Infraventral, 73
Infundibulum of brain, 326
Infundibulum of oviduct, 290, 292
Inner cell mass, 16, 21
Insectivora, 36
Insulin, 360
Intercalary arches, 70, 77
Interclavicle, 86
Interdorsals, 70, 75, 77
Intermedialia, 70
Intermediate, 23
Intermedin, 357
Internal nares, 95
Interoceptive nerves, 298
Interorbital septum, 95
Interparietal foramen, 94
Intersegmental blood vessels, 69

Interventrals, 70, 77
Intervertebral disc, 72, 84
Intestine, 178–179
  amphibians, 180
  birds, 180
  cyclostomes, 179
  fishes, 179–180
  mammals, 181–183
  reptiles, 180
Intestine, length, 181
Intrachordal centrum, 70
Invagination, 13
Iris of eye, 302–303
Islets of Langerhans, 356, 360
Isolecithal ova, 11, 15
Isthmus of pancreas, 188

Jacobson's organ, 300
Joints of bones, 67
Jugal bone, 97

Keel, 86
Keratin, 44, 56
Kidneys, 253
  cortex, 258
  medulla, 258
  mesonephric, 253, 257, 260, 264, 265
  metanephric, 253, 257–259, 260, 261, 265
  pronephric, 253, 256, 257, 260, 264
  renal pelvis, 258, 261, 267
  renal pyramids, 258
  renal sinus, 258

Lacrimal bone, 95
Lacrimal gland, 305
Lactogenic hormone, 357
Lagena of ear, 307–310
Lagomorpha, 36
Lambdoidal crest, 102
Lamina, 73
Larva, 19
Larynx, 238
  amphibians, 241
  birds, 243
  mammals, 244–245
  reptiles, 243
Lateral line organs, 299
Latimeria, 34

Leather, 44
Leydig cells (of testis), 278, 361
Ligamentum arteriosus, 212
Limb buds, 140
Linea alba, 144
Liver, 184–185
Longitudinal bundles, 144–146
Lumbosacral plexus, 336
Lumbosacral sinus, 338
Luminescent organs, 45
Lungfishes, 34
Lungs, 234, 238, 239
  development, 239
Lungs, amphibians, 242
  birds, 244
  fishes, 234, 241
  mammals, 247–248
  reptiles, 243
Lymphatic system, 192, 193, 195–196, 223–226
  amphibians, 225
  birds, 226
  fishes, 224–225
  mammals, 226
  reptiles, 226
Lymph nodes, 195

Malleolus, 124
Malleus, 93
Malpighian layer of epidermis, 42, 44, 48, 51
Mammalia, 35–37
Mammary glands, 50, 54, 57, 271
Mandible, amphibians, 95
  birds, 98
  fishes, 94
  mammals, 103
  reptiles, 97
Mandibular arch, 92
Mandibular fossa, 100
Manubrium, 89
Marrow cavity, 63
Marsupialia, 36
Maxilla, 92, 94
Meatus (external auditory), 310
Meckel's cartilage, 92, 93, 94, 95, 97
Mediastinum, 247
Medulla oblongata, 323, 324, 325, 328, 329, 330, 331

Melanin, 44, 52
Melanocyte, 23, 42, 44, 45, 52
Membranous labyrinth, 307–310
Meninges, 323
Menstruation, 362
Meroblastic ova, 13, 14
Mesenchyme, 24
Mesentery, 2
Mesethmoid, 90
Mesoderm, 1, 9, 23, 24
    intermediate, 23, 24
    lateral, 21, 23
    nephrogenic, 23, 24
    paraxial, 23, 69
    somatic, 20, 23, 24
    splanchnic, 20, 23, 24
Mesolecithal ova, 11, 13, 14
Mesonephric duct, 256, 257, 261, 264, 265
Mesonephric kidney, 276, 278, 281
Metacarpals, 110
    amphibians, 119
    birds, 121
    mammals, 125–126
    reptiles, 121
Metamerism, 1
Metamorphosis, 19
Metanephric blastema, 261
Metanephric bud, 261
Metanephric duct, 261, 262
Metanephric kidneys, 265–267
Metatarsals, 110, 119–127
Metatheria, 35, 36
Metencephalon, 321, 325, 328
Middle ear, 99
Milk line, 54
Monotremata, 36
Motor end-plates, 134, 135
Mouth, 162
    amphibians, 165
    Amphioxus, 162–163
    birds, 167–168
    cyclostomes, 163
    fishes, 163
    mammals, 168–172
    reptiles, 165–167
Müllerian ducts, *261,* 268, 276, 278, 287, 291, 292
Muscles, amphibians, 138
    birds, 138

Muscles, fishes, 137
    mammals, 138–142
Muscles, action, 135–136
    antagonistic, 135
    anterior rectus, 142
    biceps brachii, 148
    cardiac, 133
    constrictors, 146
    dorsalis trunci, 146
    epaxial, 137, 138, 144, 145, 146, 147, 150
    extensor carpi radialis, 148
    extensor carpi ulnaris, 148
    extensors, 146
    external oblique, 146, 150
    extrinsic, 140, 150
    flexor carpi ulnaris, 148
    flexors, 146
    gastrocnemius, 149
    hypaxial, 137, 138, 144, 145, 146, 147
    hypobranchial, 143
    hypoglossal, 141
    iliocostalis, 147, 150
    iliofibularis, 149
    inferior oblique, 142
    interarcual, 146
    intercostal, 147, 150
    internal oblique, 146
    interspinalis, 150
    intertransversarii, 150
    intrinsic, 140, 150
    levators, 146
    longissimus, 147, 150
    longissimus dorsi, 146, 150
    multifidus spinae, 150
    pectoralis major, 148
    pectoralis secundus (supracoracoideus), 148
    pharyngeal, 141
    posterior rectus, 142
    rectus abdominus, 146, 150
    retractor, 149
    sacrospinalis, 150
    serratus, 150
    semispinalis, 147
    skeletal, 133
    smooth, 133
    spinalis, 147
    spinalis dorsi, 150

Index

Muscles, sternohyoid, 150
  sternothyroid, 150
  stylo-pharyngeus, 141
  superior oblique, 142
  superior rectus, 141
  synergistic, 135
  thyrohyoid, 150
  tibialis anterior, 149
  transversalis, 146
  trapezius, 141
Muscles, attachments, 133–134
  development, 137–142
  innervation, 134, 140, 141, 142
  nomenclature, 136
  structure, 133–134
  tonus, 134
Muscular system, 132–152
  amphibians, 146–147
  Amphioxus, 142–143
  birds, 147–149
  cyclostomes, 143
  fishes, 144–146
  mammals, 150–151
  reptiles, 147
Myelencephalon, 321
Myelinated fibers, 316
Myelin sheath, 316
Myocommata, 137
Myomere, 137, 140
Myosepta, 72
Myotome, 24, 137, 138, 144

Nail, 49, 54, 55, 56
Nares, 236–237
Nasal bone, 92
Nasal passages, 236–237
Neognathae, 35
Neopallium, 325
Nephron, 255–256, 259–260, 261
Nephrostome, 256, 257, 264
Nerve impulse, 319
Nerves, 317
  cranial, 317, 339
  spinal, 317, 339
Nervous system, 315–354
  brain, 323–329
  cranial nerves, 348–350
  development, 319–323
    amphibians, 331–332

Nervous system, development,
    Amphioxus, 329
  birds, 332
  cyclostomes, 329
  fishes, 329–331
  mammals, 332–336
  reptiles, 332
  spinal cord, 336
    amphibians, 338
    Amphioxus, 336–338
    birds, 338
    cyclostomes, 338
    fishes, 338
    mammals, 336
    reptiles, 338
Nervous system, autonomic, 339–348
  parasympathetic, 343–344, 345, 346
  peripheral, 339
  somatic, 339
  sympathetic, 339–343, 345, 346
Nervous tissue, 24, 27
Neural arch, 70, 77
Neural crest, 23, 44, 320, 321, 323
Neural plate, 14, 319
Neural tube, 9, 14, 320
Neurilemma sheath, 316
Neuroblast, 321
Neuroglia, 27
Neuron, 315–317, 321–323
Nictitating membrane, 304, 305, 306
Nidamental gland, 287
Nipple of breast, 54, 55
Nonmyelinated fibers, 316
Norepinephrine, 345
Notch of vertebra, 74
Notochord, 1, 2, 10, 68, 69, 70, 71, 72,
    76, 77, 84, 90
Nucleus pulposus, 84

Oblique septum, 244
Occipital condyle, 93, 97
Occipital crest, 102
Occipital region, 90
Odontoid process, 79
Olfactory lobes, 325, 329, 331, 332, 333
Olfactory nerves, 299–300
Olfactory organs, 299–300
Olfactory vesicle, 90
Omosternum, 86

Ontogeny, 3, 5
Oögenesis, 278
Operculum, 34
Opisthocelous centrum, 74
Optic chiasma, 326
Optic lobes, 327, 330, 332
Optic nerve, 304
Optic vesicle, 90
Orbit, 301
Orbitosphenoid bone, 90
Organ of Corti, 310
Oronasal canal, 300
Ossification centers, 66
Osteichthyes, 34
Osteocytes, 64–65
Otic bones, 90
Otic vesicle, 307
Ova, 16, 272, 273, 274, 278, 286, 287, 288–289, 291
Ovary, 272, 273, 274, 278, 286, 287, 289, 361–362
Oviduct, 274–276, 286, 287, 288, 289, 291, 292
Oviparous, 274, 286, 287, 289
Ovoviviparous, 274, 287, 289

Palaeognathae, 35
Palate, 95, 97, 100
    primary (true), 95, 97
    secondary (false), 97, 100, 300
Palatoquadrate (pterygoquadrate), 92, 93, 95
Palpebrae (eyelids), 304, 306
Pancreas, 186–188, 360
Panniculus carnosus, 136
Pannizzae, foramen of, 205
Papillae of tongue, 301
Papillary muscles, 206
Parachordals, 90
Parallelism, 2
Parapophysis, 78
Parasympathetic nervous system, 339, 343, 344, 345
Parathohormone, 359
Parathyroid glands, 358–359
Parathyrotropic hormone, 357
Parenchyma, 24
Parietal bones, 92
Patella, 62

Pecten of eye, 306
Pedicles of vertebra, 74
Pelvic nerve, 343
Penis, 272, 282, 285–286
Perennibranchiates, 244
Perichondrium, 62
Perichordal centrum, 72
Periosteum, 64
Peripheral nervous system, 315
Perissodactyla, 37
Peritoneal fluid, 2
Peritoneum, 2
Pharyngeal arches, clefts, pouches, and slits, 1
Pharynx, 1, 160, 161, 163, 165, 166, 170, 237–238, 279, 300, 301
    amphibians, 241
    birds, 244
    cyclostomes, 239–240
    fishes, 240
    reptiles, 243
Phylogeny, 3, 5, 31
Phylum, Chordata, 33
Physoclistous swim bladder, 240
Physostomous swim bladder, 240
Pigments, 45
Pilosebaceous unit, 54, 55
Pineal body, 325–326, 329, 335
Pinna of ear, 310
Pisces, 33–40
Pitocin, 357
Pitressin, 357
Pituitary gland (hypophysis cerebri), 356–357
Placenta, 16, 22–23, 289, 293, 362
    cotyledonary, 22
    diffuse, 22
    endotheliochorial, 23
    epitheliochorial, 22
    hemochorial, 23
    hemoendothelial, 23
    syndesmochorial, 23
    vessels of, 23
    zonary, 22
Plantigrade, 126
Platysma, 136
Pleurapophyses, 79, 82
Pleurocentrum, 70
Pleuroperitoneal cavity, 2

Plexus of Auerbach and Meissner, 343
Pluma, 49
Plumula, 49
Pneumatic duct of swim bladder, 240
Polypterus, 34
Portal veins, 194, 216, 217, 220, 222
Posterior cardinal veins, 215–216
Posterior vena cava, development, 215–216, 222
Postganglionic fibers, 340, 341, 343, 344, 345, 346
Postzygapophyses, 74
Powder down, 49
Preganglionic fibers, 340, 341, 343, 345, 346
Premaxillary bone, 94
Presphenoid bone, 90
Prezygapophyses, 74
Primary brain vesicles, 320–321
Primates, 36
Primitive streak, 15
Proboscidea, 37
Procelous centrum, 74, 81
Progesterone, 291, 361–362
Pronephric duct, 256, 260–261
Pronghorn, 56
Proprioceptive nerves, 298
Prostate gland, 284
Prostatic utricle, 278, 284
Prototheria, 35
Pseudobranch, 240
Pterygoquadrate, 95
Pterylae, 49, 50
Pulmocutaneous arch, 205
Pupil, 307
Pygostyle, 82

Quadrate, 94, 95, 97
Quadratojugal, 97

Rachis of feather, 50
Rami communicantes (white and gray), 340, 341
Rathke's pouch, 326, 357
Ratitae, 35
Rattle of rattlesnake, 48
Recapitulation Theory, 4
Reflex arc, 317, 339

Reflexes, 134–135
attitudinal, 134
postural, 134
righting, 134
Renal portal veins, 216, 220, 222
Reptilia, 35
Respiration (internal, external), 233
Respiratory system, 232–250
development, 238–239
Respiratory system, amphibians, 241–242
birds, 243–244
cyclostomes, 239
fishes, 240–241
mammals, 244–248
reptiles, 243
Reproductive system, 271–295
development, 276
female, 278–279
male, 276–278
Reproductive system, female, amphibians, 287–288
Amphioxus, 286
birds, 289–291
cyclostomes, 286
fishes, 286–287
mammals, 291–293
reptiles, 288–289
male, amphibians, 281
Amphioxus, 279
birds, 282–283
cyclostomes, 279
fishes, 279
mammals, 283–286
reptiles, 281–282
Retina, 303–304
Retinacula, 140
Rhynchocephalia, 35
Ribs, 72, 78, 79, 82, 83
Rodentia, 36
Rods of retina, 303–304
Rostrum, 86

Saccule of ear, 307–310
Salivary glands, 166, 168, 169
Sarcolemma, 134
Scales, 45, 46
ctenoid, 45, 46, 47
cycloid, 34, 45, 46
dermal, 47, 48, 54, 94

Scales, epidermal, 47, 48, 54
ganoid, 34, 45, 57
imbricated, 47
placoid, 45, 46, 103
Sclerotic ossicles, 306
Sclerotome, 24, 69
Scrotum, 283
Scutes, 48
Sebaceous glands, 54
Secretin, 326
Segmentation (metamerism), 1
Sella turcica, 102
Semen, 274
Semicircular canals of ear, 307–310
Semilunar notch, 124
Semilunar valve, 207
Seminal vesicles, 278, 279, 281
Seminiferous tubules, 276, 278, 283–284, 361
Sense organs, 297–313
cutaneous, 298–299
ear, 307–313
eye, 301–307
lateral line, 299
smell, 299–300
taste, 300–301
Sensory cells, 297, 299, 300, 307, 310
Sensory fibers, 297, 299
Sensory mechanism, 317
Sertoli cells of testes, 361
Sex hormones, 360–362
Sex organs (primary, secondary), 272
Shell gland, 288, 290
Shedding, antlers, 56
feathers, 50
hair, 57
Sino-atrial node, 209
Sinusoids, 194
Sirenia, 37
Skeletogenous areas, 69
Skeleton, appendicular, 67, 68, 107–127
axial, 67, 68–107
branchial, 68, 92, 93–94, 98
dermal, 45, 48
development, 68–73
hypobranchial, 93
visceral, 92
Skin, 43–57
amphibians, 47

Skin, *Amphioxus*, 44
birds, 48–50
cyclostomes, 45
fishes, 45
mammals, 50–57
reptiles, 47–48
Skull, 89–103
development, 89–93
Skull, amphibians, 94–95
birds, 97–98
cyclostomes, 93
fishes, 93–94
mammals, 98–103
reptiles, 95–97
Somatic nervous system, 339
Somatopleure, 20, 21
Somites, 23, 24, 69
Species, 5, 32–33
Spermatogenesis, 278, 282
Spermatozoa, 9, 272, 274, 276–278, 279, 281, 282
Sphenoid region, 90
Sphenodon, 48
Spinal cord, 2, 317, 320, 321, 336–338
amphibians, 338
Amphioxus, 336
birds, 338
cyclostomes, 338
fishes, 338
mammals, 317, 336
reptiles, 338
Spine (neural, hemal), 73
Spinous layer of epidermis, 51
Spiracle, 240
Splanchnic nerve, 345
Splanchnocranium, 89, 92, 94
Splanchnopleure, 20
Spurs, 48
Squamata, 35
Squamosal bone, 95
Stapes, 93
Sternebrae, 89
Sternum, 85–86
amphibians, 86
birds, 86–87
mammals, 89
reptiles, 86
Stomach, 175–178
amphibians, 175

Stomach, birds, 175–176
cyclostomes, 175
fishes, 175
mammals, 176–178
reptiles, 175
Stroma, 24
Subphylum (Acraniata, Craniata), 33
Subunguis, 48, 56
Supradorsal, 73
Supraoccipital, 90
Sweat glands (apocrine, eccrine), 52
Swim bladder, 34, 234–236, 239, 240, 241
Sylvian fissure, 333
Sympathetic nervous system, 339, 340, 344, 345
Sympathetic trunk, 339–340, 341
Sympathicoadrenal system, 345
Synapse, 317, 339, 341, 343, 345
Synsacrum, 81
Syrinx, 243–244

Tail of fish, 119
Tapetum lucidum of eye, 306
Target organs, 356
Tarsals, 110
amphibians, 120
birds, 124
mammals, 126
reptiles, 121
Tarsometatarsus, 124
Taste, 300–301
Taxonomy, 30, 32–40
Teeth, 45, 103–107
Teat of breast, 54, 55
Telencephalon, 321, 325
Telolecithal ova, 11, 13, 14, 15, 19
Temporal bone, 92
Tendon sheath, 140
Testis, 272, 274, 276, 279, 281, 282, 283, 361
Tetrapoda, 33, 34–39
Thalamus, 326, 329, 332, 334
Thebesian veins, 208
Theca interna, 361
Thoracic duct, 226, 227
Thyroid, 357–358
Thyrotropic hormone, 357
Thyroxin, 357–358
Tissues, 24, 26

Tongue, 301
development, 170–171
innervation, 170
muscles, 171
Tongue, amphibians, 164–165
birds, 168
cyclostomes, 163
fishes, 163
mammals, 170–172
reptiles, 167
Tortoise shell, 48
Touch, 298
Trabeculae, 90
Trachea, 238, 239
amphibians, 242
birds, 243
mammals, 245–246
reptiles, 243
Transverse processes, 73, 82
Tricuspid valve, 206
Trigone of bladder, 262
Trophoblast, 16, 21
Tuberculum, 78
Tubulidentata, 37
Turbinated bones, 237–300
Tympanic bulla, 99
Tympanic membrane (eardrum), 310
Tympanum, 310

Umbilical cord, 23
Umbilical vessels, 22, 199
Uncinate process, 79, 81
Unguis, 48, 56
Unguligrade, 126
Urachus, 262
Ureter, 256, 259, 269
Urethra, 259, 267, 284
Urinary bladder, 256, 259, 262–264
amphibians, 265
fishes, 264
mammals, 267
reptiles, 265
Urine, 256, 259, 260, 265, 267
Urochordata, 33
Urodeum, 265
Urogenital papilla, 264, 279
Urogenital sinus, 261, 262, 264, 279, 293
Urogenital system, 253
development, 260–264

Urogenital system, amphibians, 265
  fishes, 264
  mammals, 267
Urostyle, 79
Uterus, 276, 278, 291, 292–293
Utricle of ear, 307–310

Vagina, 272, 276, 279, 292
Vane of feather, 50
Vasa vasorum, 194
Vegetal pole of egg, 11
Veins, 192
  development, 198–201
  structure, 194
  systemic, 194
Venous system, 215–223
  amphibians, 222
  birds, 222–223
  cyclostomes, 217
  fishes, 220–222
  mammals, 215–217
  reptiles, 222
Ventral root nerve, 321
Ventral septum, 137
Venules, 192
Vertebra, comparative anatomy, 75–85
  development, 68–73
  structure, 73–74
Vertebra, amphibians, 78–79

Vertebra, birds, 81–82
  cyclostomes, 75–76
  fishes, 76–78
  mammals, 82–85
  reptiles, 79–81
Vertebrarterial canal, 79, 81
Vibrissae, 298–299
Villi (chorionic), 22
Viviparous, 274
Vocal cords, amphibians, 241
  mammals, 245
  reptiles, 243
Vulva, 293

Whale bone (baleen), 57
White matter, 317, 324, 336, 338
Wolffian duct (mesonephric duct), 276,
  278, 279, 281, 284, 290

Xiphisternum, 86
Xiphoid processes, 86

Yolk, 11, 19
Yolk sac, 15, 16, 19, 20, 21, 198
Yolk stalk, 20, 21

Zygomatic arch, 97, 100
Zygote, 272